A-Level

Mathematics

for AQA Statistics 1

The Complete Course for AQA S1

Contents

Introduction

Introduction to Mathematical Modelling

Chapter 1

Numerical Measures

Chapter 2

Probability

Chapter 3

The Binomial Distribution

Chapter 4

The Normal Distribution

Chapter 5

Estimation

Chapter 6

Correlation and Regression

Reference

About this book

In this book you'll find...

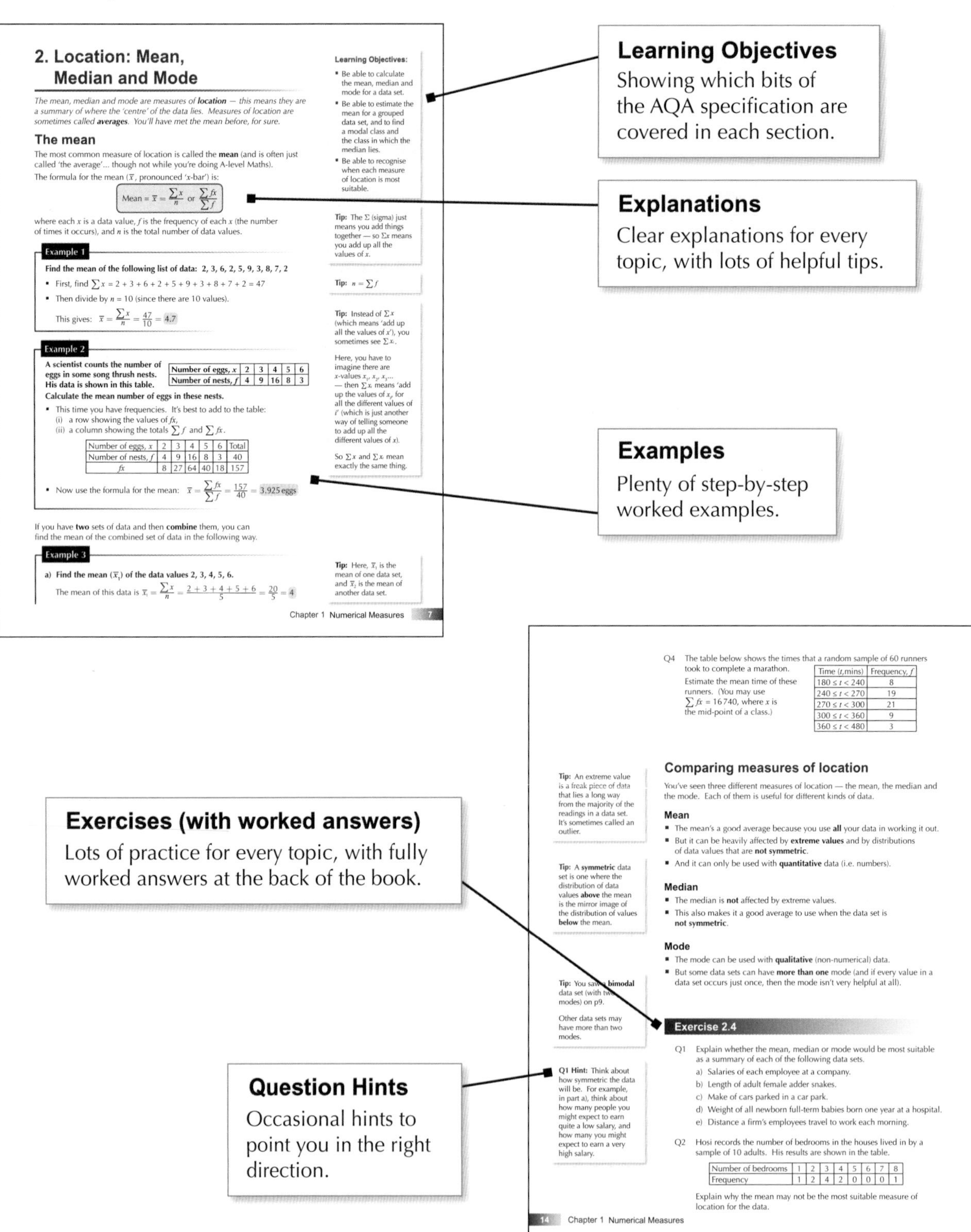

Review Exercise — Chapter 1

Q1 Calculate the mean, median and mode of the data in the table on the right.

x	0	1	2	3	4
f	5	4	4	2	1

Q2 The speeds of 60 cars travelling in a 40 mph speed limit area were measured to the nearest mph. The data is summarised in this table.

a) Calculate an estimate of the mean.

b) State the modal class.

c) Find the class which contains the median.

Speed (mph)	30 - 34	35 - 39	40 - 44	45 - 50
Frequency	12	37	9	2

Q3 Find the mean and standard deviation of the following numbers: 11, 12, 14, 17, 21, 23, 27.

Q4 The scores in an IQ test for 50 people are recorded in the table below.

Score	100 - 106	107 - 113	114 - 120	121 - 127	128 - 134
Frequency	6	11	22	9	2

Estimate the mean and variance of the distribution.

Q5 For a set of data, $n = 100$, $\sum(x - 20) = 125$, and $\sum(x - 20)^2 = 221$. Find the mean and standard deviation of x.

Q6 The time taken (to the nearest minute) for a commuter to travel to work on 20 consecutive work days is summarised in the table.

Use the linear scaling $y = x - 35.5$ to estimate the mean and standard deviation of the times, where x is the class mid-point.

Time to nearest minute	30 - 33	34 - 37	38 - 41	42 - 45
Frequency, f	3	6	7	4

Q7 Find the median and quartiles of the data below.

Amount of pocket money (in £) received per week by twenty 15-year-olds:
10, 5, 20, 50, 5, 1, 6, 5, 15, 20, 5, 7, 5, 10, 12, 4, 8, 6, 7, 30.

Q8 Two workers iron clothes. Each irons 10 items, and records the time it takes for each, to the nearest minute:

Worker A: 3 5 2 7 10 4 5 5 4 12
Worker B: 4 4 8 6 7 8 9 10 11 9

a) For worker A's times. Find: (i) the median (ii) the interquartile range

b) For worker B's times. Find: (i) the median (ii) the interquartile range

c) Make one statement comparing the two sets of data.

d) Which worker would be better to employ? Give a reason for your answer.

Review Exercises

Mixed questions covering the whole chapter, with fully worked answers.

Exam-Style Questions — Chapter 1

1 The manager of a junior football team always substitutes his first-choice attacker at half-time, and has two substitutes he can bring on, Player A and Player B. This table shows the number of goals scored by Players A and B in their last 26 appearances.

Number of goals	Player A	Player B
0	6	1
1	7	6
2	6	8
3	3	6
4	2	4
5	1	1
6	0	0
7	1	0

a) For Player A, find the mode, median, and lower and upper quartiles. *(3 marks)*

b) For Player B, find the interquartile range. *(3 marks)*

c) For Player A, calculate:

(i) the mean number of goals scored per appearance *(2 marks)*

(ii) the variance of the number of goals scored per appearance *(2 marks)*

d) The manager works out the following for Player B:
Mean = 2.35, variance = 1.46

Use this information and your answers to part c) to comment on the differences between the number of goals scored per appearance, and the spread of the data, for the two players. *(2 marks)*

2 The table shows the number of hits received by people at a paint-ball party.

No. of hits	12	13	14	15	16	17	18	19	20	21	22	23	24	25
Frequency	7	4	6	6	6	4	4	2	1	7	0	0	0	1

a) Find the mean, median and modal number(s) of hits. *(5 marks)*

b) State which of the three measures of location in part a) is least appropriate for summarising the number of hits received. Give a reason for your answer. *(2 marks)*

Exam-Style Questions

Questions in the same style as the ones you'll get in the exam, with worked solutions and mark schemes.

Formula Sheet and Statistical Tables

Containing all the formulas and statistical tables you'll be given in the S1 exam.

Glossary

All the definitions you need to know for the exam, plus other useful words.

Practice Exam Papers (on CD-ROM)

Two printable exam papers, with fully worked answers and mark schemes.

A-Level Mathematics for AQA
S1
CD-ROM
Exam Practice Papers & Worked Answers
CGP

Published by CGP

Editors:
Ali Palin, Andy Park, Charlotte Whiteley.

Contributors:
Katharine Brown, Michael Coe, Claire Creasor, Alastair Duncombe,
Anna Gainey, Claire Jackson, Gary Rowlands, Chris Worth.

ISBN: 978 1 84762 798 8

With thanks to Mona Allen, Allan Graham and Glenn Rogers for the proofreading.

Printed by Elanders Ltd, Newcastle upon Tyne.
Clipart from Corel®

Introduction to Mathematical Modelling

1. Mathematical Models in Probability and Statistics

Mathematical models are basically descriptions of things in the real world, and are usually created to help solve some kind of problem. They're usually much simpler than the real-world situations they describe, but are still useful.

These two pages cover some of the ideas behind **mathematical modelling**, and the process involved in creating a model.

You **won't** get any questions on this in the exam. However, reading through the example here should give you an idea of how statistical techniques like the ones you'll see in S1 can be used in real-world situations.

The benefits of mathematical models

Understanding real-world problems

- A technology company is going to launch a new product — the USB-Penguin.
  The company's managers would like to **maximise profits** from USB-Penguin sales. (At the very least, they need to sell enough USB-Penguins to recover the money spent on development.)
- They are trying to decide what would be the best **price** to charge for the USB-Penguin. They realise that the variables '**price**', '**sales**', and '**profit**' are linked.
  For example:
  - If the **price** is low, then **sales** should be higher.
    (i) However, if sales aren't as high as expected, the low price may mean that the company will not be able to recover the development costs.
    (ii) But if the low price encourages lots of people to buy the USB-Penguin, then **profits** could be high.
  - If the **price** is high, then they can expect to **sell fewer** USB-Penguins.
    (i) However, if sales turn out to be higher than expected, then the company will make a very big **profit**.
    (ii) But if the high price puts people off buying, then the company won't recover the development costs.
- The managers need to answer the following question:

  What is the best price to charge for the USB-Penguin to maximise profits (or to have the best chance of recovering the development costs)?

Saving money and reducing risk

They decide to try and answer the question using a **mathematical model**.

- This is a mathematical description of the situation using **equations**.
- Because real-life situations can be so complicated, some **assumptions** and **simplifications** are usually made — basically, to make the maths easier.
- The model allows possible prices to be **tried out** (in the model) and the sales and profits to be **predicted**.
- Using a model to test what might happen in various scenarios means there is less **risk** of something going **expensively wrong** in real life (such as the company losing so much money it goes out of business).

The modelling process

There are several important steps in creating a mathematical model.

① *Recognising a real-world problem*

The managers' pricing dilemma, for example.

② *Making the mathematical model*

- This will involve writing down one or more **equations**.
- For example, there might be an equation describing how the **retail price** (r) affects **sales** (s). There might also be another equation describing how the price and sales affect **profit** (P).
- Writing these equations might involve making a number of **assumptions** and **simplifications**.
  - For example, the managers might have to make their 'best guess' at the effect on sales of reducing the price.
  - And they might not take into account factors such as how increased sales might lead to more competition (as other firms make products similar to the USB-Penguin).

③ *Use the model to make some predictions*

The equations can then be used to **predict** how many USB-Penguin sales are expected at various prices, and the effect this would have on profits.

④ *Collect some real-world data*

When the USB-Penguin goes on sale, the company will be able to collect some **real-life data** — by recording the actual sales of the USB-Penguin at the price they choose.

⑤ *Analyse the real-world data*

The predicted number of sales and the actual number of sales can then be **compared**.

⑥ *Test whether the model 'works'*

Statistical tests can be carried out to test **how well** the model describes the real-world situation.

⑦ *Improve the model*

If necessary, the model can be **improved** by changing some of the equations (or adding some new ones) so that it makes predictions that are closer to what is observed in real life. This might allow the company to adapt its prices in the future so that sales and profits improve.

Tip: **Linear regression** is a form of mathematical modelling (see Chapter 6).

And **random variables** can be used to model many real-world quantities (see Chapters 3 and 4).

Tip: For example, you might **assume** that a quantity follows a **normal** distribution (see Chapter 4), or that the conditions for a **binomial** distribution are satisfied (see Chapter 3).

Tip: When **analysing** the data, you'll need to use the **numerical measures** in Chapter 1.

And you might need to see if two sets of data are **correlated** (see Chapter 6).

Tip: You'll be able to use ideas about **estimation** (see Chapter 5) to **test** the claims or ideas used in a model.

Tip: When you update the model, you need to go through steps 3 to 6 again.

1. Representing Data

Data is to statistics what fuel is to a car — without data, all the statistics knowledge in the world won't be much use. This chapter covers the essentials about data — from the tables used to represent it, through to measuring its location and dispersion.

Learning Objectives:

- Be able to recognise different types of variables.
- Be able to interpret frequency tables and grouped frequency tables.

Data basics

A lot of the subject of **statistics** involves analysing **data**.

Data consists of a number of **observations** (or **measurements**).
Each of these observations records the value of a particular **variable**.

There are different kinds of variables.

- Variables that take **non-numerical** values (i.e. they're not numbers) — these are called **qualitative** variables.
- Variables that take **numerical** values (i.e. they're numbers) — these are called **quantitative** variables.

There are then two different types of **quantitative** variables.

- A **discrete** variable can only take **certain values** within a particular range (e.g. shoe sizes) — this means there are 'gaps' between possible values (you can't take size 9.664 shoes, for example).
- A **continuous** variable can take **any value** within a particular range (e.g. lengths or masses) — there are no gaps between possible values.

Tip: Or you can think of a discrete variable changing 'in steps'.

Example 1

An employer collects information about the computers in his office. He gathers observations of the 5 variables shown in this table.

1. Manufacturer	Bell	Banana	Deucer	Deucer
2. Processor speed (in GHz)	2.6	2.1	1.8	2.2
3. Year of purchase	2009	2010	2011	2009
4. Memory (in MB)	2	3	3.1	4.8
5. Colour	Grey	Grey	Grey	Black

Which of the five variables are:

a) qualitative?

- The variables 'Manufacturer' and 'Colour' take values that are not numbers.
- So there are two qualitative variables: 'Manufacturer' and 'Colour'.

b) quantitative?

- The variables 'Processor speed', 'Year of purchase' and 'Memory' take values that are numbers.
- So there are three quantitative variables: 'Processor speed', 'Year of purchase' and 'Memory'.

Tip: 'Number of brothers' can only take whole-number values.

'Total value of 6 coins' can only take particular values. For example, they could be worth 12p or 13p, but not 12.8p.

Tip: Frequency just means 'the number of times something happens'.

Tip: Frequency tables and grouped frequency tables can also be drawn 'vertically', like this:

Number of bananas	Frequency
8	3
9	7
10	10
11	6
12	4

Tip: You don't always need to leave the bottom and top classes without a lower and upper limit — e.g. if you know for a fact that very small or very large data values are impossible.

Example 2

The variables below are all quantitative.
(i) length, (ii) weight, (iii) number of brothers, (iv) time,
(v) total value of 6 coins from down the back of my sofa

a) Which of these 5 quantitative variables are continuous?

- 'Length', 'weight' and 'time' can all take any value in a range.
- So the continuous variables are: 'length', 'weight' and 'time'.

b) Which of these 5 quantitative variables are discrete?

- 'Number of brothers' and 'total value of 6 coins' can only take certain values.
- So there are two discrete variables — these are: 'number of brothers' and 'total value of 6 coins'.

Data is often shown in the form of a **table**.
There are two types you need to be really familiar with.

- **Frequency tables** show the number of observations of various values.
  For example, this frequency table shows the number of bananas in thirty 1.5 kg bags.

Number of bananas	8	9	10	11	12
Frequency	3	7	10	6	4

- **Grouped frequency tables** show the number of observations whose values fall within certain **classes** (i.e. **ranges** or **groups of values**). They're often used when there is a large range of possible values.
  For example, this grouped frequency table shows the number of potatoes in thirty 25 kg sacks.

Number of potatoes	50-55	56-60	61-65	66-70	71-75
Frequency	1	8	12	7	2

  - Notice how grouped frequency tables **don't** tell you the **exact** value of the observations — just the most and the least they **could** be.
  - And notice how the different classes **don't overlap**. In fact, there are '**gaps**' between the classes because this is **discrete** data.

Grouped frequency tables are also used for **continuous** data. Since there are no 'gaps' between possible data values for continuous variables, there can be no gaps between classes in their grouped frequency tables either.

For example, this grouped frequency table shows the masses of 50 potatoes.

- **Inequalities** have been used to define the **class boundaries** (the upper and lower limits of each class). There are no 'gaps' and no overlaps between classes.
- The smallest class doesn't have a lower limit — so very small potatoes can still be put into one of the classes. Similarly, the largest class doesn't have an upper limit.

Mass of potato (m, in g)	Frequency
$m < 100$	7
$100 \leq m < 200$	8
$200 \leq m < 300$	16
$300 \leq m < 400$	14
$m \geq 400$	5

This grouped frequency table shows the lengths (to the nearest cm) of the same 50 potatoes.

Length of potato (l, in cm)	Frequency
4-5	5
6-7	11
8-9	15
10-11	16
12-13	3

- The shortest potato that could go in the 6-7 class would actually have a length of 5.5 cm (since 5.5 cm would be rounded up to 6 cm when measuring to the nearest cm).

  So the **lower class boundary** of the 6-7 class is 5.5 cm.
- The **upper class boundary** of the 6-7 class is the same as the lower class boundary of the 8-9 class — this is 7.5 cm. This means there are never any **gaps** between classes.
- For each class, you can find the **class width** using this formula:

$$\text{class width} = \text{upper class boundary} - \text{lower class boundary}$$

- And you can find the **mid-point** of a class using this formula:

$$\text{mid-point} = \frac{\text{lower class boundary} + \text{upper class boundary}}{2}$$

Tip: Even though a potato of length 7.5 cm would go in the 8-9 class, this is still the upper class boundary of the 6-7 class.

Tip: The upper class boundary of the 12-13 class will be 13.5 cm.

Tip: A class with a lower class boundary of 50 g and upper class boundary of 250 g can be written in different ways.

So you might see:

- '100 – 200, to the nearest 100 g'
- '50 ≤ mass < 250'
- '50–', followed by '250–' for the next class, and so on.

They all mean the same.

Example 1

A researcher measures the length (to the nearest 10 cm) of 40 cars. Her results are shown in the table. Add four columns to the table to show:
(i) the lower class boundaries
(ii) the upper class boundaries
(iii) the class widths
(iv) the class mid-points

Length (cm)	**Frequency**
250-350	**5**
360-410	**11**
420-450	**17**
460-500	**7**

- The shortest car that measures 250 cm (to the nearest 10 cm) is 245 cm long. So the lower class boundary of the 250-350 class is 245 cm.
- The upper class boundary of the 250-350 class is 355 cm (even though a car measuring 355 cm would actually go into the 360-410 class).
- Once you have the class boundaries, use the above formulas to find the class widths and the mid-points.

Length (cm)	Frequency	lower class boundary (cm)	upper class boundary (cm)	class width (cm)	mid-point (cm)
250-350	5	245	355	110	300
360-410	11	355	415	60	385
420-450	17	415	455	40	435
460-500	7	455	505	50	480

Tip: 355 cm must be the upper class boundary for the 250-350 class, because no number less than this would work.

For example, the upper class boundary can't be 354.99 cm, because then a car of length 354.999 cm wouldn't fit into any of the classes. And the upper class boundary can't be 354.999 cm, because then a car of length 354.9999 cm wouldn't fit into any of the classes. And so on.

Example 2

A researcher measures the (nose-to-tip-of-tail) length of 40 cats. His results are shown in the table.
Add two columns to the table to show:
(i) the lower class boundaries
(ii) the upper class boundaries

Length, l (mm)	**Frequency**
$250 \le l < 350$	**3**
$350 \le l < 410$	**15**
$410 \le l < 450$	**17**
$450 \le l < 500$	**5**

- The classes are written using inequalities this time. That makes it easy to tell where the class boundaries are.
- The shortest cat that can go in the $250 \le l < 350$ class measures 250 mm. The length of a cat any shorter than 250 mm wouldn't satisfy the inequality.
- Similarly, the upper class boundary of the $250 \le l < 350$ class is 350 mm.

Length, l (mm)	Frequency	lower class boundary (mm)	upper class boundary (mm)
$250 \le l < 350$	3	250	350
$350 \le l < 410$	15	350	410
$410 \le l < 450$	17	410	450
$450 \le l < 500$	5	450	500

Tip: Even though a cat of length 350 mm wouldn't go into the $250 \le l < 350$ class, the upper class boundary of this class is still 350 mm (since no number smaller than 350 mm is suitable — see page 5 for more information).

Exercise 1.1

Q1 A mechanic collects the following information about cars he services:

Make, Mileage, Colour, Number of doors, Cost of service

Write down all the variables from this list that are:

a) qualitative

b) quantitative

Q2 Amy is an athletics coach. She records the following information about each of the athletes she trains:

Number of medals won last season, Height, Mass, Shoe size

Write down all the variables from this list that are examples of:

a) discrete quantitative variables

b) continuous quantitative variables

Q3 The heights of the members of a history society are shown in the table.

a) Explain why 'height' is a continuous variable.

b) For each class, write down the:

(i) lower class boundary

(ii) upper class boundary

(iii) class width

(iv) class mid-point

Height, h (cm)	Number of members
$140 \le h < 150$	3
$150 \le h < 160$	9
$160 \le h < 170$	17
$170 \le h < 180$	12
$180 \le h < 190$	5
$190 \le h < 200$	1

2. Location: Mean, Median and Mode

The mean, median and mode are measures of ***location*** *— this means they are a summary of where the 'centre' of the data lies. Measures of location are sometimes called* ***averages****. You'll have met the mean before, for sure.*

Learning Objectives:

- Be able to calculate the mean, median and mode for a data set.
- Be able to estimate the mean for a grouped data set, and to find a modal class and the class in which the median lies.
- Be able to recognise when each measure of location is most suitable.

The mean

The most common measure of location is called the **mean** (and is often just called 'the average'... though not while you're doing A-level Maths).

The formula for the mean ($\overline{x}$, pronounced 'x-bar') is:

$$\text{Mean} = \overline{x} = \frac{\sum x}{n} \text{ or } \frac{\sum fx}{\sum f}$$

where each x is a data value, f is the frequency of each x (the number of times it occurs), and n is the total number of data values.

Tip: The Σ (sigma) just means you add things together — so Σx means you add up all the values of x.

Tip: $n = \sum f$

Example 1

Find the mean of the following list of data: 2, 3, 6, 2, 5, 9, 3, 8, 7, 2

- First, find $\sum x = 2 + 3 + 6 + 2 + 5 + 9 + 3 + 8 + 7 + 2 = 47$
- Then divide by $n = 10$ (since there are 10 values).

This gives: $\overline{x} = \frac{\sum x}{n} = \frac{47}{10} = 4.7$

Example 2

A scientist counts the number of eggs in some song thrush nests. His data is shown in this table.

Number of eggs, x	**2**	**3**	**4**	**5**	**6**
Number of nests, f	**4**	**9**	**16**	**8**	**3**

Calculate the mean number of eggs in these nests.

- This time you have frequencies. It's best to add to the table:
  (i) a row showing the values of fx,
  (ii) a column showing the totals $\sum f$ and $\sum fx$.

Number of eggs, x	2	3	4	5	6	Total
Number of nests, f	4	9	16	8	3	40
fx	8	27	64	40	18	157

- Now use the formula for the mean: $\overline{x} = \frac{\sum fx}{\sum f} = \frac{157}{40} = 3.925 \text{ eggs}$

Tip: Instead of Σx (which means 'add up all the values of x'), you sometimes see Σx_i.

Here, you have to imagine there are x-values x_1, x_2, x_3... — then Σx_i means 'add up the values of x_i, for all the different values of i' (which is just another way of telling someone to add up all the different values of x).

So Σx and Σx_i mean exactly the same thing.

If you have **two** sets of data and then **combine** them, you can find the mean of the combined set of data in the following way.

Example 3

a) Find the mean ($\overline{x}_1$) of the data values 2, 3, 4, 5, 6.

The mean of this data is $\overline{x}_1 = \frac{\sum x}{n} = \frac{2+3+4+5+6}{5} = \frac{20}{5} = 4$

Tip: Here, $\overline{x}_1$ is the mean of one data set, and $\overline{x}_2$ is the mean of another data set.

b) **Find the mean ($\bar{x}_2$) of the data values 10, 12, 14.**

The mean of this data is $\bar{x}_2 = \frac{\sum x}{n} = \frac{10 + 12 + 14}{3} = \frac{36}{3} = 12$

Tip: You **can't** just add $\bar{x}_1$ and $\bar{x}_2$ together.

And you **can't** just find the mean of $\bar{x}_1$ and $\bar{x}_2$.

c) **Find the mean ($\bar{x}$) of the combined data set 2, 3, 4, 5, 6, 10, 12, 14.**

The mean of the combined data set is

$$\bar{x} = \frac{\sum x}{n} = \frac{2 + 3 + 4 + 5 + 6 + 10 + 12 + 14}{8} = \frac{56}{8} = 7$$

If you know a data set of size n_1 has mean $\bar{x}_1$ and another data set of size n_2 has mean $\bar{x}_2$, then the combined mean is $\bar{x}$, where:

$$\bar{x} = \frac{n_1\bar{x}_1 + n_2\bar{x}_2}{n_1 + n_2}$$

Example 4

A data set consisting of 5 values has mean $\bar{x}_1 = 4$.
A second data set consisting of 3 values has mean $\bar{x}_2 = 12$.
Find the mean ($\bar{x}$) of the combined data set.

Tip: This is the same problem as in Example 3, only it's been solved using the formula.

- Here, $n_1 = 5$ and $n_2 = 3$.
- Using the formula: $\bar{x} = \frac{n_1\bar{x}_1 + n_2\bar{x}_2}{n_1 + n_2} = \frac{(5 \times 4) + (3 \times 12)}{5 + 3} = \frac{56}{8} = 7$

Exercise 2.1

Q1 Katia visits 12 shops and records the price of a loaf of bread. Her results are shown in the table below.

£1.08	£1.15	£1.25	£1.19	£1.26	£1.24
£1.15	£1.09	£1.16	£1.20	£1.05	£1.10

Work out the mean price of a loaf of bread in these shops.

Q2 Twenty students sit a maths exam. The teacher records their marks $\{x_1, \ldots, x_{20}\}$ and calculates that $\sum x = 1672$.
Work out the mean mark for these students.

Q3 The numbers of goals scored by 20 football teams in their most recent match are shown in the table.

Number of goals, x	0	1	2	3	4
Frequency, f	5	7	4	3	1

Calculate the mean number of goals scored by these teams in their most recent match.

Q4 A drama group has 15 members.
The mean age of the members is 47.4 years.

a) Work out the total of the ages of all members of the drama group.

b) A person aged 17 joins the drama group. Find the new mean age.

The mode and the median

There are two other important measures of location you need to know about — the **mode** and the **median**.

Mode = most frequently occurring data value.

Tip: The mode is often called the **modal value**.

Examples

Find the modes of the following data sets.

a) 2, 3, 6, 2, 5, 9, 3, 8, 7, 2

The most frequent data value is 2, appearing three times.

So the mode = 2.

b) 4, 3, 6, 4, 5, 9, 2, 8, 7, 5

This time there are two modes — the values 4 and 5 both appear twice.

So the modes = 4 and 5.

Tip: If a data set has two modes, then it is called **bimodal**.

c) 4, 3, 6, 11, 5, 9, 2, 8, 7, 12

This time there are no modes — each value appears just once.

The median is slightly trickier to find than the mode.

Median = value in the middle of the data set when all the data values are placed in order of size.

First put your n data values **in order**, then find the **position** of the median in the ordered list. There are two possibilities:

(i) if $\frac{n}{2}$ is a **whole number** (i.e. n is even), then the median is halfway between the values in this position and the position above.

(ii) if $\frac{n}{2}$ is **not** a **whole number** (i.e. n is odd), **round it up** to find the position of the median.

Examples

Find the medians of the following data sets.

a) 2, 3, 6, 2, 6, 9, 3, 8, 7

- Put the values in order first: 2, 2, 3, 3, 6, 6, 7, 8, 9
- There are 9 values, and $\frac{n}{2} = \frac{9}{2} = 4.5$. Rounding this up to 5 means that the median is the 5th value in the ordered list — median = 6.

b) 4, 3, 11, 4, 10, 9, 3, 8, 7, 8

- Put the values in order first: 3, 3, 4, 4, 7, 8, 8, 9, 10, 11
- There are 10 values, and $\frac{n}{2} = \frac{10}{2} = 5$.
- So the median is halfway between the 5th value in the ordered list (= 7) and the 6th value (= 8). So the median = 7.5.

Tip: The value halfway between two numbers is their mean.

If your data is in a **frequency table**, then the mode and the median are still easy to find as long as the data **isn't grouped**.

Tip: Frequency means the number of times a data value occurs.

Here, the data values are the 'numbers of letters' they received. So the frequencies are the 'numbers of houses' (that received that many letters).

Example 1

The number of letters received one day in a sample of houses is shown in this table.

Number of letters	Number of houses
0	11
1	25
2	27
3	21
4	9
5	7

a) Find the modal number of letters.

- The modal number of letters just means the mode.
- The highest frequency is for 2 letters — so the mode = 2 letters.

b) Find the median number of letters.

- It's useful to add a column to show the **cumulative frequency** — this is just a **running total** of the frequency column.

No. of letters	No. of houses (frequency)	Cumulative frequency
0	11	11
1	25	36
2	27	63
3	21	84
4	9	93
5	7	100

- The total number of houses is the final cumulative frequency, so $n = 100$.
- Since $\frac{n}{2} = \frac{100}{2} = 50$, the median is halfway between the 50th and 51st data values.
- Using the cumulative frequency, you can see that the data values in positions 37 to 63 all equal 2. This means the data values at positions 50 and 51 are both 2. So the median = 2 letters.

Example 2

The ages of the members of a local youth group are given in the table:

Age in years, x	**14**	**15**	**16**	**17**	**18**
Frequency, f	**5**	**4**	**4**	**4**	**4**

a) Find the modal age.

- The modal age just means the mode of the data.
- The highest frequency is for 14 years, so the mode = 14 years.

b) Find the median age.

- Add a row:

Age in years, x	14	15	16	17	18
Frequency, f	5	4	4	4	4
Cumulative frequency	5	9	13	17	21

- The total number of students is $n = 21$, so $\frac{n}{2} = \frac{21}{2} = 10.5$. Round up to 11 to find that the median is the 11th data value.
- Using the cumulative frequency, you can see that all the data values in positions 10 to 13 equal 16, so the median = 16 years.

Exercise 2.2

Q1 Seventeen friends took part in a charity fun run.
The amount of money that each friend raised is shown below.

£250	£19	£500	£123	£185	£101
£45	£67	£194	£77	£108	£110
£187	£216	£84	£98	£140	

a) Find the median amount of money raised by these friends.

b) Explain why it is not possible to find the mode for this data.

Q2 A financial adviser records the interest rates charged by 12 different banks to customers taking out a loan. His findings are below.

6.2% 6.9% 6.9% 8.8% 6.3% 7.4%

6.5% 6.4% 9.9% 6.2% 6.4% 6.9%

a) Write down the mode of these interest rates.

b) Find the median interest rate charged by these banks.

Q3 An online seller has received the ratings shown in this table.

a) Write down the modal customer rating.

b) Work out the median customer rating.

Rating	Number of customers
1	7
2	5
3	25
4	67
5	72

Q4 A theatre stages 35 performances of its pantomime one year. This table shows the number of completely empty rows for each performance.

Rows empty	0	1	2	3	4	5
Number of performances	10	7	6	7	4	1

a) Write down the value of the mode.

b) Work out the median number of empty rows.

Q5 Kwasi and Ben each check the number of full seconds that their computers take to start the same program on several occasions.
The table shows their results:

Time to start program (s)	3	4	5	6	7
Frequency for Kwasi's computer	3	5	4	7	3
Frequency for Ben's computer	0	6	5	6	2

a) Write down the modal speed(s) for: (i) Kwasi (ii) Ben

b) Find the median speed for: (i) Kwasi (ii) Ben

Averages of grouped data

If you have **grouped data**, you can't find exact values for the mean and median. This is because the grouping means you no longer have the exact data values. And instead of a mode, you can only find a **modal class**.

Modal class

- To find a **modal class**, you need to find the class with the **highest frequency** (assuming all the classes are the same width).

Example

Find the modal class for this data showing the heights of various shrubs.

Height of shrub to nearest cm	11-20	21-30	31-40	41-50
Number of shrubs	11	22	29	16

- In this example, all the classes are the same width (= 10 cm).
- So the modal class is the class with the highest frequency.
- This means the modal class is 31-40 cm.

Mean

- To find an **estimate** of the **mean**, you assume that every reading in a class takes the value of the class **mid-point**.
- Then you can use the formula $\bar{x} = \frac{\sum fx}{\sum f}$.

Tip: This is the formula from page 7.

Example

The heights of a number of trees were recorded. The data collected is shown in this table.

Height of tree to nearest m	0-5	6-10	11-15	16-20
Number of trees	26	17	11	6

Find an estimate of the mean height of the trees.

Tip: The frequency (f) is the 'Number of trees'.

- It's best to make another table. Include extra rows showing:
  (i) the class mid-points (x),
  (ii) the values of fx, where f is the frequency.
- And add an extra column for the totals $\sum f$ and $\sum fx$.

Height of tree to nearest m	0-5	6-10	11-15	16-20	**Total**
Class mid-point, x	2.75	8	13	18	
Number of trees, f	26	17	11	6	60 (= Σf)
fx	71.5	136	143	108	458.5 (= Σfx)

Tip: For the first class:
Lower class boundary = 0
Upper class boundary = 5.5
So the class mid-point = (0 + 5.5) ÷ 2 = 2.75

(See p5 for more information.)

- Now you can use the formula for the mean given above.

$$\text{Mean} = \bar{x} = \frac{\sum fx}{\sum f} = \frac{458.5}{60} = 7.64 \text{ m (to 2 d.p.)}$$

Median

- You can find the class which contains the median easily.
- Just divide $\sum f$ by 2 and use the rules from page 9 to find the position of the median data value in an ordered list.
- Then you can use your table to work out what class the median lies in.

Example

For the data in the previous example, find the class which contains the median data value.

- Here, f is the number of trees in each class. The total number of trees, $\sum f$, is 60. So $60 \div 2 = 30$.
- So the median value is halfway between the 30th and 31st data values. Both these data values are in the class 6-10.
- So the median lies in the 6-10 class.

Exercise 2.3

Q1 The time that 60 students took to change after PE is shown below.

Time (t, mins)	Frequency, f	Mid-point, x	fx
$3 \le t < 4$	7	3.5	24.5
$4 \le t < 5$	14	4.5	
$5 \le t < 6$	24		
$6 \le t < 8$	10		
$8 \le t < 10$	5		

Q1 Hint: Don't give your answers to too many decimal places when you're estimating something.

a) Copy and complete the table.

b) Use the table to work out an estimate of the mean time it took these children to change.

Q2 A postman records the number of letters delivered to each of 50 houses one day. The results are shown in this table.

Number of letters	Number of houses
0-2	20
3-5	16
6-8	7
9-11	5
12-14	2

a) State the modal class.

b) Estimate the mean number of letters delivered to these houses.

c) Write down the interval containing the median.

Q3 The table shows the amount of rainfall (r, in mm) recorded at some weather stations one March.

Rainfall (r, mm)	Frequency
$20 \le r < 40$	5
$40 \le r < 50$	7
$50 \le r < 60$	9
$60 \le r < 80$	15
$80 \le r < 100$	8
$100 \le r < 120$	2

a) Estimate the mean amount of rainfall, in mm, at these weather stations during this month.

b) Show that the median value of rainfall lies in the class $60 \le r < 80$.

Q4 The table below shows the times that a random sample of 60 runners took to complete a marathon.

Estimate the mean time of these runners. (You may use $\sum fx = 16740$, where x is the mid-point of a class.)

Time (t,mins)	Frequency, f
$180 \le t < 240$	8
$240 \le t < 270$	19
$270 \le t < 300$	21
$300 \le t < 360$	9
$360 \le t < 480$	3

Comparing measures of location

Tip: An extreme value is a freak piece of data that lies a long way from the majority of the readings in a data set. It's sometimes called an outlier.

You've seen three different measures of location — the mean, the median and the mode. Each of them is useful for different kinds of data.

Mean

- The mean's a good average because you use **all** your data in working it out.
- But it can be heavily affected by **extreme values** and by distributions of data values that are **not symmetric**.
- And it can only be used with **quantitative** data (i.e. numbers).

Tip: A **symmetric** data set is one where the distribution of data values **above** the mean is the mirror image of the distribution of values **below** the mean.

Median

- The median is **not** affected by extreme values.
- This also makes it a good average to use when the data set is **not symmetric**.

Mode

- The mode can be used with **qualitative** (non-numerical) data.
- But some data sets can have **more than one** mode (and if every value in a data set occurs just once, then the mode isn't very helpful at all).

Tip: You saw a **bimodal** data set (with two modes) on p9.

Other data sets may have more than two modes.

Exercise 2.4

Q1 Hint: Think about how symmetric the data will be. For example, in part a), think about how many people you might expect to earn quite a low salary, and how many you might expect to earn a very high salary.

Q1 Explain whether the mean, median or mode would be most suitable as a summary of each of the following data sets.

a) Salaries of each employee at a company.

b) Length of adult female adder snakes.

c) Make of cars parked in a car park.

d) Weight of all newborn full-term babies born one year at a hospital.

e) Distance a firm's employees travel to work each morning.

Q2 Hosi records the number of bedrooms in the houses lived in by a sample of 10 adults. His results are shown in the table.

Number of bedrooms	1	2	3	4	5	6	7	8
Frequency	1	2	4	2	0	0	0	1

Explain why the mean may not be the most suitable measure of location for the data.

3. Dispersion

A measure of location tells you roughly where the centre of the data lies. Dispersion, on the other hand, tells you how spread out the data values are. There are a few different measures of dispersion that you'll need to know about.

Learning Objectives:

- Be able to calculate the range and interquartile range.
- Be able to calculate and interpret variance and standard deviation (including with the use of linear scaling).

Range and interquartile range

Range

The **range** is about the simplest measure of dispersion you can imagine.

Range = highest value – lowest value

But the range is heavily affected by **extreme values**, so it isn't really the most useful way to measure dispersion.

Interquartile range

A more useful way to measure dispersion is to use the **interquartile range** — but first you have to find the **quartiles**. You've already seen how the median divides a data set into two halves. The quartiles are similar — there are three quartiles altogether (usually labelled Q_1, Q_2 and Q_3) and they divide the data into **four parts**.

- Q_1 is the **lower quartile** — 25% of the data is less than or equal to the lower quartile.
- Q_2 is the **median** — 50% of the data is less than or equal to the median.
- Q_3 is the **upper quartile** — 75% of the data is less than or equal to the upper quartile.

For example, the values in the data set below have been sorted so that they're in numerical order, starting with the smallest. The three quartiles are shown.

1 2 3 4 4 4 5 | 5 5 6 6 7 7 9

Q_1 (at the first 4), Q_2 (between the two 5s), Q_3 (at the second 6)

$Q_1 = 4$
$Q_2 = 5$
$Q_3 = 6$

Tip: There are various ways you can find the quartiles, and they sometimes give different results. But if you use the methods below, you'll be fine.

The quartiles are worked out in a similar way to the median — by first finding their **position** in the ordered list of data values.

To find the position of the **lower quartile** (Q_1), first work out $\frac{n}{4}$.

- if $\frac{n}{4}$ is a **whole number**, then the **lower quartile** is halfway between the values in this position and the position above.
- if $\frac{n}{4}$ is **not** a whole number, **round it up** to find the position of the lower quartile.

Tip: This is the same as the method used on page 9 for finding the median, only with $\frac{n}{2}$ replaced by $\frac{n}{4}$.

To find the position of the **upper quartile** (Q_3), first work out $\frac{3n}{4}$.

- if $\frac{3n}{4}$ is a **whole number**, then the **upper quartile** is halfway between the values in this position and the position above.
- if $\frac{3n}{4}$ is **not** a whole number, **round it up** to find the position of the upper quartile.

Tip: This is the same as the method used on page 9 for finding the median, only with $\frac{n}{2}$ replaced by $\frac{3n}{4}$.

Tip: You don't need to know the median (Q_2) to calculate the interquartile range.

Once you've found the upper and lower quartiles, you can find the **interquartile range** (IQR).

Interquartile range (IQR) = upper quartile (Q_3) – lower quartile (Q_1)

- The interquartile range is a measure of **dispersion**.
- It actually shows the range of the 'middle 50%' of the data.
- This means it's not affected by **extreme values**, but it still tells you something about how spread out the data values are.

Example 1

a) Find the median and quartiles of the following data set:
2, 5, 3, 11, 6, 8, 3, 8, 1, 6, 2, 23, 9, 11, 18, 19, 22, 7

- First put the list in order:
  1, 2, 2, 3, 3, 5, 6, 6, 7, 8, 8, 9, 11, 11, 18, 19, 22, 23
- You need Q_1, Q_2 and Q_3, so find $\frac{n}{4}$, $\frac{n}{2}$ and $\frac{3n}{4}$, where $n = 18$.
- $\frac{n}{4} = \frac{18}{4} = 4.5$. This is **not** a whole number, so round up to 5.
  This means the lower quartile is equal to the 5th term: $Q_1 = 3$
- $\frac{n}{2} = \frac{18}{2} = 9$ is a **whole number**. The median is halfway between the 9th term (= 7) and the 10th term (= 8). So $Q_2 = 7.5$
- $\frac{3n}{4} = \frac{54}{4} = 13.5$ is **not** a whole number, so round up to 14.
  This means the upper quartile is equal to the 14th term: $Q_3 = 11$

b) Find the interquartile range for the above data.

- Interquartile range = $Q_3 - Q_1 = 11 - 3 = 8$

Example 2

Find the median and interquartile range for the data below showing the number of DVDs rented from a DVD rental shop per customer in a week.

Number of rentals per customer	**1**	**2**	**3**	**4**	**5-6**
Frequency	**7**	**3**	**1**	**1**	**3**

- First add a row to the table showing cumulative frequency.

Number of rentals per customer	1	2	3	4	5-6
Frequency	7	3	1	1	3
Cumulative frequency	7	10	11	12	15

- To find the median calculate $\frac{n}{2} = \frac{15}{2} = 7.5$.
  Round up to find that the median is the 8th data value.
- Using the cumulative frequency, you can see that Q_2 is 2.

Now to find the quartiles, starting with the **lower quartile** (Q_1).

- First calculate $\frac{n}{4} = \frac{15}{4} = 3.75$.
  Round up to find that Q_1 is the 4th data value.
- Using the cumulative frequency, you can see that Q_1 is 1.

Find the **upper quartile** (Q_3) in the same way.

- First, calculate $\frac{3n}{4} = \frac{3 \times 15}{4} = 11.25$.
  Round up to find that Q_3 is the 12th value.
- So Q_3 is 4.
- So the **interquartile range** is $Q_3 - Q_1 = 4 - 1 = 3$.

Exercise 3.1

Q1 The diameters (in miles) of the eight planets in the Solar System are given below:

3032, 7521, 7926, 4222, 88 846, 74 898, 31 763, 30 778

For this data set, calculate:

a) the range

b) (i) the lower quartile (Q_1)
(ii) the upper quartile (Q_3)
(iii) the interquartile range (IQR)

Q2 Each of the three data sets below shows the speeds (in mph) of 18 different cars observed at a certain time and place.

In town at 8:45 am:
14, 16, 15, 18, 15, 17, 16, 16, 18, 16, 15, 13, 15, 14, 16, 17, 18, 15

In town at 10:45 am:
34, 29, 36, 32, 31, 38, 30, 35, 39, 31, 29, 30, 25, 29, 33, 34, 36, 31

On the motorway at 1 pm:
67, 76, 78, 71, 73, 88, 74, 69, 75, 76, 95, 71, 69, 78, 73, 76, 75, 74

For each set of data, calculate:

a) the range

b) the interquartile range (IQR)

Q3 The number of empty seats on 25 flights from Manchester to New York are shown in the table.

Empty seats	Frequency
1	2
2	5
3	7
4	1
5	4
6-8	3
9-15	3

For this data, find:

a) the lower quartile (Q_1)

b) the upper quartile (Q_3)

c) the interquartile range (IQR)

Variance and standard deviation

Variance and standard deviation are two (very closely related) measures of **dispersion** — they give you an idea of **how spread out** the data values are from the mean. The bigger the variance (or standard deviation), the more spread out your readings are.

Variance

- There are two ways to write the formula for the **variance**.
  The second one in the box below is usually much easier to use.

$$\text{variance} = \frac{\sum(x-\bar{x})^2}{n} \quad \text{or} \quad \text{variance} = \frac{\sum x^2}{n} - \bar{x}^2$$

- Here, the x-values are the data, $\bar{x}$ is the mean, and n is the total number of data values.
- The two formulas above are equivalent to each other — you can rearrange one to get the other (although you **won't** be asked to do this in the exam).

$$\frac{\sum(x-\bar{x})^2}{n} = \frac{1}{n}\sum(x^2 - 2x\bar{x} + \bar{x}^2) \quad \text{(multiplying out brackets)}$$

$$= \frac{1}{n}\sum x^2 - 2\cdot\frac{1}{n}\cdot\bar{x}\sum x + \frac{1}{n}\sum\bar{x}^2 \quad \text{(writing as 3 summations)}$$

$$= \frac{1}{n}\sum x^2 - 2\cdot\frac{1}{n}\cdot n\bar{x}^2 + \frac{1}{n}\sum\bar{x}^2 \quad \text{(since } \textstyle\sum x = n\bar{x}\text{)}$$

$$= \frac{1}{n}\sum x^2 - 2\cdot\frac{1}{n}\cdot n\bar{x}^2 + \frac{1}{n}\cdot n\bar{x}^2 \quad \text{(since } \textstyle\sum \bar{x}^2 = n\bar{x}^2\text{)}$$

$$= \frac{1}{n}\sum x^2 - \bar{x}^2 = \frac{\sum x^2}{n} - \bar{x}^2 \quad \text{(combining the 2nd and 3rd terms)}$$

$\bar{x}$ is just a number, so you can 'take it outside the summation'.

Standard deviation

The **standard deviation** is equal to the **square root** of the variance.

$$\text{Standard deviation} = \sqrt{\text{variance}}$$

The standard deviation is measured in the same units as the data values themselves — this sometimes makes it a more useful measure of dispersion than the variance.

Tip: You can remember the formula on the right as saying:

'The variance is equal to the mean of the squares ($\frac{\sum x^2}{n}$) minus the square of the mean ($\bar{x}^2$).'

The formula on the left makes it easier to understand what the variance actually is — it's 'the average of the squared deviations from the mean'.

Tip: These formulas for the variance are used when you've got data values for a whole **population**. They're not on the formula sheet — you'll need to learn them.

You might notice that there is a similar one on the formula sheet:

$$S^2 = \frac{\sum(X_i - \bar{X})^2}{n-1}$$

This is only used when you've got data from a **sample** of the population (see pages 114-118).

Tip: The variance is measured in squared units. For example, if the data values are measured in metres (m), then the variance is measured in m^2.

Examples

Find the variance and standard deviation of the following data set:
2, 3, 4, 4, 6, 11, 12

- Find the **sum** of the numbers first: $\sum x = 2 + 3 + 4 + 4 + 6 + 11 + 12 = 42$
- Then finding the **mean** is easy: $\bar{x} = \frac{\sum x}{n} = \frac{42}{7} = 6$

- Next find the **sum of the squares**: $\sum x^2 = 4 + 9 + 16 + 16 + 36 + 121 + 144 = 346$
- Now finding the '**mean of the squares**' is easy: $\frac{\sum x^2}{n} = \frac{346}{7}$
- The **variance** is the 'mean of the squares minus the square of the mean':

  Variance $= \frac{\sum x^2}{n} - \bar{x}^2 = \frac{346}{7} - 6^2 = 13.428... = 13.4$ (to 3 sig.fig.)
- Take the **square root** of the variance to find the **standard deviation**:

  Standard deviation $= \sqrt{13.428...} = 3.66$ (to 3 sig.fig.)

Tip: The alternative formula for the variance is variance $= \frac{\sum(x - \bar{x})^2}{n}$.

But it's more fiddly to use this formula than the one used in the example. This is because once you've worked out the mean, you then have to **subtract it from each individual data** value, before squaring and adding the results, and then dividing by n.

The formula used on the left involves only a **single subtraction**.

If your data is given in a **frequency table**, then the variance formula can be written like this, where f is the frequency of each x.

$$\text{variance} = \frac{\sum fx^2}{\sum f} - \bar{x}^2, \quad \text{where } \bar{x} = \frac{\sum fx}{\sum f}$$

Tip: Here, $n = \sum f$.

Tip: Remember... fx^2 means $f \times (x^2)$ — <u>not</u> $(fx)^2$.

Example

Find the variance and standard deviation of the data in this table.

x	2	3	4	5	6	7
frequency, f	2	5	5	4	1	1

- It's best to start by adding an extra row to the table showing the values of fx.

x	2	3	4	5	6	7
frequency, f	2	5	5	4	1	1
fx	4	15	20	20	6	7

- The **number** of values is: $\sum f = 2 + 5 + 5 + 4 + 1 + 1 = 18$
- The **sum** of the values is: $\sum fx = 4 + 15 + 20 + 20 + 6 + 7 = 72$
- So the **mean** of the values is: $\bar{x} = \frac{\sum fx}{\sum f} = \frac{72}{18} = 4$
- Now add two more rows to your table showing x^2 and fx^2.

x^2	4	9	16	25	36	49
fx^2	8	45	80	100	36	49

- Now you can work out $\sum fx^2$.

  $\sum fx^2 = 8 + 45 + 80 + 100 + 36 + 49 = 318$
- And now you can find the variance.

  Variance $= \frac{\sum fx^2}{\sum f} - \bar{x}^2 = \frac{318}{18} - 4^2 = 1.666... = 1.67$ (to 3 sig.fig.)
- Then take the **square root** of the variance to find the **standard deviation**:

  Standard deviation $= \sqrt{1.666...} = 1.29$ (to 3 sig.fig.)

Tip: You could also write this formula as variance $= \frac{\sum f(x - \bar{x})^2}{\sum f}$

But it's trickier to use than the formula in the blue box — again, because of all the extra subtracting you need to do.

Tip: This is the same assumption you used when you found the **mean** of grouped data on p12.

If your data is **grouped**, then you can only **estimate** the variance and standard deviation (because you don't know the actual data values — see p12).

In this case, assume that each data value is equal to the **class mid-point**. Then go through the same steps as in the example above.

Example

The heights of sunflowers in a garden were measured, and are recorded in the table below.

Height of sunflower, h (cm)	**$150 \le h < 170$**	**$170 \le h < 190$**	**$190 \le h < 210$**	**$210 \le h < 230$**
Frequency, f	**5**	**10**	**12**	**3**

Estimate the variance and the standard deviation of the heights.

- Start by adding extra rows for the class mid-points x, as well as fx, x^2 and fx^2:

Height of sunflower, h (cm)	$150 \le h < 170$	$170 \le h < 190$	$190 \le h < 210$	$210 \le h < 230$
Frequency, f	5	10	12	3
Class mid-point, x	160	180	200	220
fx	800	1800	2400	660
x^2	25 600	32 400	40 000	48 400
fx^2	128 000	324 000	480 000	145 200

- The **number** of values is: $\sum f = 5 + 10 + 12 + 3 = 30$
- The **sum** of the values is: $\sum fx = 800 + 1800 + 2400 + 660 = 5660$
- So the **mean** of the values is: $\bar{x} = \frac{\sum fx}{\sum f} = \frac{5660}{30}$
- $\sum fx^2 = 128\,000 + 324\,000 + 480\,000 + 145\,200 = 1\,077\,200$
- So variance $= \frac{\sum fx^2}{\sum f} - \bar{x}^2 = \frac{1\,077\,200}{30} - \left(\frac{5660}{30}\right)^2$

$= 311.5555...$

$= 312$ cm^2 (to 3 sig. fig.)

- And standard deviation $= \sqrt{311.5555...} = 17.7$ cm (to 3 sig. fig.)

Tip: Remember... variance takes 'squared' units.

You can use the variances (or standard deviations) of two small data sets to find the overall variance (or standard deviation) of the larger, combined set of data. But it's a bit fiddly, and so you need to do this very carefully.

Example

The mean of 10 boys' heights is 180 cm, with a standard deviation of 10 cm. The mean height of 9 girls is 165 cm, with a standard deviation of 8 cm.

Find the variance and standard deviation of the combined group of 19 heights.

You need to know the mean of the combined set of heights to be able to work out the variance. So find that first.

- Call the boys' heights x and the girls' heights y.
- First, write down the formula for the mean, and substitute in the mean for the boys ($\bar{x}$) and the total number of values (n). This gives you the **sum** of all the boys' heights, $\sum x$.
  $$\bar{x} = \frac{\sum x}{n} \Rightarrow 180 = \frac{\sum x}{10} \Rightarrow \sum x = 1800$$
- Do the same to find the sum of the girls' heights, $\sum y$.
  $$\bar{y} = \frac{\sum y}{n} \Rightarrow 165 = \frac{\sum y}{9} \Rightarrow \sum y = 1485$$
- So the sum of the heights of the combined group of boys and girls is:
  $$\sum x + \sum y = 1800 + 1485 = 3285$$
- The total number of boys and girls is 10 + 9 = 19. So the mean height of the combined group is:
  $$\frac{3285}{19} = \mathbf{172.9\ cm}$$

Tip: You could use the formula from p8 to find the combined mean:
$$\bar{x} = \frac{n_1\bar{x}_1 + n_2\bar{x}_2}{n_1 + n_2}$$

Tip: Round the fraction to 1 d.p. to give your answer. But when you use the mean in more calculations, use the fraction (or your calculator's memory) so you don't lose accuracy.

Now you need to go through a very similar process to find the sum of the squares of the combined set of heights.

- The standard deviation for the boys is 10, so the variance = $10^2 = 100$. The standard deviation for the girls is 8, so the variance = $8^2 = 64$.
- Substitute the boys' variance into the formula for the variance. This will give you the sum of the squares of their heights, $\sum x^2$.
  $$\text{variance}_x = \frac{\sum x^2}{n} - \bar{x}^2 = \frac{\sum x^2}{10} - 180^2 = 100$$
  So $\sum x^2 = 10 \times (180^2 + 100) = 325\,000$
- Now do the same for the girls to find $\sum y^2$.
  $$\text{variance}_y = \frac{\sum y^2}{n} - \bar{y}^2 = \frac{\sum y^2}{9} - 165^2 = 64$$
  So $\sum y^2 = 9 \times (165^2 + 64) = 245\,601$
- So the sum of the squares for the combined group of boys and girls is:
  $$\sum x^2 + \sum y^2 = 325\,000 + 245\,601 = \mathbf{570\,601}$$

Tip: Here, variance$_x$ is the variance of the boys' heights, and variance$_y$ is the variance of the girls' heights.

Tip: Don't use the rounded mean (172.9) — you'll lose accuracy.

- You now have all the information you need to find the variance for the combined group.

  $$\text{variance} = \frac{570\,601}{19} - \left(\frac{3285}{19}\right)^2 = 139.0415... = 139.0\text{ cm}^2 \text{ (to 1 d.p.)}$$

- And finally the standard deviation of the boys and the girls is:

  $$\text{standard deviation} = \sqrt{139.0415...} = 11.8\text{ cm (to 1 d.p.)}$$

You've seen that different measures of **location** are useful in different ways (see page 14). The same is true of measures of **dispersion** — the range, interquartile range, variance and standard deviation all have pros and cons.

Range

- The range is the **easiest** measure of dispersion to calculate.
- But it's heavily affected by even a **single** extreme value. And it depends on only **two** data values — it **doesn't** tell you anything about how spread out the rest of the values are.

Interquartile range

- It's **not** affected by **extreme values** — so if your data contains **extreme values**, then the interquartile range is a good measure of dispersion to use.
- It's fairly **tricky** to work out.

Variance

- The variance depends on **all** the data values — so no values are 'ignored'.
- But it's **tricky** to work out, and is affected by **extreme values** (meaning that 'freak' values have more influence than they deserve).
- It's also expressed in **different units** from the actual data values, so it can be difficult to interpret.

Standard deviation

- Like the variance, the standard deviation depends on **all** the data values — so no values are 'ignored'.
- It has the **same units** as the data values themselves, and so is easier to understand and interpret.
- But it is also **tricky** to work out, and affected by **extreme values**.

Exercise 3.2

Q1 The attendance figures (x) for Wessex Football Club's first six matches of the season were: 756, 755, 764, 778, 754, 759.

a) Find the mean ($\bar{x}$) of these attendance figures.

b) Calculate the sum of the squares of the attendance figures, $\sum x^2$.

c) Use your answers to find the variance of the attendance figures.

d) Hence find the standard deviation of the attendance figures.

e) Explain why the standard deviation is a reasonable measure of dispersion to use with this data.

Q2 The number of runners in the first eight Broughton marathons were:
32, 21, 75, 22, 88, 98, 71, 73

a) Calculate the variance for these figures.
b) Find the standard deviation of the number of runners.

Q3 The figures for the number of TVs (x) in the households of 20 students are shown in the table below.

x	1	2	3	4
frequency, f	7	8	4	1

a) Find the mean number of TVs ($\overline{x}$) in the 20 households.
b) By adding rows showing x^2 and fx^2 to the table, find $\sum fx^2$.
c) Calculate the variance for the data above.
d) Hence find the standard deviation.

Q4 Find the variance of the data in this frequency table.

x	7	8	9	10	11	12
frequency, f	2	3	5	7	4	2

Q5 The pulse rates while resting of a number of students were measured. They are shown in the grouped frequency table below.
(You can assume that a pulse rate is always a whole number.)

Pulse rate	56-60	61-65	66-70	71-75	76-80
frequency, f	1	2	4	8	5

a) Add four extra rows to the table showing:
 (i) the class mid-points (x)
 (ii) fx (iii) x^2 (iv) fx^2
b) Use your table to find: (i) $\sum f$ (ii) $\sum fx$ (iii) $\sum fx^2$
c) Use your answers to estimate the variance of the pulse rates.

Q6 The yields (w, in kg) of potatoes from a number of allotments are shown in the grouped frequency table on the right.

Yield, w (kg)	Frequency
$50 \leq w < 60$	23
$60 \leq w < 70$	12
$70 \leq w < 80$	15
$80 \leq w < 90$	6
$90 \leq w < 100$	2

a) Estimate the variance for this data.
b) Estimate the standard deviation.

Q7 Su and Ellen are collecting data on the durations of the eruptions of the volcano in their garden. Between them, they have recorded the duration of the last 60 eruptions.

- Su has timed 23 eruptions, with an average duration of 3.42 minutes and a standard deviation of 1.07 minutes.
- Ellen has timed 37 eruptions, with an average duration of 3.92 minutes and a standard deviation of 0.97 minutes.

They decide to combine their observations into one large data set.

a) Calculate the mean duration of all the observed eruptions.
b) Find the variance of the set of 60 durations.
c) Find the standard deviation of the set of 60 durations.

Linear scaling

Tip: Choose what to add/subtract and multiply/divide by based on what makes your data easiest to work with.

Linear scaling means doing something to all the readings in your data set to make the numbers easier to work with. That could mean:

- **adding** a number to (or **subtracting** a number from) all your readings,
- **multiplying** (or **dividing**) all your readings by a number,
- **both** of the above.

For example, finding the mean of 1831, 1832 and 1836 looks complicated. But if you subtract 1830 from each number, then finding the mean of what's left (1, 2 and 6) is much easier — it's 3. So the mean of the original numbers must be 1833 (once you've 'undone' the linear scaling). That's linear scaling in a nutshell.

- You have to change your original variable, x, to a different one, such as y (so in the example above, if $x = 1831$, then $y = 1$).
- An **original** data value x will be related to a **scaled** data value y by an equation of this form: → $y = \frac{x - \mathrm{a}}{\mathrm{b}}$ where a and b are numbers you choose.
- The mean and standard deviation of the **original** data values will then be related to the mean and standard deviation of the **scaled** data values by the following equations:

Tip: Note that if you **don't multiply or divide** your readings by anything (i.e. if b = 1), then the dispersion isn't changed.

- $\bar{y} = \frac{\bar{x} - \mathrm{a}}{\mathrm{b}}$, where $\bar{x}$ and $\bar{y}$ are the means of variables x and y
- standard deviation of $y = \frac{\text{standard deviation of } x}{\mathrm{b}}$

Example

Find the mean and standard deviation of: 1 862 020, 1 862 040, 1 862 010 and 1 862 050.

- All the **original** data values (call them x) start with the same four digits (1862) — so start by subtracting 1 862 000 from every reading to leave 20, 40, 10 and 50.
- You can then make life even simpler by dividing by 10 — giving 2, 4, 1 and 5. These are the **scaled** data values (call them y).
- So putting those steps together, each x-value is related to a corresponding y-value by the equation: $y = \frac{x - 1862000}{10}$

Tip: This means a = 1 862 000 and b = 10.

- Now work out the **mean** and **standard deviation** of the (easy-to-use) scaled values.

$$\bar{y} = \frac{2 + 4 + 1 + 5}{4} = \frac{12}{4} = 3$$

$$\text{standard deviation of } y = \sqrt{\frac{2^2 + 4^2 + 1^2 + 5^2}{4} - 3^2}$$
$$= \sqrt{\frac{46}{4} - 9} = \sqrt{2.5} = 1.58 \text{ to 3 sig. fig.}$$

Tip: Remember... standard deviation $= \sqrt{\frac{\sum x^2}{n} - \bar{x}^2}$

- Then find the mean and standard deviation of the original values using the formulas above.
- $\bar{y} = \frac{\bar{x} - \mathrm{a}}{\mathrm{b}}$, so $\bar{x} = \mathrm{a} + \mathrm{b}\bar{y}$. This means: $\bar{x} = 1862000 + 10\bar{y}$

$$= 1862000 + (10 \times 3)$$
$$= 1862030$$

- And standard deviation of $y = \frac{\text{standard deviation of } x}{\text{b}}$

  So standard deviation of x = b × standard deviation of y
  = 10 × 1.58 = 15.8 (to 3 sig. fig.)

Carry out the method in exactly the same way with **grouped** data. Remember, with grouped data, you assume that all the readings equal the **class mid-point**, and so this is the x-value that you use with the linear-scaling equation $y = \frac{x - \text{a}}{\text{b}}$.

Example

Estimate the mean and standard deviation of this data concerning job interviews using the linear scaling $y = \frac{x - 15.5}{10}$.

Length of interview, to nearest minute	**11-20**	**21-30**	**31-40**	**41-50**
Frequency, f	**17**	**21**	**27**	**15**

Tip: So here, a = 15.5 and b = 10.

- Make a new table showing the class mid-points (x) of the original data, and the scaled class mid-points (y). Also include rows for fy, y^2 and fy^2.

Length of interview, to nearest minute	11-20	21-30	31-40	41-50
Frequency, f	17	21	27	15
Class mid-point, x	15.5	25.5	35.5	45.5
Scaled value, y	0	1	2	3
fy	0	21	54	45
y^2	0	1	4	9
fy^2	0	21	108	135

Now use your table to find the mean of the **scaled** values ($\overline{y}$).

- The **number** of scaled values is: $\sum f = 17 + 21 + 27 + 15 = 80$
- The **sum** of the scaled values is: $\sum fy = 0 + 21 + 54 + 45 = 120$
- So the **mean** of the scaled values is: $\overline{y} = \frac{\sum fy}{\sum f} = \frac{120}{80} = \mathbf{1.5}$

Now for the standard deviation...

- $\sum fy^2 = 0 + 21 + 108 + 135 = 264$
- So variance $= \frac{\sum fy^2}{\sum f} - \overline{y}^2 = \frac{264}{80} - 1.5^2 = 1.05$
- This gives a standard deviation for the **scaled** data of:
  standard deviation of $y = \sqrt{1.05} = \mathbf{1.02}$ (to 3 sig. fig.).

And now you can use these figures to find the mean and standard deviation of the **original** data.

- $\overline{y} = \frac{\overline{x} - \text{a}}{\text{b}}$, so $\overline{x} = \text{a} + \text{b}\overline{y} = 15.5 + 10 \times 1.5 =$ 30.5 minutes
- And standard deviation of $y = \frac{\text{standard deviation of } x}{\text{b}}$.
  So standard deviation of x = b × standard deviation of y
  = 10 × 1.02 = 10.2 minutes (to 3 sig. fig.)
- This means the standard deviation of the interview lengths is 10.2 minutes (to 3 sig. fig.) .

Sometimes, you won't have the data itself — just some **summations**.

> **Tip:** The variables aren't x and y this time, but you can still go through exactly the same steps as before.

Example

A travel guide employee collects some data on the cost (c, in £) of a night's stay in 10 hotels in a particular town. He scales his data using $d = 10(c - 93.5)$, and calculates the summations below.

$$\sum d = 0 \text{ and } \sum d^2 = 998\,250$$

Calculate the mean and standard deviation of the original costs.

First find the **mean** of the scaled values:

- The **number** of values (n) is 10.
- So the **mean** of the scaled values is: $\bar{d} = \frac{\sum d}{n} = \frac{0}{10} = \mathbf{0}$

Now for the **standard deviation** of the scaled values:

- variance $= \frac{\sum d^2}{n} - \bar{d}^2 = \frac{998\,250}{10} - 0^2 = 99\,825$
- This gives a standard deviation for the **scaled** data of:
  standard deviation $= \sqrt{99\,825}$ = **316.0** (to 4 sig. fig.).

Now you can find the mean and standard deviation of the **original** data.

- $\bar{d} = 10(\bar{c} - 93.5)$, so $\bar{c} = 93.5 + \frac{\bar{d}}{10} = 93.5$, i.e. $\bar{c}$ = £93.50
- standard deviation of d = 10 × standard deviation of c,
  so standard deviation of $c = \frac{\text{standard deviation of } d}{10} = \frac{316.0}{10} = 31.60$

That is, standard deviation of c = £31.60 (to the nearest penny).

There are lots of different ways to ask questions about this topic.

Example

A set of 10 numbers (x-values) can be summarised as shown below:

$$\sum(x - 10) = 15 \text{ and } \sum(x - 10)^2 = 100$$

Find the mean and standard deviation of the numbers.

- You can simplify those summations if you write $y = x - 10$.
  This is the same as **scaling** the x-values.
- Rewriting the summations means: $\sum y = 15$ and $\sum y^2 = 100$
- Now you can work out the mean and standard deviation of the scaled data in the normal way.
- Mean, $\bar{y} = \frac{\sum y}{n} = \frac{15}{10} = 1.5$
- Variance of scaled data $= \frac{\sum y^2}{n} - \bar{y}^2 = \frac{100}{10} - 1.5^2 = 10 - 2.25 = 7.75$
  So standard deviation of scaled data $= \sqrt{7.75} = 2.78$ to 3 sig. fig.
- Now finding the mean and standard deviation of the x-values is easy:
  $\bar{y} = \bar{x} - 10$, so $\bar{x} = \bar{y} + 10 = 1.5 + 10 = 11.5$
  Standard deviation of x = standard deviation of y
  = 2.78 (to 3 sig. fig.)

> **Tip:** The dispersion (i.e. the standard deviation) of x is the same as the dispersion of y since you've only subtracted 10 from every number — you've not done anything to change how spread out or tightly packed they are.

Exercise 3.3

Q1 In each case below, find the mean and standard deviation of the original data sets.

a) A set of data values (x) is scaled using $y = x - 500$.
The mean of the scaled data ($\overline{y}$) is 12, and the standard deviation of the scaled data is 4.22.

b) A set of data values (x) is scaled using $y = 4x$.
The mean of the scaled data ($\overline{y}$) is 6, and the standard deviation of the scaled data is 2.14.

c) A set of data values (x) is scaled using $y = \frac{x - 20\,000}{15}$.
The mean of the scaled data ($\overline{y}$) is 12.4, and the standard deviation of the scaled data is 1.34.

Q1 Hint: In part b), $b = \frac{1}{4}$.

Q2 In each case use the given linear scaling to find the mean and standard deviation of the given data.

a) 2003, 2007, 2008 Use the scaling: $y = x - 2000$

b) 0.02, 0.17, 0.03, 0.11, 0.07 Use the scaling: $y = 100x$

c) 353.5, 351, 360, 357.5 Use the scaling: $y = 2(x - 350)$

d) –7900, –7930, –7960, –8000, –7940
Use the scaling: $y = \frac{x + 8000}{10}$

Q3 The widths (in cm) of 10 sunflower seeds in a packet are given below.
0.61, 0.67, 0.63, 0.63, 0.66, 0.65, 0.64, 0.68, 0.64, 0.62

a) Use linear scaling on the data values above (x) to form a new data set consisting of integer values (y) between 1 and 10.

b) Find the mean and standard deviation of your scaled values (y).

c) Use your answers to find the mean and standard deviation of the original values (x).

Q4 The table below summarises the weights (x, measured to the nearest gram) of 12 items on a production line.

Weight (to nearest g)	100-104	105-109	110-114	115-119
Frequency	2	6	3	1

Use the linear scaling $y = x - 102$ to estimate the mean and standard deviation of the items' weights.

Q5 Twenty pieces of data (x) have been summarised as follows:
$\sum(x + 2) = 7$ and $\sum(x + 2)^2 = 80$.
Calculate the mean and standard deviation of the data.

Comparing distributions

It's really common in the exam to be asked to **compare** two distributions.

To do this, there are different kinds of things you can say, depending on what information you have about the distributions. You can:

- Compare measures of **location**, such as the mean, median or mode.
  - You'll need to say which distribution has the higher mean/median/mode, and by how much.
  - Then say what this means **in the context of the question**.
- Compare measures of **dispersion**, such as variance, standard deviation, range, or interquartile range.
  - You'll need to say which distribution's data values are more 'tightly packed', or which distribution's values are more spread out.
  - Then say what this means **in the context of the question**.

Tip: '**...in the context of the question**' means you need to use the same 'setting' in your answer as the question uses.

For example, if the question is all about the weights of tigers in a zoo, then you need to talk about the weights of tigers in the zoo in your answer as well.

Example 1

This table summarises the marks obtained by a group of students in Maths 'Calculator' and 'Non-calculator' papers.

Comment on the location and dispersion of the distributions.

Calculator paper		Non-calculator paper
40	Lower quartile, Q_1	35
58	Median, Q_2	42
70	Upper quartile, Q_3	56
55	Mean	46.1
21.2	Standard deviation	17.8

Location:

- The mean and the median are both higher for the Calculator paper (the mean is approximately 9 marks higher, while the median is 16 marks higher).
- This means that scores were generally higher on the Calculator paper.

Dispersion:

- The interquartile range (IQR) for the Calculator paper is $Q_3 - Q_1 = 70 - 40 = 30$.
- The interquartile range (IQR) for the Non-calculator paper is $Q_3 - Q_1 = 56 - 35 = 21$.
- So the IQR and the standard deviation are both higher for the Calculator paper.
- This means the scores on the Calculator paper are more spread out than those for the Non-calculator paper.

Tip: Don't forget to give your answer in the context of the question, so here you need to talk about scores on Calculator and Non-calculator papers.

Exercise 3.4

Q1 10 men and 10 women were asked how many hours of sleep they got on a typical night. The results are shown below.

Men: 6, 7, 9, 8, 8, 6, 7, 7, 10, 5

Women: 9, 9, 7, 8, 5, 11, 10, 8, 10, 8

a) (i) Calculate the mean and median of the individual data sets.

(ii) Use your answers to compare the locations of the two data sets.

b) (i) Calculate the standard deviation of the individual data sets.

(ii) Use your answers to compare the dispersion of the two data sets.

Q2 The table below summarises data obtained by a customer about the prices of shoes (in £) from two different shops.

Simson's Sporting Supplies		**Whiteley's Fine Leather**
29	Lower quartile, Q_1	49
35	Median, Q_2	54
41	Upper quartile, Q_3	65
34.3	Mean	53.5
65	Range	78

Use the table to comment on:

a) the location of the two shops' prices

b) the dispersion of the two shops' prices

Review Exercise — Chapter 1

Q1 Calculate the mean, median and mode of the data in the table on the right.

x	0	1	2	3	4
f	5	4	4	2	1

Q2 The speeds of 60 cars travelling in a 40 mph speed limit area were measured to the nearest mph. The data is summarised in this table.

Speed (mph)	30 - 34	35 - 39	40 - 44	45 - 50
Frequency	12	37	9	2

a) Calculate an estimate of the mean.

b) State the modal class.

c) Find the class which contains the median.

Q3 Find the mean and standard deviation of the following numbers: 11, 12, 14, 17, 21, 23, 27.

Q4 The scores in an IQ test for 50 people are recorded in the table below.

Score	100 - 106	107 - 113	114 - 120	121 - 127	128 - 134
Frequency	6	11	22	9	2

Estimate the mean and variance of the distribution.

Q5 For a set of data, $n = 100$, $\sum(x - 20) = 125$, and $\sum(x - 20)^2 = 221$. Find the mean and standard deviation of x.

Q6 The time taken (to the nearest minute) for a commuter to travel to work on 20 consecutive work days is summarised in the table.

Use the linear scaling $y = x - 35.5$ to estimate the mean and standard deviation of the times, where x is the class mid-point.

Time to nearest minute	30 - 33	34 - 37	38 - 41	42 - 45
Frequency, f	3	6	7	4

Q7 Find the median and quartiles of the data below.

Amount of pocket money (in £) received per week by twenty 15-year-olds:
10, 5, 20, 50, 5, 1, 6, 5, 15, 20, 5, 7, 5, 10, 12, 4, 8, 6, 7, 30.

Q8 Two workers iron clothes. Each irons 10 items, and records the time it takes for each, to the nearest minute:

Worker A: 3 5 2 7 10 4 5 5 4 12
Worker B: 4 4 8 6 7 8 9 10 11 9

a) For worker A's times. Find: (i) the median (ii) the interquartile range

b) For worker B's times. Find: (i) the median (ii) the interquartile range

c) Make one statement comparing the two sets of data.

d) Which worker would be better to employ? Give a reason for your answer.

Exam-Style Questions — Chapter 1

1 The manager of a junior football team always substitutes his first-choice attacker at half-time, and has two substitutes he can bring on, Player A and Player B. This table shows the number of goals scored by Players A and B in their last 26 appearances.

Number of goals	Player A	Player B
0	6	1
1	7	6
2	6	8
3	3	6
4	2	4
5	1	1
6	0	0
7	1	0

a) For Player A, find the mode, median, and lower and upper quartiles. *(3 marks)*

b) For Player B, find the interquartile range. *(3 marks)*

c) For Player A, calculate:

(i) the mean number of goals scored per appearance *(2 marks)*

(ii) the variance of the number of goals scored per appearance *(2 marks)*

d) The manager works out the following for Player B:

Mean = 2.35, variance = 1.46

Use this information and your answers to part c) to comment on the differences between the number of goals scored per appearance, and the spread of the data, for the two players. *(2 marks)*

2 The table shows the number of hits received by people at a paint-ball party.

No. of hits	12	13	14	15	16	17	18	19	20	21	22	23	24	25
Frequency	7	4	6	6	6	4	4	2	1	7	0	0	0	1

a) Find the mean, median and modal number(s) of hits. *(5 marks)*

b) State which of the three measures of location in part a) is least appropriate for summarising the number of hits received. Give a reason for your answer. *(2 marks)*

3 A group of 19 people played a game. The scores, x, that the people achieved are summarised by:

$$\sum(x - 30) = 228 \text{ and } \sum(x - 30)^2 = 3040$$

a) Calculate the mean and the standard deviation of the 19 scores. *(3 marks)*

b) Show that $\sum x = 798$ and $\sum x^2 = 33\,820$. *(3 marks)*

c) Another student played the game. Her score was 32.
Find the new mean and standard deviation of all 20 scores. *(4 marks)*

4 In a supermarket two types of chocolate drops were compared.
The masses, a grams, of 20 chocolate drops of brand A are summarised by:

$$\sum a = 60.3 \qquad \sum a^2 = 219$$

The mean mass of 30 chocolate drops of brand B was 2.95 g, and the standard deviation was 1 g.

a) Find the mean mass of a brand A chocolate drop. *(1 mark)*

b) Find the standard deviation of the masses of the brand A chocolate drops. *(3 marks)*

c) Compare brands A and B. *(2 marks)*

d) Find the standard deviation of the masses of all 50 chocolate drops. *(4 marks)*

5 The scores that 16 pupils achieved in a class test are as follows:

45	56	57	61	62	63	63	64
65	66	67	69	72	74	78	89

a) Find the mean and the standard deviation of the scores. *(3 marks)*

Four students did not turn up for the test and were each awarded zero marks.

b) Find the median and interquartile range of all the scores in the class of 20. *(4 marks)*

c) Write down the mode of the test scores for the whole class of 20. *(1 mark)*

d) Explain which out of the mean, median and mode is the least appropriate measure of location for the test scores of the whole class of 20. *(1 mark)*

Chapter 2 Probability

1. Elementary Probability

Probability is a measure of how likely events are to happen. We're starting with a reminder of the basics, which you'll have seen before. But it's all important stuff as you'll be using it throughout the rest of the chapter.

Learning Objectives:

- Understand the meanings of the terms used in probability.
- Be able to calculate probabilities of events when all the outcomes are equally likely.
- Be able to assign probabilities to events using relative frequencies.

The basics of probability

- In a **trial** (or experiment), the things that can happen are called **outcomes**. For example, if you roll a six-sided dice, the numbers 1-6 are the outcomes.
- **Events** are 'groups' of one or more outcomes. So a possible event for the dice roll is that 'you roll an odd number' (corresponding to the outcomes 1, 3 and 5). If any outcome corresponding to an event happens, then you can say that the event has also happened.
- When all the possible outcomes are **equally likely**, you can work out the **probability** of an event using this formula:

$$\text{P(event)} = \frac{\text{Number of outcomes where event happens}}{\text{Total number of possible outcomes}}$$

- Remember, the probability of any event has to be **between 0** (the event is impossible) **and 1** (the event is certain to happen).

Tip: 'P(event)' is short for 'the probability of an event'.

Tip: Remember, you can write probabilities as fractions, decimals or percentages.

Example

A bag contains 15 balls — 5 are red, 6 are blue and 4 are green.
a) If one ball is selected from the bag at random, find the probability that:

i) the ball is red

- The **event** is 'a red ball is selected'.
- There are 5 red balls, so there are **5 outcomes** where the event happens and **15 possible outcomes** altogether.
- So: P(red ball) = $\frac{5}{15} = \frac{1}{3}$ ← It's usually best to simplify your answer as much as possible.

ii) the ball is red or green

- The **event** is 'a red ball or a green ball is selected'.
- There are 5 red balls and 4 green balls, so there are **9 outcomes** where the event happens and **15 possible outcomes** altogether.
- So: P(red or green ball) = $\frac{9}{15} = \frac{3}{5}$

Tip: Always check that your probability is between 0 and 1.

The random selection of one ball from this bag of 15 balls is carried out 90 times (with the ball being replaced after each selection).

b) How many times would you expect a blue ball to be selected?

- There are 6 blue balls out of 15, so each trial has P(blue ball) = $\frac{6}{15} = \frac{2}{5}$.
- In 90 trials you'd expect a blue ball to be selected $\frac{2}{5} \times 90 =$ 36 times

Tip: 36 is the 'expected frequency' of blue balls in 90 trials.

Counting outcomes

- To calculate probabilities using the 'equally likely outcomes' formula on page 33, you need to **count** the number of outcomes that correspond to the event you're interested in.
- The set of **all possible outcomes** of a trial is called the **sample space** (S). And drawing a **diagram** of the sample space can help you to count the outcomes you want.
- If a trial consists of two separate activities, then a good way to draw your sample space is as a grid.

Tip: Because the dice is being rolled twice, the outcomes here are a **combination** of the score on the first roll and the score on the second roll.

Tip: When there are two completely separate parts to an experiment, like the two dice rolls here, the total number of outcomes equals the number of outcomes for one part × the number of outcomes for the other part.

Example 1

A six-sided dice is rolled twice.

Find the probability of rolling an odd number, followed by a 1.

- Start by drawing a sample-space diagram. Draw a pair of axes, with the outcomes for the first roll on one axis and the outcomes for the second roll on the other axis.
- Mark the intersection of each pair of numbers to show every possible outcome for the two rolls combined.

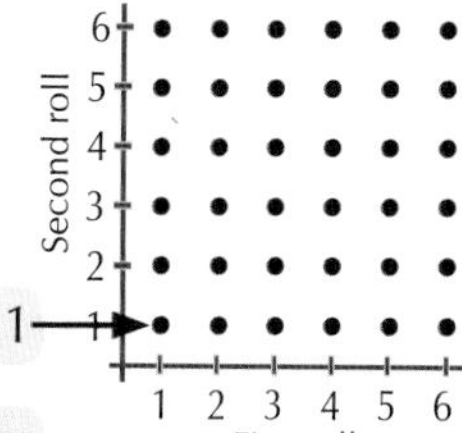

$6 \times 6 = 36$ outcomes altogether

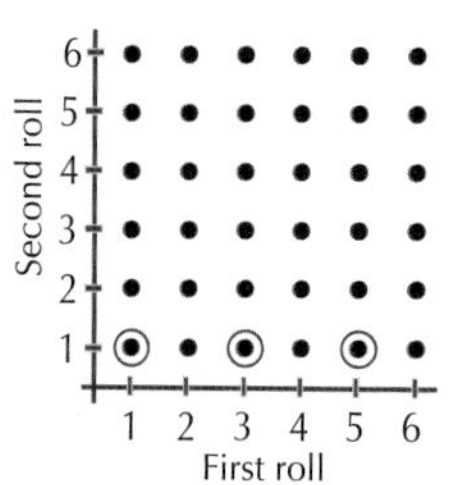

- Circle the outcomes corresponding to the event 'odd number, then 1'.
- All of the outcomes are equally likely. There are **3** outcomes where the event happens and **36** outcomes in total.

So, P(odd number, then 1) = $\frac{3}{36} = \frac{1}{12}$

Tip: A sample-space diagram can also be drawn as a table — with the outcomes for one activity along the top and the outcomes for the other activity down the left-hand side. E.g.:

	Bag A				
+	1	3	3	4	5
Bag B 1	2	4	4	5	6
2	3	5	5	6	7
4	5	7	7	8	9
4	5	7	7	8	9
5	6	8	8	9	10

Example 2

Two bags each contain five cards. Bag A contains cards numbered 1, 3, 3, 4 and 5, and bag B contains cards numbered 1, 2, 4, 4 and 5. A card is selected at random from each bag and the numbers on the two cards are added together to give a total score.

Find the probability that the total score is no more than 6.

- Start by drawing a sample-space diagram showing all the possible **total scores**.
- This time you need to show the total score for each pair of numbers at each intersection.
- Circle all the scores of 6 or less.

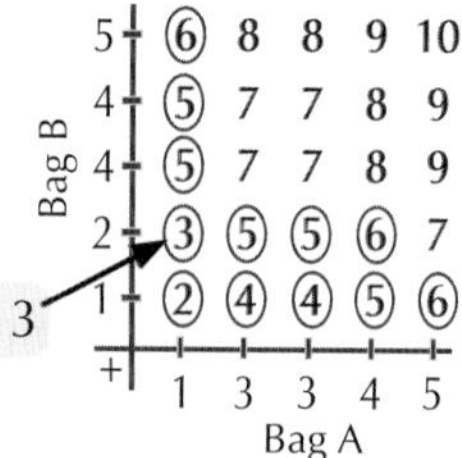

$5 \times 5 = 25$ outcomes altogether

- So now you can use the probability formula. There are **12** outcomes where the event 'total score is no more than 6' happens and **25** outcomes altogether.

  So, P(total score is no more than 6) = $\frac{12}{25}$

- Exam questions sometimes ask you to work out probabilities using information in a frequency table. It's usually a two-way table, which shows the numbers of objects in different categories for two variables.
- If the trial is a random selection from the whole group of objects, then the table represents the sample space. But instead of showing each individual outcome, the frequencies show the numbers of outcomes in the different categories.
- To find the number of outcomes that correspond to a particular event (i.e. the selection of an object with a particular characteristic), you just find the relevant frequencies.

Tip: In the example below, the variables are 'colour of pepper' and 'size of pepper', where each pepper belongs to one colour category and one size category.

Tip: Remember, the sample space is the set of all possible outcomes.

Example

The numbers of different types of pepper for sale in a greengrocer's are shown in the table below.

	Red	Yellow	Green
Small	12	14	18
Large	19	16	21

If I select one pepper at random, find the probability that it is:

a) small

- The number of outcomes corresponding to selecting a small pepper is just the number of small peppers.
  Adding up the frequencies in the 'Small' row gives 12 + 14 + 18 = **44**.
- The total number of possible outcomes is the total number of peppers, which is **100**.
- So P(small) = $\frac{44}{100} = \frac{11}{25}$

b) green

- There are 18 + 21 = 39 green peppers, so P(green) = $\frac{39}{100}$

c) large and red

- There are 19 peppers that match large and red.

  So P(large and red) = $\frac{19}{100}$

d) yellow or small

- You need to count the number of peppers that are either yellow, or small, or both.
- There are 14 + 16 = 30 yellow peppers and 12 + 14 + 18 = 44 small peppers. But if you add 30 and 44, you'll be counting the 14 peppers that are **both** yellow and small twice.
  So subtract 14 to get: 30 + 44 – 14 = **60** yellow or small peppers.
- So P(yellow or small) = $\frac{60}{100} = \frac{3}{5}$

Tip: Alternatively, you could go through each combination and add up the ones matching yellow or small — 'small and red' + 'small and yellow' + 'small and green' + 'large and yellow'.

Relative frequency

Sometimes though, you can't use the 'equally likely outcomes' approach to find probabilities.

- For example, say you have a biased dice and you want to find the probability of rolling a '4' with it.
- The dice **isn't** equally likely to land on each of the sides (the possible outcomes), so you can't use the formula on page 33.
- But let's say you roll this dice 100 times and '4' comes up 20 times. So you've rolled a '4' on 20 out of 100 rolls — the **proportion** of '4s' is 20 out of 100, or $\frac{20}{100} = \mathbf{0.2}$.
- This proportion of 0.2 is called the **relative frequency** of '4' and you can use it as an **estimate** for the **probability of rolling a '4'** with this dice.

So you can **estimate** the **probability** of an event happening using the results of an **experiment**, or what you know has **already happened** in a number of trials. Your estimate is the **relative frequency** of the event, which you work out using this formula:

Tip: The more times the experiment is done, or the more trials there are, the more accurate the estimate should be.

$$\text{Relative frequency} = \frac{\text{Number of trials where event happened}}{\text{Total number of trials carried out}}$$

Example

The table below shows the results of an Ultimate Frisbee team's last 200 matches.

	Win	Lose	Draw
Frequency	140	42	18

a) Add a third row to the table to show the relative frequency of each result.

- Just divide the frequency of each result by the total number of matches.

  'Win' = $\frac{140}{200} = \mathbf{0.7}$, 'Lose' = $\frac{42}{200} = \mathbf{0.21}$, 'Draw' = $\frac{18}{200} = \mathbf{0.09}$

Tip: Here, each of the 200 matches is a trial.

- So your table looks like this:

	Win	Lose	Draw
Frequency	140	42	18
Relative frequency	0.7	0.21	0.09

b) Estimate the probability that the team won't lose their next match.

- Using the results of their last 200 matches, the relative frequency of 'not losing' is 158 out of 200.
- So an estimate of P(won't lose their next match) = $\frac{158}{200} = 0.79$

Tip: Since you've already worked out the relative frequencies, you could simply add 0.7 and 0.09 to get the answer (see p43 for more on how to combine probabilities of different events).

Exercise 1.1

Q1 One card is selected at random from a standard pack of 52 playing cards. Find the probability of selecting each of the following:

a) the 7 of diamonds   b) the queen of spades

c) a 9 of any suit   d) a heart or a diamond

Q1 Hint: A pack of cards is split into 4 suits — hearts, diamonds, spades and clubs.

Q2 The following sample-space diagram represents a dice game where two dice are rolled and the product of the two scores is calculated:

×	1	2	3	4	5	6
1	1	2	3	4	5	6
2	2	4	6	8	10	12
3	3	6	9	12	15	18
4	4	8	12	16	20	24
5	5	10	15	20	25	30
6	6	12	18	24	30	36

a) Find the probability that the product is a prime number.

b) Find the probability that the product is less than 7.

c) Find the probability that the product is a multiple of 10.

Q3 A game involves picking a card at random from 10 cards, numbered 1 to 10, and tossing a coin.

a) Draw a sample-space diagram to show all the possible outcomes.

b) Find the probability that the card selected shows an even number and the coin shows 'tails'.

Q4 Martha rolls two fair six-sided dice and calculates a score by subtracting the smaller result from the larger.

a) Find P(the score is zero).

b) Find P(the score is greater than 5).

c) What is the most likely score? And what is its probability?

Q5 A scientist is studying the behaviour of some ladybirds. Information on the ladybirds being studied is shown below.

		Colour of ladybird		
		Red	Yellow	Orange
No. of spots	fewer than 10	20	9	1
	10 or more	15	3	2

Find the probability that a randomly selected ladybird:

a) is red or orange   b) is yellow or has fewer than 10 spots

Q6 A biased dice is rolled 60 times. The table below shows the results.

Score	1	2	3	4	5	6
Frequency	8	7	4	15	12	14

Estimate the probability that the next roll of this dice will give an odd number.

2. Solving Probability Problems

Learning Objectives:

- Understand the use of set notation to describe probabilities.
- Understand and use complementary events.
- Be able to represent a probability problem using a Venn diagram or two-way table.
- Be able to find probabilities from Venn diagrams or two-way tables.

For any probability problem there will be a set of possible outcomes, with each outcome corresponding to one or more events happening. By drawing a diagram to represent the sample space, you can show the possible events and how outcomes or probabilities are split between them.

Using Venn diagrams and tables

A **Venn diagram** shows how a collection of **objects** is split up into different **groups**, where everything in a group has something in common.

- Here, for example, the objects are **outcomes** and the groups are **events**. So the collection of objects, represented by the **rectangle**, is the set of all possible outcomes — the **sample space** (**S**). Inside the rectangle are two **circles** representing **two events**, **A** and **B**.

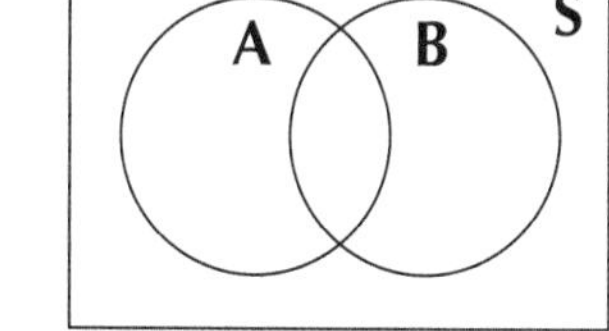

- The **circle A** represents all the outcomes corresponding to event A, and the **circle B** represents all the outcomes corresponding to event B.
- The diagram is usually labelled with the **number of outcomes** (or the **probabilities**) represented by each area.
- Since **S** is the set of **all possible outcomes**, the **total probability** in S equals **1**.

Tip: You could also draw a two-way table to represent this sort of situation — see p41.

So the two circles represent the events A and B, but other areas of the diagram also represent events, which can be expressed in terms of A and B. To describe the different areas (or events), you can use **set notation**.

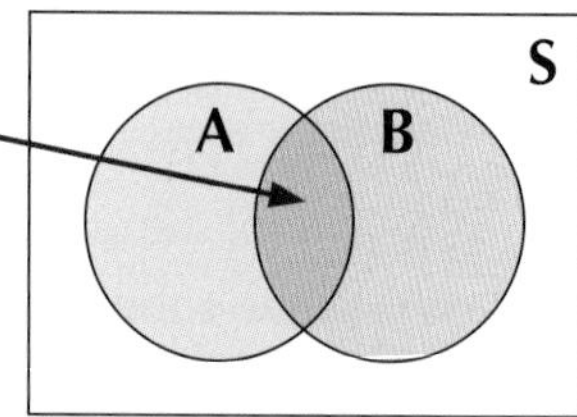

- The area where the circles overlap represents all the outcomes corresponding to **both event A and event B** happening.
- These outcomes make up an event called the **intersection** of A and B — written **A ∩ B**.

Tip: If events don't have any outcomes in common, then the circles won't overlap. These events are called **mutually exclusive** — and they're covered in detail on pages 45-46.

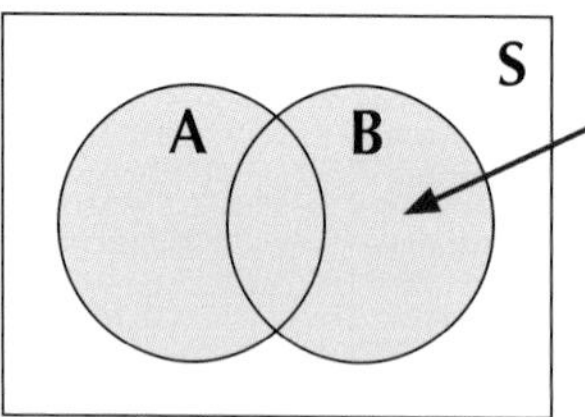

- The shaded area represents all the outcomes corresponding to **either event A or event B or both** happening.
- These outcomes make up an event called the **union** of A and B — written **A ∪ B**.

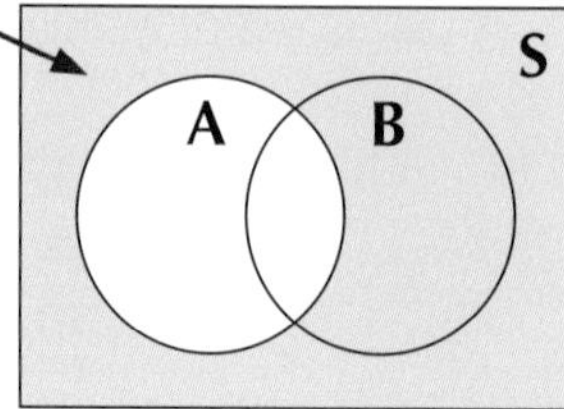

- The shaded area represents all the outcomes corresponding to **event A not** happening.
- These outcomes make up an event called the **complement of A** — written **A′** (and sometimes read as **'not A'**).
- Since an event A must either happen or not happen, and since P(S) = 1:

P(A) + P(A′) = 1 ⇒ P(A′) = 1 – P(A)

Tip: This is because if there are n outcomes altogether in S, and p of these are in event A, then $n - p$ must be in A′. $P(A) = \frac{p}{n}$, $P(A') = \frac{n-p}{n}$, which means that $P(A) + P(A') = 1$.

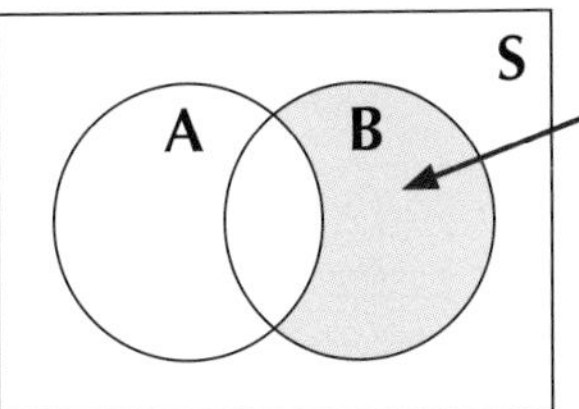

The shaded area represents all the outcomes corresponding to **event B** happening **and event A not** happening. This event is written $A' \cap B$.

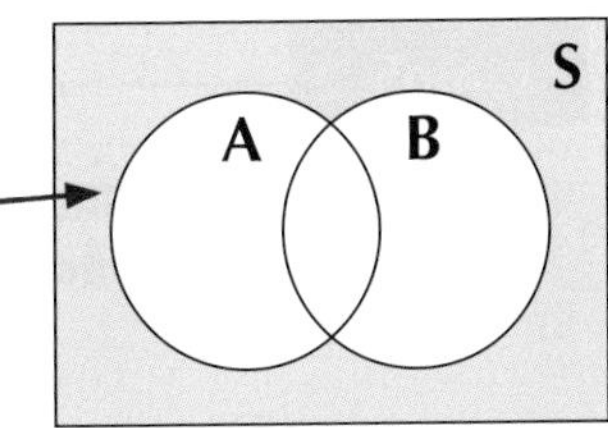

The shaded area represents all the outcomes corresponding to **event A not** happening **and event B not** happening. This event is written $A' \cap B'$.

Exam questions won't actually ask you to draw a Venn diagram, but they're often a big help in working out probabilities. Here's an example of how you can use one to make finding probabilities easier...

Example 1

There are 30 pupils in a class. 14 of the pupils are girls and 11 of the pupils have brown hair. Of the pupils with brown hair, 6 are boys. One pupil is selected at random from the class.

a) Find the probability that the pupil is a girl who doesn't have brown hair.

- Start by drawing a **Venn diagram** to represent the situation. First, you need to identify the **events**. Let **G** be the event **'pupil is a girl'** and **BH** be the event **'pupil has brown hair'**.
- Now **label** it with the numbers of **outcomes** in each area.
- You're told that there are 6 boys with brown hair, which means there are **6 pupils** who **have brown hair and aren't girls.** So label the area $BH \cap G'$ with **6** outcomes.
- There are 11 pupils in total with brown hair, so there are **11 – 6 = 5 girls with brown hair**. So label the area $G \cap BH$ with 5 outcomes.
- Now, there are 14 girls in total, so the number who **don't have brown hair** = **14 – 5 = 9**. So label the area $G \cap BH'$ with **9** outcomes.
- Finally, don't forget the outcomes that **aren't in G or BH**. There are 30 pupils altogether, so the number of **boys** who **don't have brown hair** = **30 – (9 + 5 + 6) = 10**. So label the area $G' \cap BH'$ with 10 outcomes.
- Now you can answer the question by reading from the diagram. There are **9** outcomes corresponding to the event $G \cap BH'$, out of **30** possible outcomes.
  So, P(girl who doesn't have brown hair) = $\frac{9}{30} = \frac{3}{10}$

b) Find the probability that the pupil is either a girl, or has brown hair, but not both.

- The outcomes satisfying either G or BH but not both are the outcomes in $G \cap BH'$ and $BH \cap G'$ — so that's 9 + 6 = **15** outcomes.
  So, P(either a girl or brown hair but not both) = $\frac{15}{30} = 0.5$

Tip: Each of the events needs to specify a characteristic that the selected pupil will either have or not have. Then if a pupil **has** that characteristic, they're included **inside** the circle. If they don't have the characteristic, they're outside the circle. E.g. all the girls are included in circle G, and all the boys ('not girls') are outside G.

Tip: Remember, '$\cap$' means '**and**', so the area $G \cap BH$ is the area 'girls **and** brown hair'.

Tip: There should be 14 outcomes in circle G and 11 outcomes in circle BH.

Tip: All the outcomes are equally likely, so you can use the probability formula on page 33.

Often you're given information about **probabilities** of events, rather than numbers of outcomes. You can draw the Venn diagram in the same way, but you label each area with the probability of that event.

Example 2

In any week, Carmelita goes to a maximum of two evening classes. She either goes to a dance class, to a knitting class, to both classes, or to neither class.

The probability, P(D), that she attends the dance class is 0.6, the probability, P(K), that she attends the knitting class is 0.3, and the probability that she attends both classes is 0.15.

Find the probability that in a given week:

a) She attends at least one evening class.

- Drawing a Venn diagram showing events D and K will help you to see what's going on.
- Now label each area with the probability of that event happening. Start in the middle and work outwards...

  The probability she attends both classes is 0.15, so label the area **D ∩ K** with **0.15**.

- Now you can fill in the 'attends just one class' areas, by subtracting 0.15 from each of the class probabilities.

  So **D ∩ K′** = 0.6 – 0.15 = **0.45** and **K ∩ D′** = 0.3 – 0.15 = **0.15**.

Tip: The total probability in circle D should equal P(D) = 0.6 and the total probability in circle K should equal P(K) = 0.3.

The total probability in the whole diagram should equal 1.

- Lastly, label the area **D′ ∩ K′** with the remaining probability: 1 – 0.45 – 0.15 – 0.15 = **0.25**.
- Now you want to find the probability that Carmelita attends either the dance class or the knitting class, or both — in other words, P(D ∪ K). D ∪ K is the area inside the two circles, so add up the three probabilities.

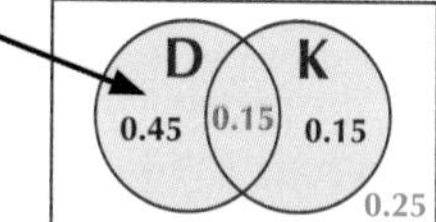

  So P(D ∪ K) = 0.45 + 0.15 + 0.15 = **0.75**

b) She attends exactly one evening class.

- This time you want the probability that Carmelita attends the dance class but not the knitting class, **or** the knitting class but not the dance class — in other words P[(D ∩ K′) or (K ∩ D′)].
- [(D ∩ K′) or (K ∩ D′)] is the shaded area.

  So P[(D ∩ K′) or (K ∩ D′)] = 0.45 + 0.15 = **0.6**

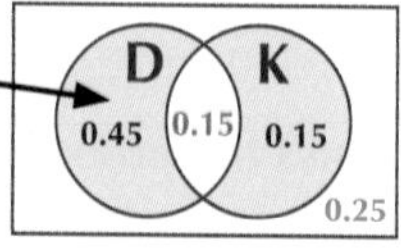

Another sort of diagram you can use to represent probability problems is a **two-way table** (or probability table).

- The idea is very similar to Venn diagrams — the **whole table** represents the **sample space** and the **cells** represent different **events** that can happen.
- You might be asked to complete a probability table in the exam, or to use one to find probabilities.
- Here's an example showing how the situation in Example 2 on the previous page can be represented using a two-way table instead.

Tip: Like Venn diagrams, two-way tables can be used to show probabilities or numbers of outcomes. For an example of a two-way table showing numbers of outcomes, see p35.

Example 3

In any week, Carmelita goes to a maximum of two evening classes. She either goes to a dance class, to a knitting class, to both classes, or to neither class.

The probability, P(D), that she attends the dance class is 0.6, the probability, P(K), that she attends the knitting class is 0.3, and the probability that she attends both classes is 0.15.

a) Draw a table of probabilities for the events D, 'not D', K and 'not K'.

- If you decide to put D along the top and K down the side, you'll need columns for events D and D′ (not D) and rows for K and K′ (not K).

Tip: It doesn't matter which event goes along the top and which goes down the side.

- Now fill in the **probabilities** you know.
  P(D) = 0.6 — so that's the **total** for **column D**.
  P(K) = 0.3 — so that's the **total** for **row K**.
  P(she attends both classes) = 0.15, so that goes in the cell in **column D and row K**.
  And the **total** probability is **1**, so that goes in the bottom-right cell.

	D	D′	Total
K	0.15		0.30
K′			
Total	0.60		1.00

- Now you can use the totals to **fill in the gaps**.
  For example, 0.3 – 0.15 = 0.15

	D	D′	Total
K	0.15	0.15	0.30
K′	0.45	0.25	0.70
Total	0.60	0.40	1.00

b) Find the probability that in a given week:

i) Carmelita attends at least one evening class.

- Now you want to find the probability that Carmelita attends either the dance class or the knitting class, or both — in other words, P(D ∪ K).
  P(D ∪ K) is made up of the probabilities in column D or row K, or both.

  So P(D ∪ K) = 0.15 + 0.45 + 0.15 = 0.75

Tip: Or you could say that P(D ∪ K) is the total of column D + the total of row K – the cell in column D and row K — see p35 for an explanation why.

ii) She attends exactly one evening class.

- This time you want the probability that Carmelita attends the dance class but not the knitting class, **or** the knitting class but not the dance class — in other words P[(D ∩ K′) or (K ∩ D′)].

- P(D ∩ K′) = 0.45 and P(K ∩ D′) = 0.15.
  So P[(D ∩ K′) or (K ∩ D′)] = 0.45 + 0.15 = 0.6

Exercise 2.1

Q1 For events A and B, P(A) = 0.4, P(B) = 0.5 and P(A ∩ B) = 0.15.

a) Draw a Venn diagram to represent events A and B.

Find:

b) P(A ∩ B′) c) P(B ∩ A′) d) P(A ∪ B) e) P(A′ ∩ B′)

Q2 A sixth form college has 144 students — 46 of the students study maths, 38 study physics and 19 study both.

a) Represent the information given above using a two-way table.

b) Find the probability that a randomly selected student from the college studies at least one of either maths or physics.

c) Given that a student studies maths, what is the probability that they also study physics?

Q2 c) Hint: You're only interested in those students who are studying maths.

Q3 Use the Venn diagram to find the probabilities below.

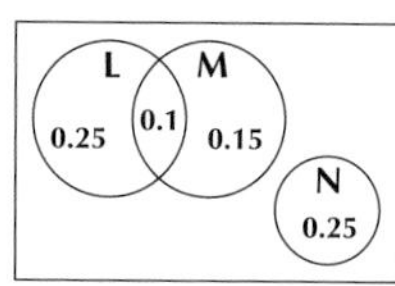

Q3 Hint: If two circles don't overlap, it means the events can't both happen.

a) P(L ∩ M) b) P(L ∩ N)

c) P(L′ ∩ N) d) P(L′ ∩ M′ ∩ N′)

e) P(L ∪ M) f) P(M′)

Q4 A group of people were asked which of the countries France and Spain they have visited.

The probability, P(F), that a randomly selected person from the group has visited France is 0.65.

The probability, P(S), that a randomly selected person from the group has visited Spain is 0.35.

The probability that a randomly selected person from the group has visited both France and Spain is 0.3.

a) Copy and complete the table of probabilities below.

	F	F′	Total
S			
S′			
Total			1.00

b) Find the probability that a randomly selected person from the group has visited:

(i) France, but not Spain

(ii) Spain, but not France

(iii) neither France nor Spain

3. Laws of Probability

There are two main probability laws you need to know — the addition law and the multiplication law. You'll see how to use these laws to find probabilities, and how you can adapt them in different circumstances.

Learning Objectives:

- Be able to use the addition law to find probabilities.
- Be able to recognise mutually exclusive events.
- Be able to use the multiplication law to find probabilities.
- Be able to recognise independent events.
- Understand how tree diagrams can be used to solve probability problems.

The addition law

For **two events**, A and B, there's a **nice formula** linking the **union** of A and B and the **intersection** of A and B — the **addition law**:

$$P(A \cup B) = P(A) + P(B) - P(A \cap B)$$

You can see why this is true, using Venn diagrams.

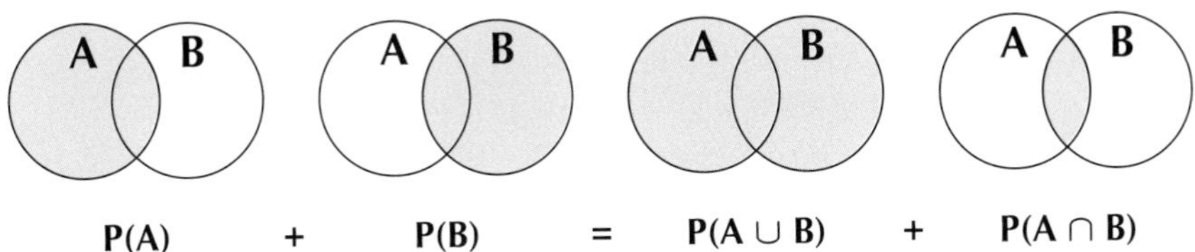

P(A) + P(B) = P(A ∪ B) + P(A ∩ B)

So to get $P(A \cup B)$ on its own, you need to subtract $P(A \cap B)$ from $P(A) + P(B)$.

Tip: If you didn't subtract $P(A \cap B)$ from $P(A) + P(B)$, you'd be counting it twice — once from A and once from B.

The addition law is **really useful** for finding missing probabilities — as long as you know three of the values in the formula, you can **rearrange** the formula to find the remaining probability.

Tip: The addition law will be on the exam formula sheet, but you should learn it anyway.

Example 1

For two events A and B, $P(A \cup B) = 0.75$, $P(A) = 0.45$ and $P(B') = 0.4$.

a) Find $P(A \cap B)$.

- To use the formula, you need to know P(A), P(B) and $P(A \cup B)$. You're missing P(B), so start by finding that. $P(B) = 1 - P(B') = 1 - 0.4 = 0.6$.
- Now rearrange the addition law formula to make $P(A \cap B)$ the subject. $P(A \cup B) = P(A) + P(B) - P(A \cap B) \Rightarrow P(A \cap B) = P(A) + P(B) - P(A \cup B)$
- And substituting in the probabilities gives: $P(A \cap B) = 0.45 + 0.6 - 0.75 =$ **0.3**

b) Find $P(A' \cap B')$.

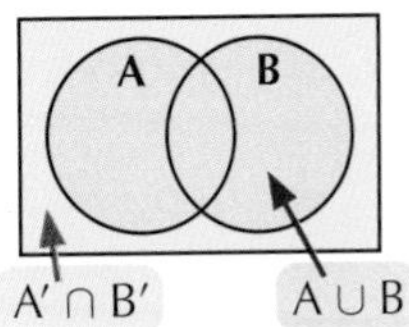

- $A' \cap B'$ is the **complement** of $A \cup B$.
- So $P(A' \cap B') = 1 - P(A \cup B) = 1 - 0.75 =$ **0.25**

Tip: Watch out for when you can use the formula $P(A) = 1 - P(A')$.

c) Find $P(A \cap B')$.

- Event A is made up of areas $A \cap B$ and $A \cap B'$ — see Tip on the right.
- So $P(A \cap B') = P(A) - P(A \cap B) = 0.45 - 0.3 =$ **0.15**

Tip: $A = A \cap B' + A \cap B$

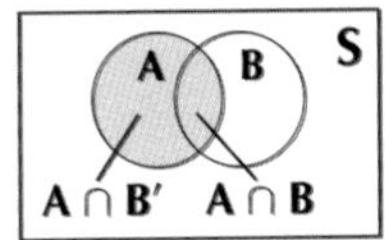

d) Find P(either event A occurs or event B occurs but not both).

- You know $P(A \cup B)$, but this includes the probability that A and B both occur, so you need to subtract $P(A \cap B)$.
- So P(event A occurs or event B occurs but not both) $= 0.75 - 0.3 =$ **0.45**

> **Tip:** $A' \cap B'$ is the complement of $A \cup B$ (see page 39).
>
> And $A' \cup B'$ is the complement of $A \cap B$, so you could answer this question by working out:
> $P(A' \cup B') = 1 - P(A \cap B)$
> $= 1 - 0.2$
> $= 0.8$

Example 2

On any given day, the probability that Jason eats an apple is 0.6, the probability that he eats a banana is 0.3, and the probability that he eats both an apple and a banana is 0.2.

a) Find the probability that he eats an apple or a banana (or both).

- Let **A** be the event 'eats an apple' and **B** be the event 'eats a banana'.
- You want to find **P(A ∪ B)**, so use the addition law:
  $P(A \cup B) = P(A) + P(B) - P(A \cap B) = 0.6 + 0.3 - 0.2 = 0.7$
- So P(he eats an apple or a banana, or both) = 0.7

b) Find the probability that he either doesn't eat an apple, or doesn't eat a banana.

- You want to find **P(A′ ∪ B′)**. You can do this using the addition law, but replacing A with A′ and B with B′. Like this:
- $P(A' \cup B') = P(A') + P(B') - P(A' \cap B')$
  $= [1 - P(A)] + [1 - P(B)] - [1 - P(A \cup B)]$
  $= (1 - 0.6) + (1 - 0.3) - (1 - 0.7) = 0.4 + 0.7 - 0.3 = 0.8$
- So P(he either doesn't eat an apple, or doesn't eat a banana) = 0.8

Exercise 3.1

Q1 If $P(A) = 0.3$, $P(B) = 0.5$ and $P(A \cap B) = 0.15$, find:

a) $P(A')$ b) $P(A \cup B)$ c) $P(A' \cap B')$

Q2 If $P(A') = 0.36$, $P(B) = 0.44$ and $P(A \cap B) = 0.27$, find:

a) $P(B')$ b) $P(A \cup B)$ c) $P(A \cap B')$ d) $P(A \cup B')$

> **Q2 d) Hint:** You have all the information you need to use the addition law, replacing B with B′.

Q3 A car is selected at random from a car park. The probability of the car being blue is 0.25 and the probability of it being an estate is 0.15. The probability of the car being a blue estate is 0.08.

a) What is the probability of the car not being blue?

b) What is the probability of the car being blue or being an estate?

c) What is the probability of the car being neither blue nor an estate?

Q4 If $P(X \cup Y) = 0.77$, $P(X) = 0.43$ and $P(Y) = 0.56$, find:

a) $P(Y')$ b) $P(X \cap Y)$ c) $P(X' \cap Y')$ d) $P(X' \cup Y')$

Q5 If $P(C' \cup D) = 0.65$, $P(C) = 0.53$ and $P(D) = 0.44$, find:

a) $P(C' \cap D)$ b) $P(C' \cap D')$ c) $P(C' \cup D')$ d) $P(C \cap D)$

Q6 The probability that a student has read 'To Kill a Mockingbird' is 0.62. The probability that a student hasn't read 'Animal Farm' is 0.66. The probability that a student has read at least one of these two books is 0.79. Find:

a) The probability that a student has read both the books.

b) The probability that a student has read 'Animal Farm' but hasn't read 'To Kill a Mockingbird'.

c) The probability that a student has read neither of the books.

Mutually exclusive events

Events can happen at the same time when they have one or more outcomes in common. For example, the events 'I roll a 3' and 'I roll an odd number', both happen if the outcome of my dice roll is a '3'. Events which have **no outcomes** in **common**, **can't happen** at the same time. These events are called **mutually exclusive** (or just 'exclusive').

- If A and B are mutually exclusive events, then $\mathbf{P(A \cap B) = 0}$.
- And since the **intersection** is **zero**, a Venn diagram would show the events as non-overlapping circles.

Tip: A Venn diagram for mutually exclusive events A and B might look like this.

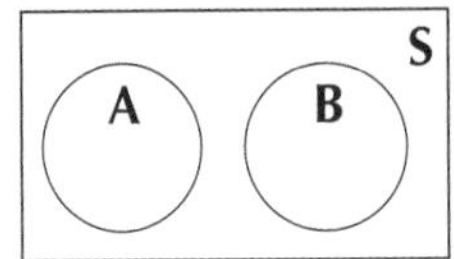

We defined the addition law on page 43 as $P(A \cup B) = P(A) + P(B) - P(A \cap B)$. When A and B are mutually exclusive, we can substitute $P(A \cap B) = 0$, to give a slightly simpler version.

For two events, A and B, where A and B are **mutually exclusive**:

$$\mathbf{P(A \cup B) = P(A) + P(B)}$$

And you can write a general form of this for n mutually exclusive events. For mutually exclusive events $A_1, A_2, ..., A_n$:

$$\mathbf{P(A_1 \cup A_2 \cup ... \cup A_n) = P(A_1) + P(A_2) + ... + P(A_n)}$$

Tip: With n mutually exclusive events, $A_1, ..., A_n$, none of the events can happen at the same time as **any** of the others.

In other words, **only one** out of $A_1, ..., A_n$ can happen at a time.

Example

A card is selected at random from a standard pack of 52 cards. Find the probability that the card is either a picture card (a Jack, Queen or King), or the 7, 8 or 9 of clubs.

- Start by defining the two events. Let A be the event 'select a picture card' and B be the event 'select the 7, 8 or 9 of clubs'.
- You want to find the probability of A or B, $P(A \cup B)$. The card **can't** be both a picture card **and** the 7, 8, or 9 of clubs, so A and B are mutually exclusive, which means that $P(A \cup B) = P(A) + P(B)$.
- Using the formula for equally likely outcomes:

  $P(A) = \frac{12}{52}$ and $P(B) = \frac{3}{52}$

  12 outcomes where event happens out of a total of 52

  3 outcomes where event happens out of a total of 52

- So the probability of A or B is $P(A \cup B) = P(A) + P(B)$

  $= \frac{12}{52} + \frac{3}{52} = \frac{15}{52}$

- This means P(card is either a picture card or the 7, 8 or 9 of clubs) $= \frac{15}{52}$

To show whether or not events A and B are mutually exclusive, you just need to show whether the intersection of A and B is zero or non-zero — i.e. whether $P(A \cap B) = 0$ or $P(A \cap B) \neq 0$.

Tip: You could also show that $P(A \cup B) \neq P(A) + P(B)$ — that's the same as showing that $P(A \cap B) \neq 0$.

Tip: Drawing a Venn diagram can be helpful to see areas.

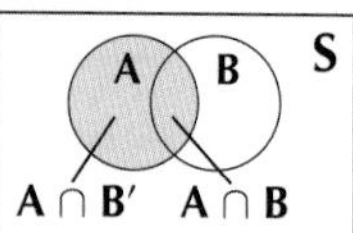

Examples

a) For two events, A and B, $P(A) = 0.38$, $P(B) = 0.24$ and $P(A \cup B) = 0.6$. Show whether events A and B are mutually exclusive.

- The easiest way to do this is to use the addition law to find $P(A \cap B)$.
  $P(A \cup B) = P(A) + P(B) - P(A \cap B)$
  $\Rightarrow P(A \cap B) = P(A) + P(B) - P(A \cup B) = 0.38 + 0.24 - 0.6 = 0.02$
- So, $P(A \cap B) \neq 0$, which means that A and B are **not mutually exclusive**.

b) For two events, A and B, $P(A) = 0.75$ and $P(A \cap B') = 0.75$. Show whether events A and B are mutually exclusive.

- This one looks a bit trickier, but you just need to think about the different areas that make up event A.
  $P(A) = P(A \cap B) + P(A \cap B')$
  $\Rightarrow P(A \cap B) = P(A) - P(A \cap B') = 0.75 - 0.75 = 0$
- So, $P(A \cap B) = 0$, which means that A and B **are mutually exclusive**.

Exercise 3.2

Q1 If X and Y are mutually exclusive events, with $P(X) = 0.48$ and $P(Y) = 0.37$, find:

a) $P(X \cap Y)$ b) $P(X \cup Y)$ c) $P(X' \cap Y')$

Q2 Fred occasionally likes to wear a brightly coloured tie to work. On any given workday, he wears a grey tie, navy tie, orange tie or red tie with probabilities 0.6, 0.35, 0.03 and 0.02 respectively.

Find the probability that on a given workday his tie is orange or red.

Q3 Dave is planning his evening. The probabilities that he will go bowling, to the cinema and out for dinner are 0.17, 0.43 and 0.22 respectively. Given that he only has time to do one activity, find:

a) The probability that he either goes bowling or to the cinema.

b) The probability that he doesn't do any of the 3 activities.

Q4 For events A, B and C, $P(A) = 0.28$, $P(B) = 0.66$, $P(C) = 0.49$, $P(A \cup B) = 0.86$, $P(A \cup C) = 0.77$ and $P(B \cup C) = 0.92$.

Find each of the probabilities below and say whether each pair of events is mutually exclusive.

a) $P(A \cap B)$ b) $P(A \cap C)$ c) $P(B \cap C)$

Q5 For events C and D, $P(C') = 0.6$, $P(D) = 0.25$ and $P(C \cap D') = 0.4$.

a) Show that C and D are mutually exclusive. b) Find $P(C \cup D)$

Q6 A box contains 50 biscuits. Of the biscuits, 20 are chocolate-coated and the rest are plain. Half of all the biscuits are in wrappers. One biscuit is selected at random from the box.

If P is the event 'the biscuit is plain', and W is the event 'the biscuit is in a wrapper', show that the events P and W are not mutually exclusive.

The multiplication law — conditional probability

A probability is conditional if it **depends** on what has already happened.

The probability that an event B happens, **given** that an event A has already happened, is called the conditional probability of 'B given A', written **P(B | A)**.

You can work out the probability of **B given A**, using this formula:

$$P(B \mid A) = \frac{P(A \cap B)}{P(A)}$$

Tip: Events A and B might be occurring at the **same time** — i.e. P(B | A) is the probability of B occurring, given that A occurs.

Tip: The probability of A given B is:
$P(A \mid B) = \frac{P(A \cap B)}{P(B)}$

Here's an explanation of where this formula comes from...

Event A has happened and for B|A to happen, B will also happen.

- If you know that A has already happened, then the only remaining possible outcomes must be the ones corresponding to A.
- And the only remaining possible outcomes corresponding to B also happening must be the ones in A ∩ B.

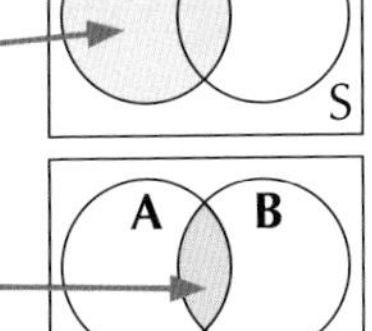

- Using the **probability formula** (and assuming event **A** has **already happened**):

$$P(B \mid A) = \frac{\text{number of possible outcomes corresponding to B}}{\text{total number of possible outcomes}} = \frac{\text{number of outcomes in } A \cap B}{\text{number of outcomes in A}}$$

- So if $n(A \cap B)$ = number of outcomes in A ∩ B, and $n(A)$ = number of outcomes in A:

$$P(B \mid A) = \frac{n(A \cap B)}{n(A)}$$

- Now, if we divide the top and bottom of the fraction by $n(S)$ (the total number of outcomes in S), its value doesn't change, but we can write it in a different way:

$$\mathbf{P(B \mid A)} = \frac{n(A \cap B)}{n(A)} = \frac{n(A \cap B)/n(S)}{n(A)/n(S)} = \mathbf{\frac{P(A \cap B)}{P(A)}}$$ ← the formula in the box above

And if we rearrange this formula for conditional probabilities, we get our second important probability law, called the **multiplication law**.

For events A and B:

$$\mathbf{P(A \cap B) = P(A)P(B \mid A)}$$

Tip: The multiplication law is given in this form on your exam formula sheet. But you can easily rearrange it into the form given above to find, say, P(B|A).

- So this law says that to find the probability that A **and** B **both** happen, you multiply the probability of A by the probability of B given that A has happened.
- Or you can write this the other way around, by swapping A and B: **P(A ∩ B) = P(B)P(A | B)**.

Tip: Just replace B with B′ in the multiplication law.

Example 1

For events A and B: P(A) = 0.6, P(B) = 0.5, P(A ∩ B) = 0.3, P(B′ | A) = 0.5.

a) Find P(A | B).

Using the formula for conditional probability:

$$P(A \mid B) = \frac{P(A \cap B)}{P(B)} = \frac{0.3}{0.5} = 0.6$$

b) Find P(A ∩ B′).

Using the multiplication law:
$$P(A \cap B') = P(A)P(B' \mid A) = 0.6 \times 0.5 = 0.3$$

Example 2

This table represents two events, C and D. The numbers of outcomes corresponding to the events C, 'not C', D and 'not D' are shown.

	C	C′	Total
D	5	7	12
D′	3	5	8
Total	8	12	20

If one of the 20 possible outcomes is selected at random:

a) Find P(C | D).

- Using the conditional probability formula: $P(C \mid D) = \frac{P(C \cap D)}{P(D)}$
- $P(C \cap D) = \frac{\text{Number of outcomes in } C \cap D}{\text{Total number of outcomes}} = \frac{5}{20}$, and

  $P(D) = \frac{\text{Number of outcomes in } D}{\text{Total number of outcomes}} = \frac{12}{20}$
- So $P(C \mid D) = \frac{5}{20} \div \frac{12}{20} = \frac{5}{20} \times \frac{20}{12} = \frac{5}{12}$

b) Find P(D | C′).

- Using the conditional probability formula: $P(D \mid C') = \frac{P(D \cap C')}{P(C')}$
- $P(D \cap C') = \frac{\text{Number of outcomes in } D \cap C'}{\text{Total number of outcomes}} = \frac{7}{20}$, and

  $P(C') = \frac{\text{Number of outcomes in } C'}{\text{Total number of outcomes}} = \frac{12}{20}$
- So $P(D \mid C') = \frac{7}{20} \div \frac{12}{20} = \frac{7}{20} \times \frac{20}{12} = \frac{7}{12}$

c) Find P(D′ | C′).

- Given the event C′, there are two possibilities — either event D will happen, (D | C′), or event D will not happen, (D′ | C′).
  So (D′ | C′) is the complement of (D | C′).
- This means that $P(D' \mid C') = 1 - P(D \mid C') = 1 - \frac{7}{12} = \frac{5}{12}$

Example 3

Vikram either walks or runs to the bus stop. The probability that he walks is 0.4. The probability that he catches the bus is 0.54. If he walks to the bus stop, the probability that he catches the bus is 0.3.

Find the probability that:

a) Vikram walks to the bus stop and catches the bus.

- Start by writing down the probabilities you know for the events W, 'Vikram walks to the bus stop', and C, 'Vikram catches the bus':

  $P(W) = 0.4$, $P(C) = 0.54$ and $P(C | W) = 0.3$

- You can find $P(C \cap W)$ using the **multiplication law**:

  $P(C \cap W) = P(C | W)P(W) = 0.3 \times 0.4 = 0.12$

b) Find the probability that Vikram catches the bus, given that he runs to the bus stop.

- This is the probability $P(C | W') = \frac{P(C \cap W')}{P(W')}$
- $\mathbf{P(C \cap W')} = P(C) - P(C \cap W) = 0.54 - 0.12 = \mathbf{0.42}$ and $\mathbf{P(W')} = 1 - P(W) = 1 - 0.4 = \mathbf{0.6}$.
- So, $P(C | W') = \frac{P(C \cap W')}{P(W')} = \frac{0.42}{0.6} = 0.7$
- So P(Vikram catches the bus, given that he runs to the bus stop) = 0.7

Tip: The probability that Vikram catches the bus, given that he walks to the bus stop, is 0.3.

Tip: He either walks or runs to the bus stop, so P(runs) = P(W′).

Tip: You could use a two-way table or Venn diagram to help you see that $P(C \cap W') = P(C) - P(C \cap W)$. E.g.

	W	**W′**	**Total**
C	0.12	**0.42**	0.54
C′	0.28	0.18	0.46
Total	0.4	0.6	1.00

Exercise 3.3

Q1 If $P(G) = 0.7$, $P(H) = 0.63$ and $P(G \cap H) = 0.24$, find:

a) $P(G | H)$ b) $P(H | G)$

Q2 $P(A) = 0.68$, $P(B') = 0.44$, $P(C) = 0.44$, $P(A \cap B) = 0.34$, $P(A \cap C) = 0.16$ and $P(B \cap C') = 0.49$. Find:

a) $P(B | A)$ b) $P(A | C)$ c) $P(C' | B)$

Q3 In a group of eleven footballers, five are over 6 feet tall.
Two of the three players who can play in goal are over 6 feet tall.
One of the players is selected at random.

a) If the player is over 6 feet tall, what is the probability that they can play in goal?

b) If the player can play in goal, what is the probability that they are over 6 feet tall?

Q4 Nida and Sally regularly go shopping together. On any given shopping trip, the probability that Nida buys shoes is 0.6. The probability that Sally buys shoes is 0.7 if Nida buys shoes, but decreases to 0.3 if Nida doesn't buy shoes.

Find the probability that, on any given shopping trip:

a) Nida and Sally both buy shoes

b) neither Nida nor Sally buy shoes

Q5 Given that $P(X) = 0.44$, $P(Y') = 0.72$, $P(Z) = 0.61$, $P(X|Y) = 0.75$, $P(Z|X) = 0.25$, $P(Y \cap Z') = 0.2$ and $P(X \cap Y \mid Z) = \frac{7}{61}$, find:

a) $P(Y)$ b) $P(X \cap Y)$ c) $P(X \cap Z)$

d) $P(Y|Z')$ e) $P(X \cap Y \cap Z)$

Independent events

If the probability of an event B happening **doesn't depend** on whether an event A has happened or not, events A and B are **independent**.

- For example, if a dice is rolled twice, the events A = 'first roll is a 4' and B = 'second roll is a 4', are independent, because the number rolled on the second roll doesn't depend on the number rolled on the first roll.
- Or, suppose a card is selected at random from a pack of cards, then replaced, then a second card is selected at random. The events A = 'first card is a 7' and B = 'second card is a 7', are independent because P(B) is unaffected by what was selected on the first pick.

Tip: If the first card **isn't** replaced, then A and B are not independent (B is conditional on A). If A happens, $P(B) = \frac{3}{51}$, but if A doesn't happen, $P(B) = \frac{4}{51}$.

If A and B are **independent**, then P(B) is the same, whether A happens or not. And that means you have the following results:

- $\mathbf{P(B \mid A) = P(B \mid A') = P(B)}$. Similarly, $\mathbf{P(A \mid B) = P(A \mid B') = P(A)}$.
- The **conditional probability** formula becomes: $P(B \mid A) = \mathbf{P(B)} = \dfrac{\mathbf{P(A \cap B)}}{\mathbf{P(A)}}$
- The **multiplication law** becomes: $\mathbf{P(A \cap B)} = P(A)P(B \mid A) = \mathbf{P(A)P(B)}$

So, for two events, A and B, where A and B are **independent**:

$$P(A \cap B) = P(A)P(B)$$

And you can write a general form of this for n independent events. For independent events $A_1, A_2, ..., A_n$:

$$P(A_1 \cap A_2 \cap ... \cap A_n) = P(A_1)P(A_2) ... P(A_n)$$

Example 1

V and W are independent events, where P(V) = 0.2 and P(W) = 0.6.

a) Find $P(V \cap W)$.

Put these probabilities into the **multiplication law** for independent events:

$P(V \cap W) = P(V)P(W) = 0.2 \times 0.6 = 0.12$

b) Find $P(V \cup W)$.

You know the probability of each event and the probability of the intersection, so you can use the **addition law** to find the union:

$P(V \cup W) = P(V) + P(W) - P(V \cap W) = 0.2 + 0.6 - 0.12 = 0.68$

Example 2

Alex takes his dog for a walk each morning in a popular dog-walking area.

On any given walk, the probability that Alex sees a terrier, P(T), is 0.7, the probability that Alex sees a greyhound, P(G), is 0.45, and the probability that Alex sees a poodle, P(P), is 0.2.

Assuming that the events T, G and P are independent, find the probability that on any given walk Alex sees:

a) all 3 breeds of dog

- You have 3 independent events, so using the multiplication law:
- $P(T \cap G \cap P) = P(T) \times P(G) \times P(P)$
  $= 0.7 \times 0.45 \times 0.2$
  $= 0.063$

b) none of the 3 breeds of dog

- This is $P(T' \cap G' \cap P')$.
- $P(T') = 1 - 0.7 = 0.3$, $P(G') = 1 - 0.45 = 0.55$, $P(P') = 1 - 0.2 = 0.8$.
- So $P(T' \cap G' \cap P') = P(T') \times P(G') \times P(P')$
  $= 0.3 \times 0.55 \times 0.8$
  $= 0.132$

c) exactly 2 of the 3 breeds of dog

- There are **three** different ways of getting the event 'exactly 2 breeds':
  'Terrier and greyhound, but not poodle' — $T \cap G \cap P'$
  'Terrier and poodle, but not greyhound' — $T \cap G' \cap P$
  'Greyhound and poodle, but not terrier' — $T' \cap G \cap P$
- $P(T \cap G \cap P') = P(T) \times P(G) \times P(P') = 0.7 \times 0.45 \times 0.8 = 0.252$
  $P(T \cap G' \cap P) = P(T) \times P(G') \times P(P) = 0.7 \times 0.55 \times 0.2 = 0.077$
  $P(T' \cap G \cap P) = P(T') \times P(G) \times P(P) = 0.3 \times 0.45 \times 0.2 = 0.027$
- Since only one of these three events can happen, you can use the **addition law for mutually exclusive** events to find:
  $P[(T \cap G \cap P') \cup (T \cap G' \cap P) \cup (T' \cap G \cap P)]$
  $= P(T \cap G \cap P') + P(T \cap G' \cap P) + P(T' \cap G \cap P)$
  $= 0.252 + 0.077 + 0.027$
  $= 0.356$
- So P(Alex sees exactly 2 of the 3 breeds of dog) = 0.356

Tip: Here you're using the **multiplication** rule for independent events, followed by the **addition** law for mutually exclusive events.

To show that events A and B are independent, you just need to show that **one** of the following statements is true:

> **Tip:** If one of these is true, then the other one will also be true.

- $P(B \mid A) = P(B)$ [or $P(A \mid B) = P(A)$]
- $P(A) \times P(B) = P(A \cap B)$

Example

A scientist is investigating the likelihood that a person will catch two infectious diseases, after being exposed to one and then the other. The probability of catching the first disease is 0.25, the probability of catching the second disease is 0.5, and the probability of catching both diseases is 0.2.

Show that the events 'catch first disease' and 'catch second disease' are not independent.

- Let A = 'catch first disease' and B = 'catch second disease'.
- There are several different ways to show the result, but it's probably easiest to compare $P(A) \times P(B)$ with $P(A \cap B)$.
- $P(A) = 0.25$, $P(B) = 0.5$ and $P(A \cap B) = 0.2$
  $P(A) \times P(B) = 0.25 \times 0.5 = 0.125 \neq 0.2$

  So, since $P(A) \times P(B) \neq P(A \cap B)$, the events 'catch first disease' and 'catch second disease' are not independent.

> **Tip:** You could also show that:
> $P(B \mid A) = \frac{P(A \cap B)}{P(A)} = \frac{0.2}{0.25} = 0.8 \neq P(B) = 0.5$,
> or $P(A \mid B) = \frac{P(A \cap B)}{P(B)} = \frac{0.2}{0.5} = 0.4 \neq P(A) = 0.25$.

Exercise 3.4

Q1 If X and Y are independent events, with $P(X) = 0.62$ and $P(Y) = 0.32$, calculate $P(X \cap Y)$.

Q2 $P(A \cap B) = 0.45$ and $P(B') = 0.25$. If A and B are independent events, what is $P(A)$?

Q3 Events M and N are independent, with $P(M) = 0.4$ and $P(N) = 0.7$. Calculate the following probabilities:

a) $P(M \cap N)$ b) $P(M \cup N)$ c) $P(M \cap N')$

> **Q3 Hint:** If M and N are independent, then M and N′ are also independent.

Q4 A card is picked at random from a standard pack of 52 cards. The card is replaced and the pack is shuffled, before a second card is picked at random.

a) What is the probability that both cards picked are 'hearts'?

b) Find the probability that the 'ace of hearts' is chosen both times.

Q5 For events A, B and C: $P(A) = \frac{3}{11}$, $P(B) = \frac{1}{3}$, $P(C) = \frac{15}{28}$, $P(A \cap B) = \frac{1}{11}$, $P(A \cap C) = \frac{2}{15}$ and $P(B \cap C) = \frac{5}{28}$.

Show whether or not each of the pairs of events, (A and B), (A and C) and (B and C) are independent.

Q6 X, Y and Z are independent events, with P(X) = 0.84, P(Y) = 0.68 and P(Z) = 0.48. Find the following probabilities:

a) $P(X \cap Y)$ b) $P(Y' \cap Z')$ c) $P(Y | Z)$ d) $P(Z' | Y')$ e) $P(Y | X')$

Q7 Jess, Keisha and Lucy go shopping independently. The probabilities that they will buy a DVD are 0.66, 0.5 and 0.3 respectively.

a) What is the probability that all three of them buy a DVD?

b) What is the probability that at least two of them buy a DVD?

Tree diagrams

Tree diagrams show probabilities for **sequences** of two or more events.

You won't be asked to draw a tree diagram in your exam, but you can use them to help you answer some of the trickier probability questions.

Here's a tree diagram representing two trials. There are two possible results for the first trial — events A and A′, and there are two possible results for the second trial — events B and B′.

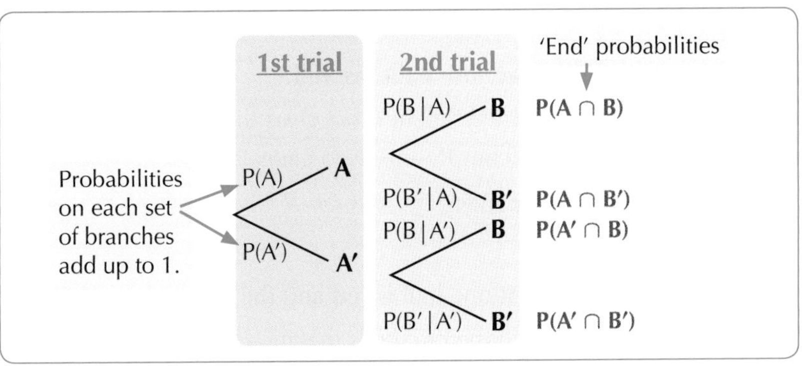

Tip: The 'end' probabilities are the probabilities of the different sequences of events.

Answers to questions are often found by adding the relevant 'end' probabilities.

- Each '**chunk**' of the diagram represents one **trial**.
- Each **branch** of a 'chunk' is a **possible result** of the trial.
- To find the **probability** of a sequence of events, you **multiply along the branches** representing those events.
- The **total** of the '**end**' probabilities is always **1**.

Tree diagrams for independent events

Tree diagrams for **independent** events look a bit simpler than the one above.

- Events A and B have no effect on each other, so $P(B | A) = P(B)$, and so on.
- So for the diagram above, the second set of branches would look slightly different:

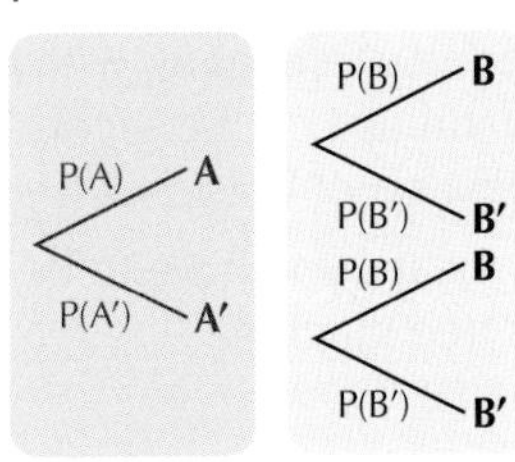

Example

A bag contains 10 balls, 6 of which are red and 4 of which are purple. One ball is selected from the bag at random, then replaced. A second ball is then selected at random.

a) Draw a tree diagram to show this information.

- There are **two trials** — '1st ball selection' and '2nd ball selection'.
- Each trial has **two possible results** — 'red' and 'purple'.
- The **probability** of selecting a **red** ball on each pick is **0.6** and the probability of selecting a **purple** ball on each pick is **0.4**.
- So you can draw a **tree diagram** like this:

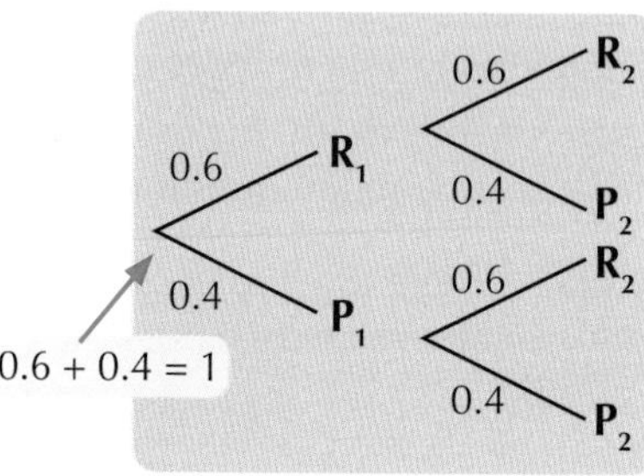

R_1 = 'first ball is red'
R_2 = 'second ball is red'
P_1 = 'first ball is purple'
P_2 = 'second ball is purple'

Tip: Here, the selection is done '**with replacement**' — so the result of the second selection is independent of the result of the first.

b) Find the probability that both balls are red.

- There is **1 'path'** along the branches that gives the result 'red and red'.
- Multiply along the branches R_1 and R_2 to give:
  $P(R_1 \cap R_2) = 0.6 \times 0.6 = 0.36$

Tip: You can answer questions like b) and c) without using a tree diagram, but very often if you draw one, it helps to make things clearer.

Tip: This is the same as using the multiplication law for independent events R_1 and R_2.

c) Find the probability that one ball is red and the other is purple.

- There are **2 'paths'** along the branches that give the result 'red and purple' — (R_1 and P_2) and (P_1 and R_2).
- Multiply along these pairs of branches to give:
  $\mathbf{P(R_1 \cap P_2)} = 0.6 \times 0.4 = \mathbf{0.24}$ and $\mathbf{P(P_1 \cap R_2)} = 0.4 \times 0.6 = \mathbf{0.24}$
- Now, you want to find the probability of (R_1 and P_2) **or** (P_1 and R_2), so you **add** these two probabilities together:
  P(1 red and 1 purple) $= P(R_1 \cap P_2) + P(P_1 \cap R_2) = 0.24 + 0.24 = 0.48$

Tip: This is the same as using the multiplication law for independent events twice, followed by the addition law for mutually exclusive events.

Tree diagrams for dependent events

When you're dealing with events that **depend** on each other, the probabilities on the second set of branches are **conditional** on those on the first set of branches (see the diagram on the previous page).

This means you have to be a bit more careful when you're labelling your tree diagram.

Example 1

A box of 6 biscuits contains 5 chocolate biscuits and 1 lemon biscuit. George takes out a biscuit at random and eats it. He then takes out another biscuit at random.

a) Draw a tree diagram to show this information.

- There are **two trials** — '1st biscuit selection' and '2nd biscuit selection'. Let $\mathbf{C}_i$ = 'biscuit i is chocolate' and $\mathbf{L}_i$ = 'biscuit i is lemon', for i = 1, 2.
- The probability of selecting a **chocolate** biscuit on the first pick is $\frac{5}{6}$ and the probability of selecting a **lemon** biscuit on the first pick is $\frac{1}{6}$.
- The probabilities for the **second** biscuit are **conditional**:
  - If the first pick is **chocolate**, then: P(choc) = $\frac{4}{5}$ — i.e. $\mathbf{P(C_2 \mid C_1) = \frac{4}{5}}$, and P(lemon) = $\frac{1}{5}$ — i.e. $\mathbf{P(L_2 \mid C_1) = \frac{1}{5}}$.
  - If the first pick is **lemon**, then there are no lemon biscuits left, so: P(choc) = 1 — i.e. $\mathbf{P(C_2 \mid L_1) = 1}$ and P(lemon) = 0 — i.e. $\mathbf{P(L_2 \mid L_1) = 0}$.
- So you can draw a **tree diagram** like this:

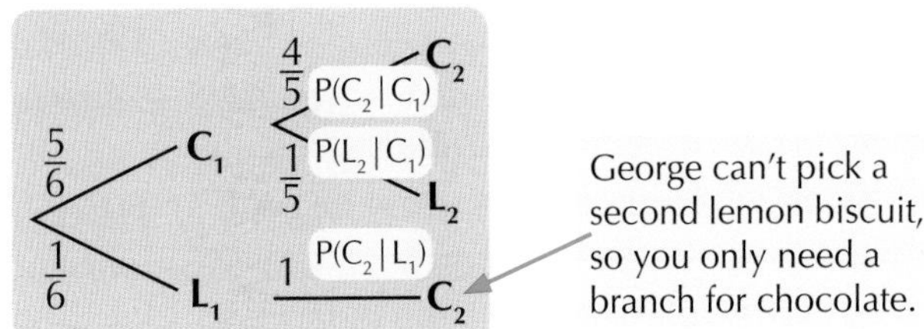

Tip: Here, the selection is done '**without replacement**' — so the result of the second selection is conditional on the result of the first.

Tip: If George took out a third biscuit, you'd get a third set of branches, looking like this:

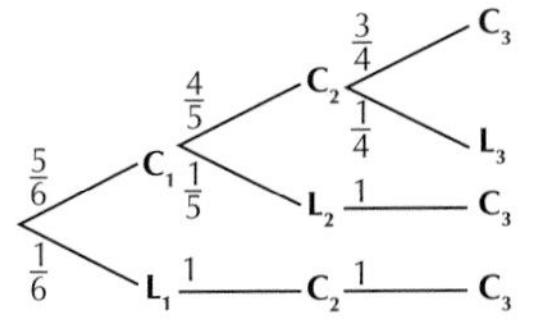

b) Find the probability that George takes out two chocolate biscuits.

- There is **1 'path'** along the branches that gives this result.
- Multiply along the branches C_1 and C_2 to give:
  $P(C_1 \cap C_2) = P(C_1)P(C_2 \mid C_1) = \frac{5}{6} \times \frac{4}{5} = \frac{20}{30} = \frac{2}{3}$
- So P(George takes out two chocolate biscuits) = $\frac{2}{3}$

c) Find the probability that the second biscuit he takes is chocolate.

- There are **2 'paths'** along the branches that give the result 'second biscuit is chocolate' — (C_1 and C_2) and (L_1 and C_2).
- You've already found $P(C_1 \cap C_2)$, so find $P(L_1 \cap C_2)$ in the same way:
  $\mathbf{P(L_1 \cap C_2)} = P(L_1)P(C_2 \mid L_1) = \frac{1}{6} \times 1 = \mathbf{\frac{1}{6}}$
- Now **add** the probabilities for the two 'paths' together:
  P(2nd biscuit is chocolate) = $P(C_1 \cap C_2) + P(L_1 \cap C_2) = \frac{2}{3} + \frac{1}{6} = \frac{5}{6}$

Tip: Another way to find P(2nd biscuit is choc) is to find P(2nd biscuit is lemon) and subtract this probability from 1. Sometimes finding the complement and subtracting it from 1 is an easier way to find a probability.

Example 2

Horace is either late for school or on time for school, and when he gets to school he is either shouted at or not shouted at. The probability that he's late for school is 0.4. If he's late, the probability that he's shouted at is 0.7. If he's on time, the probability that he's shouted at is 0.2.

Given that Horace is shouted at, what is the probability that he was late?

- It's best to take complicated questions like this step by step. You're given information about two events: Let **L** = 'Horace is late' and let **S** = 'Horace is shouted at'.
- Start by writing down the probability you want to find: that's **P(L | S)**.

  Using the conditional probability formula: $P(L \mid S) = \frac{P(L \cap S)}{P(S)}$

- So you need to find $P(L \cap S)$ and P(S) — and the easiest way is by drawing a **tree diagram** using the information in the question:

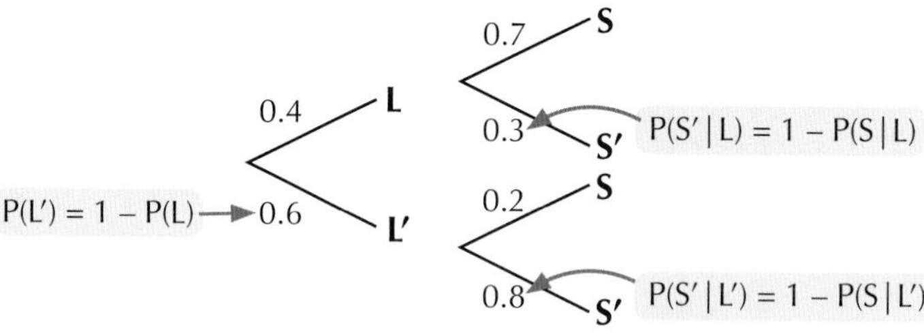

Tip: Be careful with questions like this... The question tells you the probability of S conditional on L (and L'). But you need to think of the situation the 'other way round' — with L conditional on S. So don't just rush in.

Tip: In general, if B depends on A, then A depends on B.

Here, S depends on L, so L depends on S.

- Using the tree diagram:

  $\mathbf{P(L \cap S)} = P(L)P(S \mid L) = 0.4 \times 0.7 = \mathbf{0.28}$

  $\mathbf{P(S)} = P(L \cap S) + P(L' \cap S) = 0.28 + P(L')(S \mid L')$
  $= 0.28 + 0.6 \times 0.2$
  $= \mathbf{0.4}$

- So, $P(L \mid S) = \frac{P(L \cap S)}{P(S)} = \frac{0.28}{0.4} = 0.7$
- This means P(Horace was late, given he is shouted at) = 0.7

An event can often occur via more than one set of results. E.g. in the example above, the event 'Horace is shouted at' occurs for the sets of results 'late and shouted at' and '**not** late and shouted at'.

- But sometimes the different sets of results are actually just the same results arranged in different orders, with each arrangement resulting in the same 'end' probability.
- Where this is the case, you can find the probability of the event simply by finding the probability of one of the sets of results and multiplying by the number of ways the results can be arranged.

There's an example on the next page.

Example 3

There are 10 CDs on a shelf: 5 jazz, 3 polka and 2 opera. Jamie picks 3 CDs off the shelf at random, without replacing them.

What is the probability that he picks one CD of each type of music?

- There are **three trials** — the three CD selections. Let J_i = 'CD i is jazz', P_i = 'CD i is polka' and O_i = 'CD i is opera', for $i = 1, 2, 3$.
- You know that $P(J_1) = \frac{5}{10}$, $P(P_1) = \frac{3}{10}$ and $P(O_1) = \frac{2}{10}$, and the probabilities for the second and third CDs are **conditional**.
- So you can draw a **tree diagram** like the one below (I've only labelled the paths you're interested in).

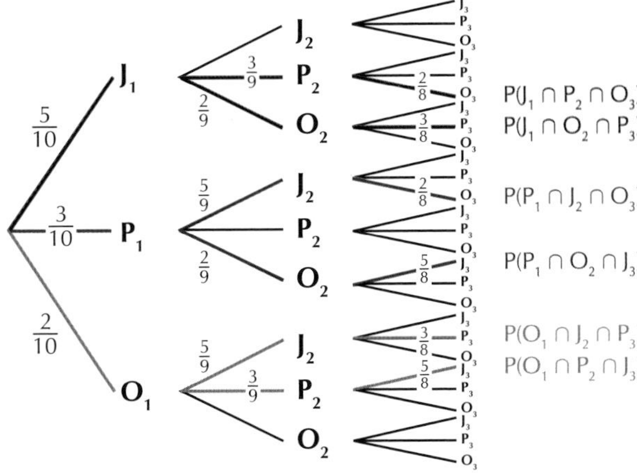

- So one way to get one CD of each type is to pick jazz first, then polka, then opera. $P(J_1 \cap P_2 \cap O_3) = \frac{5}{10} \times \frac{3}{9} \times \frac{2}{8} = \frac{5 \times 3 \times 2}{10 \times 9 \times 8} = \mathbf{\frac{30}{720}} = \mathbf{\frac{1}{24}}$.
- But that's just **one possible order** for the jazz CD, the polka CD and the opera CD. Instead, you could pick, e.g., jazz, then opera, then polka.
- In fact, you can see from the tree diagram that there are **6 possible orders** for arranging the jazz CD, the polka CD and the opera CD.
- And each of these arrangements results in the **same 'end' probability**. You always multiply 5 jazz, by 3 polka, by 2 opera on the top — i.e. the numerator is $5 \times 3 \times 2 = 30$. And there are always 10 possible CDs for the first pick, 9 left for the second and 8 left for the third — i.e. the denominator is $10 \times 9 \times 8 = 720$.
- So the probability of Jamie picking one CD of each type is the probability of one of the arrangements multiplied by the number of arrangements, which is $6 \times \frac{1}{24} = \frac{1}{4}$.

To understand **why** there are 6 possible arrangements for the 3 CDs, it helps to consider the number of possibilities at each selection.

- There are 3 possibilities for the first CD.
- Then there are 2 possibilities for the second CD.
- And that leaves just 1 possibility for the third CD.
- So there must be **3 × 2 × 1 = 6** ways to pick one CD of each type.

Tip: For more on counting different arrangements, see p64.

You can use this reasoning to work out the number of different arrangements without drawing a tree diagram if you prefer.

Exercise 3.5

Q1 The probability that Jake will win two consecutive darts matches is shown on the tree diagram.

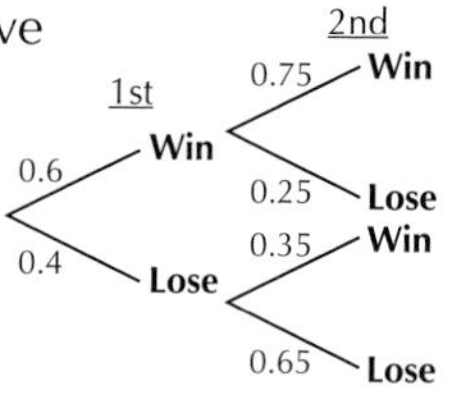

a) Explain whether the events 'wins 1st match' and 'wins 2nd match' are independent?

b) Find the probability that Jake will win:

(i) both matches (ii) at least one match

Q2 A game involves rolling a fair, six-sided dice and tossing a fair coin. A player wins if they roll a '6' and the coin shows 'tails'.

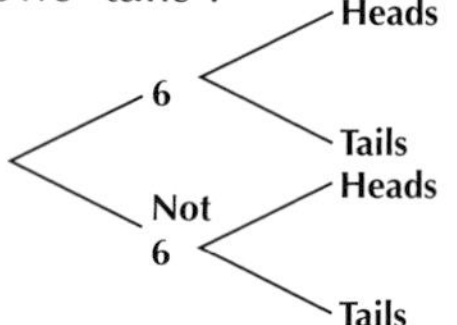

a) Complete the tree diagram by showing the probability on each branch.

b) Find the probability that a person wins the game.

Q3 The probability that a randomly selected Year 13 student has passed their driving test is 0.3. The probability that they intend to go to university, given that they have passed their driving test, is 0.75.

a) Assuming that 'passed driving test' and 'intend to go to university' are independent, draw a tree diagram to show this information.

b) Find the probability that a randomly selected student hasn't passed their driving test and does not intend to go to university.

c) What is the probability that a student picked at random does not intend to go to university?

Q4 A restaurant has found that if a diner orders a roast dinner, the probability that they order apple pie for pudding is 0.72. If they order a different main course, they order apple pie with probability 0.33. The probability that a diner orders a roast dinner is 0.56.

By drawing a tree diagram, find the probability that a randomly selected diner will order apple pie for pudding.

Q5 A group of people were asked about their mobile phones. 62% of them own a smartphone and 53.9% of them have a contract costing more than £25 a month. Of the people with a smartphone, 29% have a contract costing £25 a month or less.

Use a tree diagram to find the probability that a person from the group owns a smartphone, given that their contract costs more than £25 a month.

Q6 Dave, Juan and Callum often go mountain-biking together. On any given ride, Dave, Juan and Callum fall off their bikes with independent probabilities 0.3, 0.4 and 0.6 respectively.

a) Using a tree diagram or otherwise, calculate the probability that on any given ride, at least 2 of the 3 friends fall off their bikes.

b) Find the probability that Dave doesn't fall off on 4 consecutive rides.

Review Exercise — Chapter 2

Q1 A fair, six-sided dice and a fair coin are thrown and a score is recorded.
If a head is thrown, the score is double the number on the dice.
If a tail is thrown, the score is the number on the dice plus 4.

a) Draw a sample-space diagram to represent all the possible outcomes.

b) What is the probability of scoring more than 5?

c) If a tail is thrown, what is the probability that the score is an even number?

Q2 The hot-beverage choices of a company's 30 workers are shown in the table below.
If one worker is selected at random, find the probability that he or she:

a) drinks coffee

b) drinks milky tea without sugar

c) either drinks tea or takes only sugar

Drink	Milk or sugar: Only milk	Only sugar	Both	Neither
Tea	7	4	6	1
Coffee	5	3	2	2

Q3 The probability that a randomly selected student from a sixth-form college eats sausages for dinner is 0.5, that they eat chips is 0.2 and that they eat sausages and chips together is 0.02.
Find the probability that a student selected in this way eats:

a) chips but not sausages

b) either chips or sausages but not both

Q4 Arabella rolls two fair, six-sided dice and calculates her score by adding the two results together.

a) What is the probability that her score is a prime number?

b) What is the probability that her score is a square number?

Let P be the event 'Arabella's score is a prime number' and S be the event 'Arabella's score is a square number'.

c) Explain whether or not the events P and S are mutually exclusive.

d) Find $P(P \cup S)$.

Arabella carries out the experiment twice. Let S_1 be the event 'score from first pair of rolls is a square number' and S_2 be the event 'score from second pair of rolls is a square number'.

e) Explain whether or not the events S_1 and S_2 are independent.

f) Find $P(S_1 \cap S_2)$.

Q5 A school orchestra is made up of pupils in either the upper or the lower school.
40% of the orchestra members are boys. Of the boys, 30% are in the upper school.
Of the girls in the orchestra, 50% are in the upper school.

A member of the orchestra is chosen at random. By drawing a tree diagram or otherwise, find the probability that the orchestra member is:

a) in the lower school, given that they are a boy

b) a girl in the lower school

c) in the upper school

Exam-Style Questions — Chapter 2

1 Gwen only ever buys two brands of soap — brand A and brand B. On her weekly shopping trip, she might buy brand A soap, brand B soap, both brands of soap or neither brand.

a) Copy and complete the table of probabilities below for the events A ('buys brand A'), A' ('not A'), B ('buys brand B') and B' ('not B'). *(3 marks)*

	A	A'	Total
B	0.05		0.10
B'			
Total	0.40		1.00

b) Find the probability that, on any given shopping trip, Gwen doesn't buy soap. *(1 mark)*

2 A jar contains counters of 3 different colours. There are 3 red counters, 4 white counters and 5 green counters. Two random counters are removed from the jar one at a time. Once removed, the colour of the counter is noted. The first counter is not replaced before the second one is drawn.

a) Find the probability that the second counter is green. *(2 marks)*

b) Find the probability that both the counters are red. *(2 marks)*

c) Find the probability that the two counters are not both the same colour. *(3 marks)*

3 Event J and Event K are independent events, where P(J) = 0.7 and P(K) = 0.1.

a) Find:

(i) $P(J \cap K)$ *(1 mark)*

(ii) $P(J \cup K)$ *(2 marks)*

b) If L is the event that neither J or K occurs, find $P(L \mid K')$. *(3 marks)*

4 When Albert eats in a certain restaurant, he always eats either chicken or beef for his main course. And he always eats either sponge pudding or ice cream for his dessert.

The probability that he eats chicken is $\frac{1}{3}$, the probability that he eats ice cream given that he eats chicken is $\frac{2}{5}$, and the probability that he eats ice cream given that he eats beef is $\frac{3}{4}$.

a) Find the probability that he eats either chicken or ice cream, but not both. *(3 marks)*

b) Find the probability that he eats ice cream. *(3 marks)*

c) Find the probability that he has eaten chicken, given that he is eating ice cream. *(3 marks)*

5 A film club with 20 members meets once a week. 14 of the members go every week and 13 plan to renew their membership for another year. Of those planning to renew their membership, 10 go every week.

One member of the club is selected at random.

a) Find the probability that the person selected plans to renew their membership and goes to the club every week. *(3 marks)*

b) Find the probability that the person selected goes to the club every week, but doesn't plan to renew their membership. *(2 marks)*

c) Show whether or not going to the club every week and renewing membership are independent. *(2 marks)*

6 For a particular biased dice, the event 'roll a 6' is called event B. P(B) = 0.2.

This biased dice and a fair, six-sided dice are rolled together.

a) Write down the probability that the biased dice doesn't show a 6. *(1 mark)*

b) Find the probability that at least one of the dice shows a 6. *(2 marks)*

c) Find the probability that exactly one of the dice shows a 6, given that at least one of them shows a 6. *(4 marks)*

Chapter 3 The Binomial Distribution

1. Probability Distributions

Learning Objectives:

- Understand what is meant by a discrete random variable.
- Understand the concept of a probability distribution.
- Understand the concepts of a probability function and a cumulative distribution function, and be familiar with their properties.

This chapter's all about the binomial distribution. But before we get into that, you'll probably want to know what a probability distribution is.
This section will cover the basics that you need for the rest of the chapter.

Discrete random variables

First things first... you'll need to know what a discrete random variable is:

- A **variable** is just something that can take a variety of values — its value isn't fixed.
- A **random variable** is a variable that takes different values with different probabilities.
- A **discrete random variable** is a random variable with 'gaps' between its possible values.

A **discrete random variable** is usually represented by an **upper case letter** such as X. The **particular values** that X can take are represented by the **lower case letter** x.

For example, if you toss a fair coin twice and count the number of heads, then X is 'number of heads' and x could be 0, 1 or 2.

Tip: Remember from Chapter 1 that for a **discrete variable** there are gaps between the values that it can take. See page 3.

Every **discrete random variable**, X, has an '**expected value**' (or **mean**) **E(*X*)**.

- In theory, it's what you'd **expect** the mean of the data to be if you took lots of readings.
- In practice, the mean is unlikely to be exactly E(X), but it should be pretty close.

Just like you can find the **mean** of a discrete random variable, you can also find its **variance, Var(*X*)**.

- Again, it's a theoretical value — it's the '**expected variance**' of a large number of readings.
- And the **standard deviation** of a discrete random variable is just the square root of its variance: $\text{standard deviation} = \sqrt{\text{variance}} = \sqrt{\text{Var}(X)}$

Tip: Remember:

The **mean** is the most common measure of location — it gives you an idea of where the 'centre' of the distribution is (p7).

The **standard deviation** and **variance** are both measures of dispersion — they tell you how spread out a distribution is from the mean (p18).

Probability distributions and functions

A **probability distribution** for a discrete random variable, X, gives **every possible** value, x, that X can take and its **corresponding probability**, $P(X = x)$.

The probabilities can be represented in **tables**... or you might even be given a **formula** to work them out.

A **probability function** is a formula that generates the probability of X taking the value x, for every possible x. It is written $\mathbf{P(X = x)}$ or sometimes just $\mathbf{p(x)}$.

Example

A fair coin is tossed once and the number of heads, X, is counted. Write down the probability function of X.

- To write down the probability function, you need to work out the **possible values**, x, that X can take and the **probability** of each value.

  The outcome can either be heads or tails, so X can either take the value **0** (if it lands on tails) or **1** (if it lands on heads).

  The probability of each outcome is $\frac{1}{2}$, since the coin is fair.

- Now you can write down the probability function:

  $$P(X = x) = \frac{1}{2} \qquad x = 0, 1$$

  List the possible values of x after the 'formula'.

- If you put a possible value, x, into this formula, it'll give you the probability of X taking that value.

Tip: The probability of X taking any value other than 0 or 1 is zero — it's impossible.

Tip: Even though it's described as a 'formula', the probability function can just be a number.

There's an important rule about probabilities that you'll use in solving lots of discrete-random-variable problems:

The **probabilities** of **all** the possible values that a discrete random variable can take **add up to 1**.

For a **discrete random variable** X:

$$\sum_{\text{all } x} P(X = x) = 1$$

Tip: Remember that Σ (sigma) just means you add things together — so $\Sigma\, P(X = x)$ means you add up all the values of $P(X = x)$.

We can check this works for the **fair coin** in the previous example above:

$$\sum_{\text{all } x} P(X = x) = \sum_{x=0,1} P(X = x) = P(X = 0) + P(X = 1) = \frac{1}{2} + \frac{1}{2} = 1 \checkmark$$

The only values of x are 0 and 1.

The probability of each outcome is $\frac{1}{2}$.

The cumulative distribution function

The **cumulative distribution function** (or c.d.f.) of a discrete random variable X, written $\mathbf{F(x)}$, gives the probability that X will be **less than or equal to** a particular value x. It's like a **running total** of probabilities.

To find $F(x_0)$ for a given value x_0, you **add up** all of the probabilities of the values X can take which are less than or equal to x_0.

$$F(x_0) = P(X \leq x_0) = \sum_{x \leq x_0} P(X = x)$$

2. Binomial Distributions

Learning Objectives:

- Be able to calculate and use binomial coefficients.
- Know and be able to apply the conditions that give rise to a binomial distribution.
- Be able to find probabilities for the binomial distribution using the binomial probability function.

Binomial distributions are a really important type of discrete probability distribution. We'll come back to probability distributions later, because first you need to know all about binomial coefficients.

Binomial coefficients

It's really important in probability to be able to **count** the possible **arrangements** of various objects. This is because **different** arrangements of outcomes can sometimes correspond to the **same** event — there's more detail about this on the next few pages.

It's slightly easier to get your head round some of these ideas if you think about things that are less 'abstract' than outcomes. So first of all, think about arranging n **different** objects on a shelf.

> n **different** objects can be arranged in $n!$ ('n factorial') different orders, where $n! = n \times (n-1) \times (n-2) \times ... \times 3 \times 2 \times 1$.

Examples

a) In how many orders can 4 different ornaments be arranged on a shelf?

- Imagine placing the ornaments on the shelf one at a time, starting on the left. You have 4 choices for the first ornament, 3 choices for the second ornament, 2 choices for the third ornament, and 1 choice for the last ornament. So there are $4 \times 3 \times 2 \times 1 = 4! =$ 24 different orders.

b) In how many orders can 8 different objects be arranged?

- There are $8! =$ 40 320 different orders.

Keep thinking about arranging n objects on a shelf — but this time, imagine that x of those objects are the **same**.

> n objects, of which x are **identical**, can be arranged in $\frac{n!}{x!}$ orders.

Tip: 2 objects can be arranged in 2! (= 2) different orders.

Examples

a) In how many different orders can 5 objects be arranged if 2 of those objects are identical?

- Imagine those 2 identical objects were actually different. Then there would be $5! = 120$ possible orders.
- But because those 2 objects are **identical**, you can **swap them round** without making a different arrangement. So there are really only $120 \div 2 =$ 60 different orders in which to arrange the objects.

Tip: This is $\frac{5!}{2!} = \frac{120}{2} = 60$.

b) In how many different orders can 7 objects be arranged if 4 of those objects are identical?

- If all 7 objects were different, there would be 7! possible orders.
- But those 4 identical objects can be swapped around in 4! ways (since there are 4! different ways to arrange 4 objects).
- So there are $\frac{n!}{x!} = \frac{7!}{4!} = \frac{5040}{24} = 210$ possible orders for the 7 objects.

Tip: If you had 7 objects where:

(i) 4 of those were identical to each other, and

(ii) 2 of the remaining objects were also identical to each other,

...then you'd have to divide 7! (= 5040) by 4! (= 24) **and** by 2! (= 2) to get 105 different arrangements.

Now imagine that you have n objects, but x of these are identical to each other, and the other $n - x$ are also identical to each other (so there are really only two different types of object — x of one type, and $n - x$ of the other).

> x objects of one type and $(n - x)$ objects of another type can be arranged in $\frac{n!}{x!(n-x)!}$ different orders.

You might have seen the expression $\frac{n!}{x!(n-x)!}$ before — it's called a **binomial coefficient**.

Tip: Binomial coefficients can be written in different ways: $\binom{n}{x} = {}^nC_x = \frac{n!}{x!(n-x)!}$

Example

In how many different orders can 8 identical blue books and 5 identical green books be arranged on a shelf?

- You have two different types of object — so the number of possible orders is given by a binomial coefficient.
- $n = 13$ and $x = 8$ (or 5), so there are $\binom{13}{8} = \frac{13!}{8!5!} = 1287$ orders.

Tip: It doesn't matter whether x represents the number of green books or the number of blue books, since: $\binom{13}{5} = \binom{13}{8} = \frac{13!}{5!8!}$

Counting 'numbers of arrangements' crops up in all sorts of places.

Examples

a) How many ways are there to select 11 players from a squad of 16?

- This is basically a 'number of different arrangements' problem.
- Imagine the 16 players are lined up — then you could 'pick' or 'not pick' players by giving each of them a sign marked with a tick or a cross.
- So just find the number of ways to order 11 ticks and 5 crosses — this is $\binom{16}{11} = \frac{16!}{11!5!} = 4368$.

Tip: Notice how binomial coefficients get large very quickly. This is because $n!$ grows **very** quickly as n gets bigger.

b) How many ways are there to pick 6 lottery numbers from 49?

- Again, numbers are either 'picked' or 'unpicked', so there are $\binom{49}{6} = \frac{49!}{6!43!} = 13\,983\,816$ possibilities.

Okay... it's time to get back to the subject of **probability**...

This chapter is all about **success** and **failure** — at least, there'll be a lot of situations where there are only **two** possible outcomes, and these outcomes are often **labelled** 'success' and 'failure'.

- For example, when you toss a coin, there are two possible outcomes — heads and tails. So 'success' could be heads, while 'failure' could be tails.

You're going to be working out the probability of getting x successes (in any order) when you try something n times in total (i.e. in n 'trials').

- For example, if you toss a coin 3 times, then you're going to find the probability of getting, say, 2 heads (so here, $n = 3$ and $x = 2$).

Tip: Or you could call tails 'success' and heads 'failure' — it doesn't matter which is which.

But the probability of getting x successes in n trials depends **in part** on how many ways there are to arrange those x successes and $(n - x)$ failures.

- So to find the probability of getting 2 heads in 3 coin tosses, you'd need to find out how many ways there are to get 2 heads and 1 tail in any order.
- You could get:
  (i) heads on 1st and 2nd tosses, tails on the 3rd
  (ii) heads on 1st and 3rd tosses, tails on the 2nd
  (iii) heads on 2nd and 3rd tosses, tails on the 1st

These different arrangements of successes and failures are really important when you're finding the total probability of '2 heads and 1 tail'.

Tip: The 'in part' is explained on page 67.

Tip: These 3 possible arrangements of heads and tails are given by the binomial coefficient $\binom{3}{2} = \frac{3!}{2!1!} = 3$

Tip: See the next page for finding probabilities.

Examples

15 coins are tossed. How many ways are there to get:

a) 9 heads and 6 tails?

- This is $\binom{15}{9} = \frac{15!}{9!(15-9)!} = \frac{15!}{9! \times 6!} = 5005$

b) 6 heads and 9 tails?

- This is $\binom{15}{6} = \frac{15!}{6!(15-6)!} = \frac{15!}{6! \times 9!} = 5005$

Tip: You get the same answer for '9 heads and 6 tails' and '6 heads and 9 tails'.

This is why it doesn't matter whether you call heads 'success' or 'failure' — there are just as many ways to arrange '9 successes and 6 failures' as there are ways to arrange '6 successes and 9 failures'.

In fact, $\binom{n}{x} = \binom{n}{n-x}$ for any n and x.

Exercise 2.1

Q1 a) In how many ways can the letters of STARLING be arranged?
b) In how many ways can the letters of STARLINGS be arranged?
c) In how many ways can the letters of STARTER be arranged?

Q2 A school football squad consists of 20 players. The coach has to choose 11 of these players to make up the team. How many different ways are there to choose 11 players out of 20?

Q3 Ten 'success or failure' trials are carried out. In how many different ways can the following be arranged:
a) 3 successes and 7 failures? b) 5 successes and 5 failures?

Q4 Eleven 'success or failure' trials are carried out. In how many different ways can the results be arranged if there are:
a) 4 successes? b) 6 successes? c) 8 successes?

Tip: A **trial** means a situation where there are different possible outcomes. So tossing a coin is a trial, because there are two different possible outcomes. Rolling a dice is also a trial, because there are six different possible outcomes.

The binomial distribution

I said on page 66 that the probability of getting x successes in n trials depended **in part** on the number of ways those x successes could be arranged.

But there's another factor as well — the **probability of success** in any of those trials. The examples below both involve finding the probability of getting 3 successes in 4 trials.

Examples

a) I roll a fair dice 4 times.
Find the probability of getting a five or a six on 3 of those rolls.

- First, note that each roll of the dice is **independent** of the others. That means you can **multiply** individual probabilities together.
- Now... '**success**' here means rolling a 5 or a 6.
  This has a probability of $\frac{2}{6}$, or $\frac{1}{3}$.
  So '**failure**' means rolling a 1, 2, 3 or 4 — with probability $1 - \frac{1}{3} = \frac{2}{3}$.
- There are $\binom{4}{3} = 4$ different possible orders that these 3 'successes' and 1 'failure' could happen in.

  So P(3 successes) = P(success) × P(success) × P(success) × P(failure)
  + P(success) × P(success) × P(failure) × P(success)
  + P(success) × P(failure) × P(success) × P(success)
  + P(failure) × P(success) × P(success) × P(success)
- Each line above contains the same probabilities — each line will equal $[\text{P(success)}]^3 \times \text{P(failure)} = \left(\frac{1}{3}\right)^3 \times \frac{2}{3}$.
- So if you add up all four lines, you find:
  $\text{P(3 successes)} = 4 \times [\text{P(success)}]^3 \times \text{P(failure)}$
  $= 4 \times \left(\frac{1}{3}\right)^3 \times \frac{2}{3} = \frac{8}{81} =$ **0.0988 (to 3 sig. fig.)**

b) I roll a fair dice 4 times.
Find the probability of getting a six on 3 of those rolls.

- This time, '**success**' means rolling a 6 — this has probability $\frac{1}{6}$.
  And '**failure**' means a 1, 2, 3, 4 or 5 — this has probability $1 - \frac{1}{6} = \frac{5}{6}$.
- You could go through exactly the same process as in a) — you still have $n = 4$ and $x = 3$, so there are still 4 ways to arrange the 3 successes and 1 failure — the only difference would be the probabilities.
- So this time:
  $\text{P(3 successes)} = 4 \times [\text{P(success)}]^3 \times \text{P(failure)}$
  $= 4 \times \left(\frac{1}{6}\right)^3 \times \frac{5}{6} = \frac{4 \times 5}{6^4} = \frac{20}{1296} =$ **0.0154 (to 3 sig. fig.)**

Tip: If the probability of an event (X) happening is p (i.e. P(X) = p), then the probability that X doesn't happen is $1 - p$ (i.e. P(X′) = $1 - p$, where X′ is the event "not X", i.e. X doesn't happen).

Tip: The 4 different arrangements shown are the $\binom{4}{3} = \frac{4!}{3! \times 1!} = 4$ ways to arrange 3 successes and 1 failure.

Tip: Remember (p45)... if events A and B are mutually exclusive, then P(A or B) = P(A) + P(B).

Tip: Remember (p50)... if events A and B are independent, then P(A and B) = P(A) × P(B).

Tip: Notice how, although the final probability is different for these two examples, the formula for working it out is the same:
P(3 successes)
= 4 × [P(success)]^3
× P(failure)

We're now ready to return to probability distributions and functions — more specifically, the binomial distribution and its probability function.

You could use exactly the same logic as in the previous example to work out the formula for the probability of x successes in n trials, for any values of x and n.

This is what you'd get:

$$\text{P}(x \text{ successes in } n \text{ trials}) = \binom{n}{x} \times [\text{P(success)}]^x \times [\text{P(failure)}]^{n-x}$$

This is the **probability function** for the **binomial distribution**.
It tells you the probability that in a total of n separate trials, there will be x successes, for any value of x from 0 to n.

There are **5 conditions** that lead to a binomial distribution.
If just one of these conditions is **not met**, then the logic you've just seen to get the above formula won't hold, and you **won't** have a binomial distribution.

A random variable X follows a **binomial distribution** as long as these 5 conditions are satisfied:

1) There is a **fixed** number (n) of trials.
2) Each trial involves either '**success**' or '**failure**'.
3) All the trials are **independent**.
4) The probability of 'success' (p) is the **same** in each trial.
5) The variable is the **total** number of **successes** in the n trials.

In this case, $\mathbf{P}(X = x) = \binom{n}{x} \times p^x \times (1-p)^{n-x}$ for $x = 0, 1, 2,..., n$,

and you can write $X \sim \text{B}(n, p)$.

Tip: Remember... a **probability function** lets you work out the probability of a discrete random variable taking its possible values (p63).

Tip: Binomial random variables are **discrete**, since they only take values 0, 1, 2,..., n.

Tip: n and p are the two **parameters** of the binomial distribution. (Or n is sometimes called the '**index**'.)

Tip: The notation $X \sim \text{B}(n, p)$ gives you all the information you need to list all the possible values of X and their corresponding probabilities.

For $X \sim \text{B}(n, p)$, the possible values of x are 0, 1, 2, ..., n and their probabilities are given by the probability function in the blue box.

Examples

Which of the random variables described below would follow a binomial distribution? For those that do, state the distribution's parameters.

a) **The number of faulty items (T) produced in a factory per day, if the probability of each item being faulty is 0.01 and there are 10 000 items produced every day.**
Binomial — there's a fixed number (10 000) of trials with two possible results ('faulty' or 'not faulty'), a constant probability of 'success', and T is the total number of 'faulty' items.
So (as long as faulty items occur independently) $T \sim \text{B}(10\,000, 0.01)$.

b) **The number of red cards (R) drawn from a standard, shuffled 52-card pack in 10 picks, not replacing the cards each time.**
Not binomial, since the probability of 'success' changes each time (as the cards are not replaced).

c) **The number of red cards (R) drawn from a standard, shuffled 52-card pack in 10 picks, replacing the cards each time.**
Binomial — there's a fixed number (10) of independent trials with two possible results ('red' or 'black/not red'), a constant probability of success (as the cards are replaced), and R is the number of red cards drawn. So $R \sim \text{B}(10, 0.5)$.

d) **The number of times (T) I have to toss a coin before I get heads.**
Not binomial, since the number of trials isn't fixed.

e) **The number of left-handed people (L) in a sample of 500 randomly chosen people if the fraction of left-handed people in the population as a whole is 0.13.**
Binomial — there's a fixed number (500) of independent trials with two possible results ('left-handed' or 'not left-handed'), a constant probability of success (0.13), and L is the number of left-handers. So $L \sim B(500, 0.13)$.

Sometimes you might need to make an **assumption** in order to justify using a binomial distribution. Any assumption you need to make will be in order to satisfy one of the 5 conditions for a binomial distribution on the previous page.

Examples

State any assumptions you need to make for the random variables described below to follow a binomial distribution.

a) **The total number of defective widgets (N) produced by a machine in a day, if it produces 5000 widgets every day.**

- There's a fixed number (5000) of trials, and each trial has two possible results ('defective' or 'not defective'). N is the number of 'successes' over the 5000 trials.
- That leaves two conditions to satisfy. So you'd need to assume that the trials are **independent** (e.g. that one defective widget doesn't lead to another), and that the probability of a defective widget being produced is **always the same** (if the machine needed to 'warm up' every morning before it started working properly, then this might not be true).

b) **The number of games of chess Tina wins against Mihir (X) if they play 6 games, where in the past Tina has won 60% of their games.**

- There's a fixed number (6) of trials, and each trial has two possible results ('Tina wins' or 'Tina doesn't win'). X is the number of 'successes' over the 6 games.
- So you'd need to assume that the trials are **independent** (e.g. that Tina losing one game won't lead to her getting disheartened and losing another as a result), and that the probability of Tina winning remains **constant** (which it might not if one of them practises lots between games and improves, for example).

Exercise 2.2

Q1 In each of the following situations, explain whether or not the random variable follows a binomial distribution. For those that follow a binomial distribution, state the parameters n and p.

a) The number of spins (X) of a five-sided spinner (numbered 1-5) until a 3 is obtained.

b) The number of defective light bulbs (X) in a batch of 2000 bulbs that have been recently produced, where the production process randomly produces 0.5% defective light bulbs.

c) The number of boys (Y) out of the next 10 children born in a hospital, assuming each birth is equally likely to produce a girl or a boy.

Q2 Based on previous experience, a circus performer successfully completes his circus act on 95% of occasions. Over the next few weeks, he will perform his circus act on 15 occasions and X is the number of occasions on which he successfully completes the act.

State the assumptions that would need to be made in order for X to be modelled by a binomial distribution.

Q3 Ahmed picks 10 cards from a standard, shuffled pack of 52 cards, and counts the number of picture cards (i.e. jacks, queens or kings). State the conditions under which the number of picture cards (X) would follow a binomial distribution, and give the parameters of this distribution.

Q4 A sewing machine operator sews buttons onto jackets.
The probability that a button sewed by this operator falls off a jacket before it leaves the factory is 0.001. On one particular day, the sewing machine operator sews 650 buttons, and X is the number of these buttons that fall off a jacket before it leaves the factory.

Can X be modelled by a binomial distribution? State any assumptions you make and state the value of any parameters.

Using the binomial probability function

You've seen the conditions that give rise to a binomial probability distribution. And you've seen where the binomial probability function (below) comes from.

> For a random variable X, where $X \sim \mathrm{B}(n, p)$:
>
> $\mathrm{P}(X = x) = \binom{n}{x} \times p^x \times (1-p)^{n-x}$ for $x = 0, 1, 2, ..., n$.

Now you need to make sure you know how to use it.

Examples

If $X \sim$ B(12, 0.16), find:

a) P(X = 0)

- Use the formula with $n = 12$, $p = 0.16$ and $x = 0$:

$$\mathrm{P}(X = 0) = \binom{n}{x} \times p^x \times (1-p)^{n-x} = \binom{12}{0} \times 0.16^0 \times (1 - 0.16)^{12-0}$$
$$= \frac{12!}{0!12!} \times 0.16^0 \times 0.84^{12}$$
$$= 0.123 \text{ (to 3 sig. fig.)}$$

b) P(X = 2)

- Use the formula with $n = 12$, $p = 0.16$ and $x = 2$:

$$\mathrm{P}(X = 2) = \binom{n}{x} \times p^x \times (1-p)^{n-x} = \binom{12}{2} \times 0.16^2 \times (1 - 0.16)^{12-2}$$
$$= \frac{12!}{2!10!} \times 0.16^2 \times 0.84^{10}$$
$$= 0.296 \text{ (to 3 sig. fig.)}$$

Tip: To find P($X = a$) just put $x = a$ into the binomial distribution function.

Tip: Remember... $a^0 = 1$ for any number a.

Don't be put off if the question is asked in some kind of context.

Examples

I spin the fair spinner on the right 7 times. Find the probability that I roll:

a) 2 fives

- For this part, call 'roll a five' a success, and 'roll anything other than a five' a failure.
- Then $\mathrm{P(roll\ 2\ fives)} = \binom{7}{2} \times \left(\frac{1}{5}\right)^2 \times \left(\frac{4}{5}\right)^5$

$$= \frac{7!}{2!5!} \times \frac{1}{25} \times \frac{1024}{3125} = 0.275 \text{ (to 3 sig. fig.)}$$

Tip: p = P(roll a five) $= \frac{1}{5}$

b) 3 fives

- Again, call 'roll a five' a success, and 'roll anything other than a five' a failure.
- Then $\mathrm{P(roll\ 3\ fives)} = \binom{7}{3} \times \left(\frac{1}{5}\right)^3 \times \left(\frac{4}{5}\right)^4$

$$= \frac{7!}{3!4!} \times \frac{1}{125} \times \frac{256}{625} = 0.115 \text{ (to 3 sig. fig.)}$$

c) 4 numbers less than three

- This time, success means 'roll a one or a two', while failure is now 'roll a three, four or five'.
- So

$$\text{P(roll 4 numbers less than three)} = \binom{7}{4} \times \left(\frac{2}{5}\right)^4 \times \left(\frac{3}{5}\right)^3$$
$$= \frac{7!}{4!3!} \times \frac{16}{625} \times \frac{27}{125} = 0.194 \text{ (to 3 sig. fig.)}$$

Tip: p = P(roll a one or a two) $= \frac{2}{5}$

Sometimes you might need to find several individual probabilities, and then add the results together.

Examples

If $X \sim B(6, 0.32)$, find:

a) $P(X \leq 2)$

- If $X \leq 2$, then X can be 0, 1 or 2.
- So use the formula to find $P(X = 0)$, $P(X = 1)$ and $P(X = 2)$, and then add the results together.
- This time, $n = 6$ and $p = 0.32$.
- $$P(X = 0) = \binom{n}{x} \times p^x \times (1 - p)^{n-x} = \binom{6}{0} \times 0.32^0 \times (1 - 0.32)^{6-0}$$
$$= \frac{6!}{0!6!} \times 0.32^0 \times 0.68^6$$
$$= \mathbf{0.0988...}$$
- $$P(X = 1) = \binom{n}{x} \times p^x \times (1 - p)^{n-x} = \binom{6}{1} \times 0.32^1 \times (1 - 0.32)^{6-1}$$
$$= \frac{6!}{1!5!} \times 0.32^1 \times 0.68^5$$
$$= \mathbf{0.2791...}$$
- $$P(X = 2) = \binom{n}{x} \times p^x \times (1 - p)^{n-x} = \binom{6}{2} \times 0.32^2 \times (1 - 0.32)^{6-2}$$
$$= \frac{6!}{2!4!} \times 0.32^2 \times 0.68^4$$
$$= \mathbf{0.3284...}$$
- So $P(X \leq 2) = P(X = 0) + P(X = 1) + P(X = 2)$
$= 0.0988... + 0.2791... + 0.3284... = 0.706$ (to 3 sig. fig.)

Tip: Remember... if $X \sim B(n, p)$, then X can only take integer values from 0 to n.

Tip: Remember (p45)... if events A and B are mutually exclusive then you **add** their probabilities to find the probability of **either** A **or** B happening.

b) $P(2 \leq X < 4)$

- If $2 \leq X < 4$, then X can be 2 or 3.
- You've already found $P(X = 2)$, so you just need to find $P(X = 3)$ now.
- $$P(X = 3) = \binom{n}{x} \times p^x \times (1 - p)^{n-x} = \binom{6}{3} \times 0.32^3 \times (1 - 0.32)^{6-3}$$
$$= \frac{6!}{3!3!} \times 0.32^3 \times 0.68^3$$
$$= \mathbf{0.2060...}$$
- So $P(2 \leq X < 4) = P(X = 2) + P(X = 3)$
$= 0.3284... + 0.2060... = 0.534$ (to 3 sig. fig.)

Sometimes you're better off using a bit of cunning and coming at things from a different direction entirely.

Example

If $X \sim B(8, 0.83)$, find $P(X \leq 6)$:

- You could use the method in the previous examples, and find $P(X \leq 6)$ by working out $P(X = 0) + P(X = 1) + \ldots + P(X = 6)$.
- But remember... $P(X \leq 6) = 1 - P(X > 6) = 1 - P(X = 7) - P(X = 8)$.
- So instead, use the formula to find $P(X = 7)$ and $P(X = 8)$, and then subtract them both from 1.
- So using $n = 8$ and $p = 0.83$.
- $P(X = 7) = \binom{n}{x} \times p^x \times (1 - p)^{n-x} = \binom{8}{7} \times 0.83^7 \times (1 - 0.83)^{8-7}$

$$= \frac{8!}{7!1!} \times 0.83^7 \times 0.17^1$$

$$= \mathbf{0.3690...}$$

- $P(X = 8) = \binom{n}{x} \times p^x \times (1 - p)^{n-x} = \binom{8}{8} \times 0.83^8 \times (1 - 0.83)^{8-8}$

$$= \frac{8!}{8!0!} \times 0.83^8 \times 0.17^0$$

$$= \mathbf{0.2252...}$$

- So $P(X \leq 6) = 1 - P(X = 7) - P(X = 8) = 1 - 0.3690... - 0.2252...$
  $= 0.406$ (to 3 sig. fig.)

Tip: Remember (p63)... $\sum_{\text{all } x} P(X = x) = 1$

Tip: You'll get the same answer by adding up $P(X = 0) + P(X = 1) + \ldots + P(X = 6)$, but it'll be a lot more work than this method.

Example

When I toss a grape in the air and try to catch it in my mouth, my probability of success is always 0.8. The number of grapes I catch in 10 throws is described by the discrete random variable X.

a) How is X distributed? Name the type of distribution, and give the values of any parameters.

- There's a fixed number (10) of independent trials with two possible results ('catch' and 'not catch'), a constant probability of success (0.8), and X is the total number of catches.
- Therefore X follows a binomial distribution, $X \sim B(10, 0.8)$

b) Find the probability of me catching at least 9 grapes in 10 throws.

- P(at least 9 catches) = P(9 catches) + P(10 catches)

$$= \left\{\binom{10}{9} \times 0.8^9 \times 0.2^1\right\} + \left\{\binom{10}{10} \times 0.8^{10} \times 0.2^0\right\}$$

$= 0.2684... + 0.1073... = 0.376$ (to 3 sig. fig.)

Exercise 2.3

Q1 Find the probabilities below.
Give your answers to 3 significant figures.

a) For $X \sim B(10, 0.14)$:

(i) $P(X = 2)$ (ii) $P(X = 4)$ (iii) $P(X = 5)$

b) For $X \sim B(8, 0.27)$:

(i) $P(X = 3)$ (ii) $P(X = 5)$ (iii) $P(X = 7)$

Q2 Find the probabilities below.
Give your answers to 3 significant figures.

a) For $X \sim B(20, 0.16)$:

(i) $P(X < 2)$ (ii) $P(X \leq 3)$ (iii) $P(1 < X \leq 4)$

b) For $X \sim B(30, 0.88)$:

(i) $P(X > 28)$ (ii) $P(25 < X < 28)$ (iii) $P(X \geq 27)$

Q3 Find the probabilities below.
Give your answers to 3 significant figures.

a) For $X \sim B(5, \frac{1}{2})$:

(i) $P(X \leq 4)$ (ii) $P(X > 1)$ (iii) $P(1 \leq X \leq 4)$

b) For $X \sim B(8, \frac{2}{3})$:

(i) $P(X < 7)$ (ii) $P(X \geq 2)$ (iii) $P(0 \leq X \leq 8)$

Q4 A fair, six-sided dice is rolled 5 times.
What is the probability of obtaining exactly 2 sixes?

Q5 A multiple-choice test has three possible answers to each question, only one of which is correct. A student guesses the answer to each of the twelve questions at random. The random variable X is the number of correct answers.

a) State the distribution of X.

b) Find the probability that the student gets fewer than three questions correct.

Q6 A biased coin is tossed ten times.
The probability of it landing on heads is 0.65 for each toss.

a) State the distribution of X, where X is the total number of heads obtained.

b) Find $P(4 < X \leq 7)$.

Q7 5% of the items made using a particular production process are defective. A quality control manager samples 15 items at random. What is the probability that there are between 1 and 3 defective items (inclusive)?

3. Using Binomial Tables

Doing one calculation to work out a probability using the binomial probability function is bad enough. Doing lots of them and adding the results together is worse... potentially much worse. Fortunately, there are binomial tables.

Learning Objectives:

- Be able to use binomial tables to find probabilities.
- Be able to use binomial tables to find values for a random variable given a probability.

Using tables to find probabilities

Binomial tables reduce the amount of 'calculator work' you have to do to answer questions on the binomial distribution.

Here's an example of a problem solved **without** binomial tables.

Example 1

I have an unfair coin. When I toss this coin, the probability of getting heads is 0.08. Find the probability that it will land on heads fewer than 3 times when I toss it 12 times in total.

- If the random variable X represents the number of heads I get in 12 tosses, then $X \sim B(12, 0.08)$. You need to find $P(X \leq 2)$.
- $P(X \leq 2) = P(X = 0) + P(X = 1) + P(X = 2)$

$$= \left\{\binom{12}{0} \times 0.08^0 \times 0.92^{12}\right\} + \left\{\binom{12}{1} \times 0.08^1 \times 0.92^{11}\right\} + \left\{\binom{12}{2} \times 0.08^2 \times 0.92^{10}\right\}$$

$$= 0.367666... + 0.383651... + 0.183485...$$

$$= 0.9348 \text{ (to 4 sig. fig.)}$$

Tip: For more on c.d.f.s of discrete random variables, see p63.

But it's much quicker to use tables of the binomial **cumulative distribution function** (c.d.f.). These tables show $P(X \leq x)$, for $X \sim B(n, p)$.

So have another look at the problem in the previous example.
Here, $X \sim B(12, 0.08)$, and you need to find $P(X \leq 2)$.

- First find the table for the correct value of n. The table below is for $n = 12$.
- Then find the right value of p across the top of the table — here, $p = 0.08$.

The cumulative binomial distribution function
This table gives the probability $P(X \leqslant x)$, where the random variable $X \sim B(n, p)$.

① Find n... ② ...then find p.

p	0.01	0.02	0.03	0.04	0.05	0.06	0.07	0.08	0.09	...
x	$n = 12$									
0	0.8864	0.7847	0.6938	0.6127	0.5404	0.4759	0.4186	0.3677	0.3225	...
1	0.9938	0.9769	0.9514	0.9191	0.8816	0.8405	0.7967	0.7513	0.7052	...
2	0.9998	0.9985	0.9952	0.9893	0.9804	0.9684	0.9532	0.9348	0.9134	...
3	1.0000	0.9999	0.9997	0.9990	0.9978	0.9957	0.9925	0.9880	0.9820	...
4		1.0000	1.0000	0.9999	0.9998	0.9996	0.9991	0.9984	0.9973	...
5				1.0000	1.0000	1.0000	0.9999	0.9998	0.9997	...
6							1.0000	1.0000	1.0000	...
...										...

- The numbers underneath your value of p then tell you $P(X \leq x)$ for all the different values of x down the left-hand side of the table. Here, you need $P(X \leq 2)$.
- So reading across, the table tells you $P(X \leq 2) = \mathbf{0.9348}$.

Tip: The full set of binomial tables is on pages 161-166.

These tables are the same ones that'll be in the formula booklet you'll get in your exam.

Only tables for certain values of n are included (the biggest value included is $n = 50$). So sometimes you still have to find probabilities in other ways (e.g. using the probability function).

Once the entries in a column reach 1.0000, all entries below it will also be 1.0000. So for $p = 0.01$ in this table, $P(X \leq 3) = 1.0000 = P(X \leq 4) = ... = P(X \leq 12)$.

Example 2

I have an unfair coin. When I toss this coin, the probability of getting heads is 0.08. Find the probability that it will land on heads fewer than 6 times when I toss it 12 times in total.

- Since $n = 12$ again, you can use the extract from the $n = 12$ table at the bottom of the previous page.
- And since $p = 0.08$, the probability you need will also be in the highlighted column.
- But this time, you need to find $P(X \leq 5)$, so find $x = 5$ down the left-hand side of the table, and then read across.
- This tells you that $P(X \leq 5) = 0.9998$.

Tip: You could work out all the individual probabilities and add them together, but it would take a lot longer.

For these next examples, the value of n is also 12, so you'll still be using the $n = 12$ table. The value of p is different, though — so you'll need to use a different column.

But be warned... in these examples, looking up the value in the table is just the start of the solution.

Example 3

I have a different unfair coin. When I toss this coin, the probability of getting heads is 0.4. Find the probability that it will land on heads more than 4 times when I toss it 12 times in total.

- This time, $p = 0.4$ — so find $p = 0.4$ along the top of the table, and look at the entries in that column.
- The tables only show $P(X \leq x)$, whereas you need to find $P(X > 4)$. But $P(X > 4) = 1 - P(X \leq 4)$ — so you can still use the information in the table to quickly find the answer.
- Find the entry for $x = 4$ — this tells you $P(X \leq 4) = \mathbf{0.4382}$.
- So $P(X > 4) = 1 - P(X \leq 4) = 1 - 0.4382 = 0.5618$.

Tip: $p = 0.4$ is not featured in the extract of the table on the previous page. You'll need to look at the full table for $n = 12$ on p162.

Tip: Again...

$$\sum_{\text{all } x} P(X = x) = 1$$

With a bit of cunning, you can get binomial tables to tell you almost anything you want to know...

Example 4

The probability of getting heads when I toss my unfair coin is 0.4. When I toss this coin 12 times in total, find the probability that:

a) it will land on heads exactly 6 times.

- Again, $p = 0.4$ — so use the '$p = 0.4$' column in the table for $n = 12$.
- To find $P(X = 6)$, use the fact that $P(X \leq 6) = P(X \leq 5) + P(X = 6)$. This means $P(X = 6) = P(X \leq 6) - P(X \leq 5)$ — and you can find both $P(X \leq 6)$ and $P(X \leq 5)$ from the table.
- So $P(X = 6) = P(X \leq 6) - P(X \leq 5) = 0.8418 - 0.6652 = 0.1766$.

Tip: Remember... if A and B are mutually exclusive events, then P(A or B) = P(A) + P(B).

If you call A the event '$X \leq 5$', and B the event '$X = 6$', then:

P(A or B)
$= P(X \leq 5 \text{ or } X = 6)$
$= P(X \leq 6)$.

And so using the rule above:

$P(X = 6)$
$= P(X \leq 6) - P(X \leq 5)$

b) it will land on heads more than 3 times but fewer than 6 times.

- This time you need to find $P(3 < X < 6)$.
  This is the same as $P(3 < X \le 5)$.
- But $P(X \le 5) = P(X \le 3) + P(3 < X \le 5)$.
  This means $P(3 < X \le 5) = P(X \le 5) - P(X \le 3)$
  — and you can find both $P(X \le 5)$ and $P(X \le 3)$ from the table.
- So $P(3 < X < 6) = P(X \le 5) - P(X \le 3) = 0.6652 - 0.2253 = 0.4399$.

Tip: This time, call A the event '$X \le 3$', and B the event '$3 < X \le 5$' — then A and B are mutually exclusive, with
P(A or B)
$= P(X \le 3 \text{ or } 3 < X \le 5)$
$= P(X \le 5)$

Then using the formula P(A or B) = P(A) + P(B) for mutually exclusive events, you get:
$P(X \le 5)$
$= P(X \le 3) + P(3 < X \le 5)$

There's an easy way to remember which probability to subtract from which other probability. For example, suppose you need to find $P(a < X \le b)$.

- Use the table to find **$P(X \le b)$** — the probability that X is less than or equal to the largest value satisfying the inequality '$a < X \le b$'...
- ...**and subtract $P(X \le a)$** to 'remove' the probability that X takes one of the smaller values not satisfying the inequality '$a < X \le b$'.

Examples

If $X \sim B(12, 0.45)$, find:

a) $P(5 < X \le 8)$

- The largest value satisfying the inequality $5 < X \le 8$ is $X = 8$.
  So you need to find $P(X \le 8)$.
- Using the table for $n = 12$ and $p = 0.45$, $P(X \le 8) = \mathbf{0.9644}$.
- You need to subtract the probability $P(X \le 5)$, since $X = 5$ doesn't satisfy the inequality $5 < X \le 8$, and neither does any value smaller than 5.
- From the table, $P(X \le 5) = \mathbf{0.5269}$.
- So $P(5 < X \le 8) = P(X \le 8) - P(X \le 5) = 0.9644 - 0.5269 = 0.4375$

Tip: $n = 12$ again — so refer to the same table as before.

b) $P(4 \le X < 10)$

- The largest value satisfying the inequality $4 \le X < 10$ is $X = 9$.
  So you need to find $P(X \le 9)$.
- Using the table for $n = 12$ and $p = 0.45$, $P(X \le 9) = \mathbf{0.9921}$.
- Now subtract the probability $P(X \le 3)$, since $X = 3$ doesn't satisfy the inequality $4 \le X < 10$, and neither does any value smaller than 3.
- From the table, $P(X \le 3) = \mathbf{0.1345}$.
- So $P(4 \le X < 10) = P(X \le 9) - P(X \le 3) = 0.9921 - 0.1345 = 0.8576$

Tip: The inequality $4 \le X < 10$ can be written as $3 < X \le 9$.

Using the tables is relatively straightforward as long as you can find the value of p you need. But the values of p only go as high as $p = 0.5$ — so if $p > 0.5$, you need to think about things slightly differently.

- Suppose $X \sim B(12, 0.65)$, and you need to find $P(X \le 5)$.
- This means you need to find the probability of 5 or fewer 'successes', when the probability of 'success' is $p = 0.65$.
- But you can switch things round and say you need to find the probability of 7 or more 'failures', where the probability of 'failure' is $1 - p = 0.35$.
- It's easiest if you rewrite the problem using a new variable, Y, say.
  Y will represent the number of 'failures' in 12 trials, so $Y \sim B(12, 0.35)$.

- You can use tables to find $P(Y \geq 7) = 1 - P(Y < 7)$
$= 1 - P(Y \leq 6)$
$= 1 - 0.9154 = \mathbf{0.0846}$
- So the probability of 7 or more 'failures' if the probability of 'failure' is 0.35 is 0.0846. This must equal the probability of 5 or fewer 'successes' if the probability of 'success' is 0.65.
- So if $X \sim B(12, 0.65)$, then $P(X \leq 5) = \mathbf{0.0846}$.

Where $X \sim B(n, p)$, but $p > 0.5$...
First define $Y = n - X$, where $Y \sim B(n, 1 - p)$.
Then, for constants k and h:
- $P(X \leq k) = P(Y \geq n - k)$ and $P(X < k) = P(Y > n - k)$
- $P(X \geq k) = P(Y \leq n - k)$ and $P(X > k) = P(Y < n - k)$
- $P(h < X \leq k) = P(n - k \leq Y < n - h)$

Tip: $h < X \leq k$ means that $X > h$ and $X \leq k$.
So $Y < n - h$ and $Y \geq n - k$.
In other words: $n - k \leq Y < n - h$.

Notice that, as well as having been subtracted from n, both k and h have 'swapped sides' in the inequality, and the $\leq$ and $<$ signs have moved with them.

Examples

The probability of this spinner landing on blue is 0.7. The spinner is spun 12 times, and the random variable X represents the number of times the spinner lands on blue.

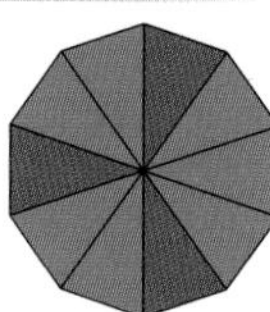

a) Find $P(X > 8)$.
- Since X represents the number of 'blues' in 12 spins, $X \sim B(12, 0.7)$.
- Because $p = 0.7$, you won't be able to use the tables directly.
So define a new random variable Y, where Y represents the number of 'reds' in 12 spins. Since the spinner can only land on either red or blue, $P(\text{red}) = 1 - P(\text{blue}) = 1 - 0.7 = 0.3$. This means $Y \sim B(12, 0.3)$.
- Then $P(X > 8) = P(Y < 4) = P(Y \leq 3) = 0.4925$

b) Find $P(X \leq 4)$.
- $P(X \leq 4) = P(Y \geq 8) = 1 - P(Y < 8) = 1 - P(Y \leq 7) = 1 - 0.9905 = 0.0095$

c) Find $P(5 \leq X < 8)$.
- $P(5 \leq X < 8) = P(4 < Y \leq 7) = P(Y \leq 7) - P(Y \leq 4)$
$= 0.9905 - 0.7237 = 0.2668$

Exercise 3.1

Q1 Hint: The binomial tables start on page 161.

Q1 The random variable $X \sim B(10, 0.25)$.
Use the binomial table for $n = 10$ to find:

a) $P(X \leq 2)$ b) $P(X \leq 7)$ c) $P(X \leq 9)$
d) $P(X < 5)$ e) $P(X < 4)$ f) $P(X < 6)$

Q2 The random variable $X \sim B(15, 0.4)$.
Use the appropriate binomial table to find:

a) $P(X > 3)$ b) $P(X > 6)$ c) $P(X > 10)$
d) $P(X \geq 5)$ e) $P(X \geq 3)$ f) $P(X \geq 13)$

Q3 The random variable $X \sim B(20, 0.35)$.
Use the appropriate binomial table to find:

a) $P(X = 7)$ b) $P(X = 12)$ c) $P(2 < X \leq 4)$

d) $P(10 < X \leq 15)$ e) $P(7 \leq X \leq 10)$ f) $P(3 \leq X < 11)$

Q4 The random variable $X \sim B(25, 0.8)$.
Use the appropriate binomial table to find:

a) $P(X \geq 17)$ b) $P(X \geq 20)$ c) $P(X > 14)$

d) $P(X = 21)$ e) $P(3 \leq X < 14)$ f) $P(12 \leq X < 18)$

Q5 Seven fair coins are tossed. What is the probability of tossing more than four heads?

Q6 In a production process it is known that approximately 5% of items are faulty. In a random sample of 25 objects, estimate the probability that fewer than 6 are faulty.

Using binomial tables 'backwards'

Sometimes, you'll need to use the tables 'the other way round'.

- So far you've been given a value for x, and you've had to find a probability such as $P(X \leq x)$, $P(X > x)$, $P(X = x)$,... and so on.
- But you could be given a probability (c, say) and asked to find a value of x.
- These kinds of questions can get quite complicated.

Examples

If $X \sim B(25, 0.2)$, find:

a) c if $P(X \leq c) = 0.7800$

- Use the binomial table for $n = 25$, and the column for $p = 0.2$.
- Going down the column, you can see that $P(X \leq 6) = 0.7800$, so $c = 6$.

b) d if $P(X \geq d) = 0.7660$

- If $P(X \geq d) = 0.7660$, then $P(X < d) = P(X \leq d - 1)$
$= 1 - 0.7660 = 0.2340$.
- Using the table, you can see that $P(X \leq 3) = 0.2340$.
- This means that $d - 1 = 3$, which gives $d = 4$.

Here are some slightly trickier examples.

Examples

If $X \sim B(30, 0.4)$, find:

a) the maximum value a such that $P(X \leq a) < 0.05$.

- Use the binomial table for $n = 30$, and the column for $p = 0.4$.
- You can see that $P(X \leq 7) = 0.0435$ and $P(X \leq 8) = 0.0940$.
- So the maximum value a such that $P(X \leq a) < 0.05$ is $a = 7$.

Tip: Remember... $P(X \leq b) = 1 - P(X > b)$.

So if $P(X > b) < 0.05$, then $P(X \leq b) > 0.95$.

b) the minimum value b such that $P(X > b) < 0.05$.

- This time you need the smallest value of b with $P(X > b) < 0.05$. But if $P(X > b) < 0.05$, then $P(X \leq b) > 0.95$. So you need the smallest value of b with $P(X \leq b) > 0.95$.
- Using the same binomial table as before, you can see that $P(X \leq 15) = 0.9029$ and $P(X \leq 16) = 0.9519$.
- So the minimum value of b with $P(X \leq b) > 0.95$ is $b = 16$. This means that the minimum value of b with $P(X > b) < 0.05$ must also be $b = 16$.

This kind of question occurs in real-life situations.

Tip: This situation satisfies the conditions for a binomial distribution, since:

(i) there are a fixed number (20) of trials (i.e. each question is a trial),

(ii) the only possible outcomes of each trial are success or failure,

(iii) the trials are all independent — guessing the correct answer to one question doesn't make a student any more or less likely to guess the next answer correctly,

(iv) the probability of success in each trial is always 0.2,

(iv) the variable X is the total number of successes in the 20 trials.

Example

A teacher sets her class a multiple-choice test. In this test there are 20 questions, and each question has 5 possible answers.
The teacher wants to make it very unlikely that a student who guesses the answer to every question would pass the test.
How high should the pass mark be to give a student guessing the answer to every question less than a 10% probability of passing the test?

- Since each question has 5 possible answers, the probability of correctly guessing the answer to each question must be 0.2.
- There are 20 questions altogether, so if the random variable X is the overall score of a student who always guesses, then $X \sim B(20, 0.2)$.
- You need to find the minimum value m such that $P(X \geq m) < 0.1$, i.e. the minimum value m with $P(X < m) > 0.9$ or $P(X \leq m - 1) > 0.9$.
- From tables, $P(X \leq 5) = 0.8042$, but $P(X \leq 6) = 0.9133$.
- So the probability of a student who always guesses getting more than 5 answers correct is $P(X > 5) = 1 - P(X \leq 5) = 1 - 0.8042 = 0.1958$. But the probability of a student who always guesses getting more than 6 answers correct is $P(X > 6) = 1 - P(X \leq 6) = 1 - 0.9133 = 0.0867$.
- So the pass mark should be set at 7 or more. Then the probability that a student who always guesses will pass the test is less than 10%.

Exercise 3.2

For all the questions below, use binomial tables to find your answers.

Q1 The random variable $X \sim B(8, 0.35)$.
Find the values of a, b, c and d such that:

a) $P(X \leq a) = 0.4278$ b) $P(X < b) = 0.9747$

c) $P(X > c) = 0.8309$ d) $P(X \geq d) = 0.1061$

Q2 & Q3 Hint: With these wordy questions, read everything carefully and be very careful with the inequality signs.

Q2 A teacher is writing a multiple-choice test, with 4 options for each of the 30 questions. He wants the probability of someone passing the test by guessing the answer to each question to be 10% or less.

a) What is the lowest score that should be set as the pass mark?

b) Another teacher says the probability of passing by guessing should be less than 1%. What should the minimum pass score be now?

Q3 In a fairground competition, a fair coin is tossed 20 times by a contestant. If the contestant scores x heads or more, they win a prize. If the random variable X represents the number of heads obtained, find the minimum number of heads that are needed to win if the probability of winning is to be kept below 0.05.

4. Mean and Variance

You saw that it is possible to find the mean and variance of a discrete random variable earlier in the chapter. In this section, you're going to work out the mean and variance of a discrete random variable following a binomial distribution.

Learning Objectives:

- Be able to calculate the mean and variance of a random variable following a binomial distribution.
- Be able to find n or p given values for $E(X)$ or $Var(X)$.

Mean and variance of the binomial distribution

The mean

Remember... the **mean** of a random variable is also called its **expected value**. It's a kind of 'theoretical mean' — what you'd expect the mean to be if you gathered a large number of observations of the random variable (p62).

So suppose you have a random variable $X \sim B(n, p)$. The mean of X would be the 'average' number of successes if you performed lots of sets of n trials.

The mean (expected value) of X can be written either as μ or $E(X)$, and is given by the formula below.

> If $X \sim B(n, p)$, then:
> **Mean (or Expected Value) = $\mu = E(X) = np$**

Tip: This formula will be in your formula booklet. But it's worth committing to memory, because it's so important.

Keep in mind that this is a 'theoretical mean' — the mean of experimental results is unlikely to match it **exactly**.

Tip: Greek letters (e.g. μ) often show something based purely on theory rather than experimental results.

Examples

Find the expected values of the following random variables.

a) $X \sim B(20, 0.2)$

- Just put the parameters of the distribution into the formula. $E(X) = np = 20 \times 0.2 = 4$

b) $X \sim B(155, 0.37)$

- Again, just use the formula. $E(X) = np = 155 \times 0.37 = 57.35$

Example

What's the expected number of sixes when I roll a fair dice 30 times? Interpret your answer.

- If the random variable X represents the number of sixes in 30 rolls, then $X \sim B(30, \frac{1}{6})$.
- So the expected value of X is $E(X) = 30 \times \frac{1}{6} = 5$
- If I were to repeatedly roll the dice 30 times, and find the **average** number of sixes in each set of 30 rolls, then I would expect it to end up pretty close to 5. And the more sets of 30 rolls I did, the closer to 5 I'd expect the average to be.

Tip: Notice that the probability of getting exactly 5 sixes on my next set of 30 rolls

$= \binom{30}{5} \times \left(\frac{1}{6}\right)^5 \times \left(\frac{5}{6}\right)^{25}$

$= 0.192$ (to 3 sig. fig.)

So I'm much more likely **not** to get exactly 5 sixes ($= 1 - 0.192 = 0.808$).

This is why it only makes sense to talk about the mean as a 'long-term average', and not as 'what I expect to happen next'.

The variance and standard deviation

The **variance** of a random variable is a kind of 'theoretical variance' — again, it's what you'd expect the variance to be if you gathered a large number of observations of the random variable (p62).

So the variance of a random variable $X \sim B(n, p)$ would be the expected variance if you performed lots of sets of n trials.

The variance of a random variable can be written either as σ^2 or $\text{Var}(X)$.

The **standard deviation** of a random variable is the positive square root of the variance, and is usually written σ.

Tip: For a binomial distribution, P(success) is usually called p, and P(failure) is sometimes called q $(= 1 - p)$.

If $X \sim B(n, p)$, then:

$$\textbf{Variance} = \text{Var}(X) = \sigma^2 = np(1-p) = npq$$

$$\textbf{Standard Deviation} = \sigma = \sqrt{np(1-p)} = \sqrt{npq}$$

Like with the mean... the variance of experimental results is unlikely to match this 'theoretical variance' **exactly**.

Examples

Find the variance and standard deviation of these random variables.

a) $X \sim B(400, 0.1)$

- First find $q = 1 - p$. — Since $p = 0.1$, $q = 1 - 0.1 = \mathbf{0.9}$.
- Then use the formula for the variance. — $\text{Var}(X) = \sigma^2 = npq = 400 \times 0.1 \times 0.9 = 36$
- Take the square root to find the standard deviation. — Standard deviation $= \sigma = \sqrt{36} = 6$

b) $X \sim B(155, 0.37)$

- Find $q = 1 - p$. — Since $p = 0.37$, $q = 1 - 0.37 = \mathbf{0.63}$.
- Calculate the variance. — $\text{Var}(X) = \sigma^2 = npq = 155 \times 0.37 \times 0.63 = 36.1305$
- Find the standard deviation. — Standard deviation $= \sigma = \sqrt{36.1305} = 6.01$ (to 3 sig. fig.)

Examples

If $X \sim B(25, 0.2)$, find:

a) $P(X \leq \mu)$

- Find the mean. — $\mu = 25 \times 0.2 = 5$
- Use tables to find $P(X \leq \mu)$. — $P(X \leq \mu) = P(X \leq 5) = 0.6167$

Tip: See p75 for more about using binomial tables.

b) $P(X \leq \mu - \sigma)$

- Find the variance, and then the standard deviation. — $\sigma^2 = 25 \times 0.2 \times 0.8 = 4$, which gives $\sigma = 2$.
- Use tables to find $P(X \leq \mu - \sigma)$. — $P(X \leq \mu - \sigma) = P(X \leq 3) = 0.2340$

c) $P(X \leq \mu - 2\sigma)$

- You'll need to use tables again. — $P(X \leq \mu - 2\sigma) = P(X \leq 1) = 0.0274$

You could be given E(X) and/or Var(X), and asked to find n and/or p.

Example 1

If $X \sim B(200, p)$ and $E(X) = 60$, find p.

$E(X) = 200 \times p = 60$, so $p = \frac{60}{200} = 0.3$

Example 2

A random variable $X \sim B(n, p)$.
If $E(X) = 10$ and $Var(X) = 9$, find n and p.

- Write down what you know about E(X) and Var(X). This gives you two equations involving n and p.

$E(X) = np = 10$
$Var(X) = np(1 - p) = 9$

- Divide Var(X) by E(X) — this will give you an equation just involving p, since the n's cancel.

$$\frac{Var(X)}{E(X)} = \frac{np(1-p)}{np} = 1 - p$$
$$\frac{Var(X)}{E(X)} = \frac{9}{10} = 0.9$$

- Solve to find p.

So $1 - p = 0.9$, which means $p = 0.1$

- Use your value for p to find n.

$E(X) = np = 10$, so $n = 10 \div 0.1 = 100$

Exercise 4.1

Q1 For each of the following random variables, find:
(i) the mean (μ)
(ii) the variance (σ^2)
(iii) the standard deviation (σ)

a) $X \sim B(10, 0.9)$ b) $X \sim B(25, 0.7)$ c) $X \sim B(50, 0.05)$
d) $X \sim B(70, 0.85)$ e) $X \sim B(15, 0.1)$ f) $X \sim B(100, 0.35)$

Q2 A biased coin has a probability of 0.6 of landing on heads. The random variable X represents the number of heads obtained in 60 tosses of the coin.

a) State the distribution of X.
b) Find the mean and the variance of X.

Q3 The random variable Y represents the number of times a biased coin lands on heads when it is tossed 150 times.
If $E(Y) = 30$, find:

a) the probability (p) of this coin landing on heads,
b) the variance of Y.

Q4 In a raffle, each ticket sold has a probability of 0.1 of winning a prize.

a) If 1600 tickets are sold in total and X represents the number of winning tickets sold, find the expected number of winning tickets (E(X)).
b) Calculate σ^2, the variance of X.

5. Modelling Real Problems

Learning Objective:

- Be able to apply knowledge of the binomial distribution to real-life situations.

Exam questions often involve a 'realistic-sounding' situation. So it's not enough just to know everything about the binomial distribution — you have to know how to apply that knowledge in real life as well.

Modelling real problems with B(n, p)

The first step with a real-world problem is to **model** it using a sensible probability distribution. If the situation satisfies all the conditions on page 68, then you'll need to use a **binomial distribution**.

When you've decided how to model the situation, you can 'do the maths'. You may then need to **interpret** your solution in the **context** of the question.

Tip: You might need to make some **assumptions** before using a binomial distribution. If so, you should write down what those assumptions are (unless you've already been told in the question to assume that those things are true).

Example 1

A market researcher is interviewing people in a busy city centre. It is assumed that the probability of each person he approaches agreeing to an interview is 0.3, and that each person can be considered an independent trial. During one session, he approaches 30 people.

a) Suggest a suitable model to describe the number of people (X) who agree to an interview.

- In this situation:
  (i) there's a **fixed number** (30) of trials,
  (ii) all the trials are **independent**,
  (iii) there are **two possible results** ('agree to an interview' and 'do not agree to an interview'),
  (iv) there's a **constant** probability of success (0.3),
  (v) X is the **total number** of people agreeing to an interview.

All the conditions for a binomial distribution are satisfied.

In fact, $X \sim B(30, 0.3)$.

Tip: See p75 for more about binomial tables.

b) Find the probability that more than 10 people agree to an interview.

- It's a binomial distribution, so use the binomial tables.

$P(X > 10) = 1 - P(X \leq 10)$
$= 1 - 0.7304 = 0.2696$

c) Find the expected number of people who will agree to an interview, and the variance of X.

- Use the formula for the mean (expected value) of a binomial distribution.

$E(X) = np = 30 \times 0.3 = 9$

So the researcher could expect 9 people to agree to an interview.

- Use the formula for the variance of a binomial distribution.

Variance $= np(1 - p)$
$= 30 \times 0.3 \times (1 - 0.3) = 6.3$

d) The researcher counts those agreeing to an interview in 100 samples of 30. He finds the mean is 8.9 and the variance is 3.2. Comment on the assumptions that the probability of a person agreeing to an interview is 0.3, and that each person can be considered an independent trial.

- The observed mean is approximately the same as the mean predicted by the model — so the assumption that the probability of a person agreeing to an interview is 0.3 seems justified.
- The observed variance is **very** different from the theoretical variance. This suggests at least one of the conditions for a binomial distribution is **not** satisfied, and the only real possibility left is the independence of the trials. So this assumption is unlikely to be valid.

Tip: You're asked to comment on **two** assumptions in d), so take them one at a time.

i) The mean number of 'successes' in each set of 30 trials is 8.9 — so based on this data, you would estimate the probability of 'success' as $\frac{8.9}{30} = 0.296...$, which is very close to 0.3. So that first assumption seems reasonable.

ii) So the only condition left to satisfy for a binomial distribution is the independence of the trials. Now... if the trials *were* all independent, then you'd expect an observed variance close to 6.3. But because the observed variance is **very** different, it seems **unlikely** that this last condition for a binomial distribution can be satisfied.

Example 2

A student has to take a 50-question multiple-choice exam. Each question has five possible answers of which only one is correct.

He believes he can pass the exam by guessing answers at random.

a) How many questions could the student be expected to guess correctly?

- Define your random variable first, and say how it will be distributed.

Let X be the number of correct guesses in 50 questions. Then $X \sim B(50, 0.2)$.

- Then you can use the formula for the mean (expected value).

$E(X) = np = 50 \times 0.2$
$= 10$ questions

b) If the pass mark is 15, what is the probability that the student will pass the exam?

- You need to find $P(X \geq 15)$.
- Remember... the tables only tell you $P(X \leq x)$.

$P(X \geq 15) = 1 - P(X < 15)$
$= 1 - P(X \leq 14)$
$= 1 - 0.9393 = 0.0607$

c) The examiner decides to set the pass mark so that it is at least 3 standard deviations above the expected number of correct guesses. What should the minimum pass mark be?

- You need the standard deviation of X — so start by finding the variance.

$\text{Var}(X) = np(1 - p)$
$= 50 \times 0.2 \times 0.8 = 8$

So the standard deviation $= \sqrt{8}$
$= \mathbf{2.828...}$

- Now you need to think about what the question is actually asking.

This means the pass mark needs to be at least $10 + (3 \times 2.828...) \approx 18.5$ — i.e. the minimum pass mark should be 19.

Tip: You don't always need to write down the 5 conditions for a binomial distribution — but you should make sure they're satisfied.

You **will** have to specify what values n and p take though.

Example 3

I am spinning a coin that I know is three times as likely to land on heads as it is on tails.

a) What is the probability that it lands on tails for the first time on the third spin?

- First you need to know the probabilities for heads and tails.

P(heads) = 3 × P(tails).
But P(heads) + P(tails) = 1.
This means that P(heads) = 0.75 and P(tails) = 0.25.

- If it lands on tails for the first time on the third spin, then the first two spins must have been heads.
- Since all the spins are independent, you know that:
  P(heads then heads then tails)
  = P(heads) × P(heads) × P(tails)

P(lands on tails for the first time on the third spin)
$= 0.75 \times 0.75 \times 0.25$
$= 0.141$ (to 3 sig. fig.)

Tip: Careful... this doesn't need you to use one of the binomial formulas.

Tip: Here, the order of the results matters, so you **don't** need to multiply by a binomial coefficient — i.e. the first result **must** be heads, the second **must** be heads and the third **must** be tails.

It's not like on p67, where there were various possible orders that the results could have happened in.

b) What is the probability that in 10 spins, it lands on heads at least 7 times?

- First define your random variable, and state how it is distributed.

If X represents the number of heads in 10 spins, then $X \sim B(10, 0.75)$.

- $p = 0.75$ isn't in your tables, so define a new binomial random variable Y with probability of success $p = 0.25$.

The number of tails in 10 spins can be described by the random variable $Y = 10 - X$, where $Y \sim B(10, 0.25)$.

- You need the probability of 'at least 7 heads' — this is the same as the probability of '3 or fewer tails'.

$P(X \geq 7) = P(Y \leq 3) = 0.7759$

Exercise 5.1

Q1 A hairdresser hands out leaflets. She knows there is always a probability of 0.25 that a passer-by will take a leaflet. During a five-minute period, 50 people pass the hairdresser.

a) Suggest a suitable model for X, the number of passers-by who take a leaflet in the five-minute period. Explain why this is a suitable model.

b) What is the probability that more than 4 people take a leaflet?

c) What is the probability that exactly 10 people take a leaflet?

d) What is the expected number of people who will take a leaflet in this period?

e) Find the standard deviation (σ) of X.

Q2 Jasmine plants 15 randomly selected seeds in each of her plant trays. She knows that 35% of this type of plant grow with yellow flowers, while the remainder grow with white flowers. All her seeds grow successfully, and Jasmine counts how many plants in each tray grow with yellow flowers.

a) Find the probability that a randomly selected tray has exactly 5 plants with yellow flowers.

b) Find the probability that a randomly selected tray contains more plants with yellow flowers than plants with white flowers.

Q3 In the UK, the probability of any particular person in a random sample having hazel eyes is 0.15. A random sample of size n is taken, and X represents the number of people in this sample with hazel eyes. It is known that $E(X) = 6$.

a) Find the value of n.

b) Find the probability that fewer than 6 people have hazel eyes in this sample.

c) In a random sample of a different size, the expected number of people with hazel eyes is calculated to be 24. If Y represents the number of people in this sample with hazel eyes, find $Var(Y)$.

Review Exercise — Chapter 3

Q1 State whether the function $P(X = x) = \frac{2}{3}$ $x = 0, 1, 2$ could be a probability function. Explain your answer.

Q1 Hint: Remember the important rule about discrete probability functions from page 63.

Q2 In how many different orders can the following be arranged?

a) 15 identical red balls, plus 6 other balls, all of different colours.

b) 4 red counters, 4 blue counters, 4 yellow counters and 4 green counters.

c) 7 green counters and 5 blue counters.

Q3 Use the binomial probability function to find the probability of the following.

a) Getting exactly 5 heads when you spin a fair coin 10 times.

b) Getting exactly 9 heads when you spin a fair coin 10 times.

Q4 Which of the following would follow a binomial distribution? Explain your answers.

a) The number of prime numbers you throw in 30 throws of a standard dice.

b) The number of people in a particular class at a school who get 'heads' when they flip a coin.

c) The number of aces in a 7-card hand dealt from a standard pack of 52 cards.

d) The number of shots I have to take before I score from the free-throw line in basketball.

Q5 What is the probability of the following?

a) Getting at least 5 heads when you spin a fair coin 10 times.

b) Getting at least 9 heads when you spin a fair coin 10 times.

Q6 If $X \sim B(14, 0.27)$, find:

a) $P(X = 4)$ b) $P(X < 2)$ c) $P(5 < X \leq 8)$

Q7 If $X \sim B(25, 0.15)$ and $Y \sim B(15, 0.65)$ find:

a) $P(X \leq 3)$ b) $P(X \leq 7)$ c) $P(X \leq 15)$

d) $P(Y \leq 3)$ e) $P(Y \leq 7)$ f) $P(Y \leq 15)$

Q8 Find the required probability for each of the following binomial distributions.

a) $P(X \leq 15)$ if $X \sim B(20, 0.4)$ b) $P(X < 4)$ if $X \sim B(40, 0.15)$

c) $P(X > 7)$ if $X \sim B(25, 0.45)$ d) $P(X \geq 40)$ if $X \sim B(50, 0.8)$

e) $P(X = 20)$ if $X \sim B(30, 0.7)$ f) $P(X = 7)$ if $X \sim B(10, 0.75)$

Q9 If $X \sim B(30, 0.35)$, find:

a) a if $P(X \leq a) = 0.8737$ b) b if $P(X \geq b) = 0.8762$

c) the maximum value c such that $P(X \leq c) < 0.05$.

Q10 Find the mean and variance of the following random variables.

a) $X \sim B(20, 0.4)$ b) $X \sim B(40, 0.15)$ c) $X \sim B(25, 0.45)$

d) $X \sim B(50, 0.8)$ e) $X \sim B(30, 0.7)$ f) $X \sim B(45, 0.012)$

Exam-Style Questions — Chapter 3

1 The probability of an apple bought from a local farm containing a maggot is 0.15.

a) Find the probability that in a random sample of 40 apples there are:

(i) fewer than 6 apples containing maggots,

(2 marks)

(ii) more than 2 apples containing maggots,

(2 marks)

(iii) exactly 12 apples containing maggots.

(2 marks)

b) These apples are sold in crates of 40. Rosie buys 3 crates.

Find the probability that more than 1 crate contains more than 2 apples with maggots.

(3 marks)

Jim claims that the number of apples containing maggots, M, in a bag of 5 bought from his shop can be modelled by a binomial distribution with $n = 5$ and $p = \frac{1}{10}$.

c) (i) Calculate the mean and variance of M, if you assume Jim's claim to be correct.

(2 marks)

(ii) In 30 bags of 5 apples bought from Jim's shop, the number of apples containing maggots per bag had a mean of 0.5 and a variance of 0.5.

Using this, and your answer to part c) (i), comment on Jim's claim.

(2 marks)

2 Simon tries to solve the crossword puzzle in his newspaper every day for two weeks. He either succeeds in solving the puzzle, or he fails to solve it.

a) Simon believes that this situation can be modelled by a random variable, X, following a binomial distribution.

(i) State two conditions needed for a binomial distribution to arise here.

(2 marks)

(ii) State which quantity would follow a binomial distribution (assuming the above conditions are satisfied).

(1 mark)

b) Simon believes that $X \sim B(14, p)$. If $P(X = 4) = P(X = 5)$, find p.

(5 marks)

The newspaper also publishes a separate, cryptic crossword puzzle every other day. Simon attempts to solve all such puzzles during the same two-week period. Again, he either succeeds or fails to solve the puzzle. Simon says that the number of cryptic crossword puzzles he solves can be modelled by a random variable $Y \sim B(7, 0.2)$.

c) Assuming that all Simon's claims about the two types of puzzle are correct, how many puzzles in total would you expect Simon to solve in this two-week period?

(3 marks)

3 A darts player gets a 'treble-20' with each dart with a probability of 0.75.

a) The player throws 3 darts.
Find the probability that he gets a 'treble-20' with at least 2 of the darts. *(2 marks)*

b) He throws another 5 sets of 3 darts.
In how many sets would he be expected to get a 'treble-20' with at least 2 darts? *(2 marks)*

c) He now throws another 30 darts for a charity challenge.

(i) If he gets a 'treble-20' with at least 26 of the darts, he wins a major prize for the charity.
What is the probability that he wins the major prize? *(2 marks)*

(ii) If he gets a 'treble-20' with between 22 and 25 of the darts (inclusive), he wins a minor prize for the charity.
What is the probability that he wins the minor prize? *(3 marks)*

4 Jessica has a bag of coins. Some of the coins are bronze and some are silver.
Jessica picks a coin at random, makes a note of whether it is bronze or silver, replaces it in the bag and then gives the bag a shake. She repeats this process n times in total.
The probability of her picking a bronze coin each time is 0.3.

a) Given that the expected number of bronze coins she obtains is 7.5, find n. *(2 marks)*

b) Using this value of n, find the probability that Jessica picks bronze and silver coins in the ratio $1:4$. *(2 marks)*

5 The probability that any egg from a particular farm will be cracked by the time it reaches the supermarket shelves is 0.06. These eggs are sold in boxes of 12.

a) If X represents the number of cracked eggs in a randomly selected box of 12, find:

(i) the probability that there will be no cracked eggs, *(2 marks)*

(ii) the probability that there will be more than 2 cracked eggs. *(3 marks)*

b) A supermarket always orders 50 boxes of 12 eggs at a time.

(i) State how Y will be distributed, where Y is the number of boxes per order containing more than 2 cracked eggs. *(1 mark)*

(ii) Find the probability that at least one box in an order contains more than 2 cracked eggs. *(2 marks)*

Chapter 4 The Normal Distribution

1. The Normal Distribution

Learning Objectives:

- Know the shape and properties of the normal distribution.
- Know that probabilities are shown by the area under the normal curve.
- Be able to use the correct notation to describe a normal distribution.

In this section you'll be introduced to the normal distribution. Many variables can be modelled by a normal distribution, and this can be very useful, as you'll see later on.

The normal distribution

The shape of a normal distribution

The distributions of lots of quantities in the real world follow a **particular pattern** — with most of the data values falling **somewhere in the middle**, and only a small proportion taking much higher or lower values.

- For example, this histogram shows the distribution of the weights of some hedgehogs.
- Most of the weights lie close to the mean weight — with similar numbers distributed symmetrically above and below.

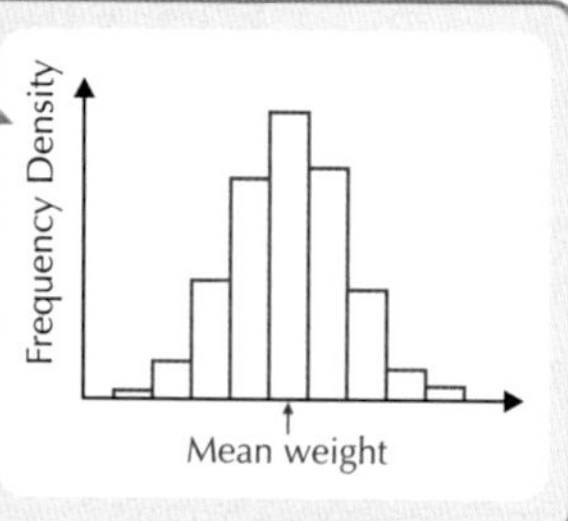

Tip: Remember from p3... **continuous** variables can take any value within a certain range, unlike discrete variables, which have 'gaps' between values.

- A quantity like this can often be **modelled** by a **normal distribution**.
- A normal distribution is **continuous**, so can easily model continuous variables — such as height, weight, length, etc.

Tip: A **random variable** is a variable that takes different values with specific probabilities. You covered discrete random variables briefly in Chapter 3 (p62). It's a similar idea here, but the variable is continuous — it can take any value in a certain range.

If X is a **continuous random variable** that follows a **normal** distribution, you can describe the probability distribution of X using just two measures — its **mean**, μ, and **variance**, σ^2.

- Whatever the values of μ and σ^2, the **graph** of a normal distribution always looks like the **curve** below.

- The curve is '**bell**-shaped'.
- There's a **peak** at the **mean**, μ.
- It's **symmetrical** about the mean — so values the same distance above and below the mean are equally likely.

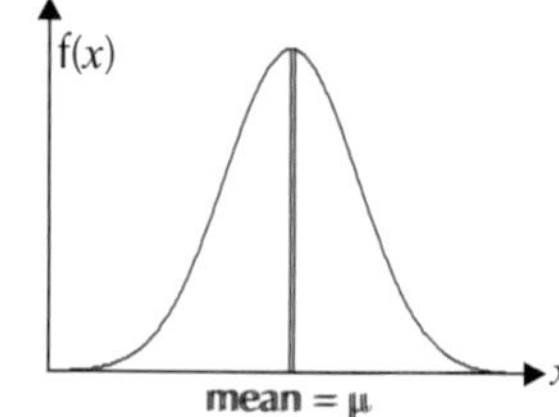

Tip: The vertical axis is labelled $f(x)$ because the equation of the curve is a function of x. It's called the probability density function, but you don't need to know about these in S1.

- You can see that the shape of the normal curve **approximately fits** the shape of the hedgehog distribution above. The peak at the mean reflects the fact that values close to the mean are most likely.
- The width and height of the curve depend on the **variance** of the normal distribution. The three graphs on the next page all show normal distributions with the **same mean** (μ), but **different variances** (σ^2).

Tip: For a normal distribution, mean = median = mode.

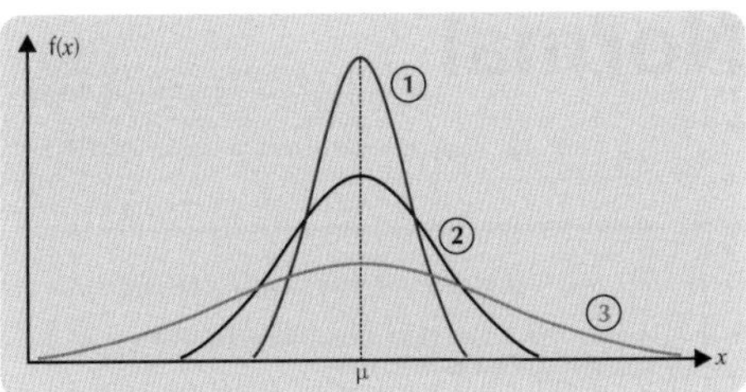

- The **larger** the variance the **wider** the curve, so **graph 3** has the **largest** variance and **graph 1** has the **smallest** variance.
- The **total area** under the curve is always the **same**, so a wider curve needs to have a lower height.

The area under a normal curve

The **area** under a normal curve shows **probabilities**.

- The **total area** under the curve represents the **total probability** of the random variable taking one of its possible values. And since the total probability is 1, the **total area under the curve** must also be **1**.
- The **probability** of the variable taking a value **between two limits** is the **area under the curve** between those limits.
- The probability of the variable taking any **single value**, $P(X = x)$, is always **zero** because the area under the curve at a single **point** always equals zero.
- This means that for any **normally distributed** random variable, X, and any k: $\mathbf{P(X < k) = P(X \leq k)}$

> **Tip:** These blue bullet points are true for all continuous random variables. You'll see more about this in S2.

> **Tip:** You'll see how to find and use areas under the normal curve over the next few pages.

> **Tip:** This is because: $P(X \leq k) = P(X < k) + P(X = k)$ (since the events $X < k$ and $X = k$ are mutually exclusive — see p45). So, since $P(X = k) = 0$: $P(X \leq k) = P(X < k) + 0 = P(X < k)$

There are some **facts** about the **area** under the curve that apply to **all** normal distributions.

- **68%** of the total **area** lies within **±1** standard deviation (±σ) of the mean.
- **95%** of the total **area** lies within **±2** standard deviations (±2σ) of the mean.
- **99.7%** of the total **area** lies within **±3** standard deviations (±3σ) of the mean.

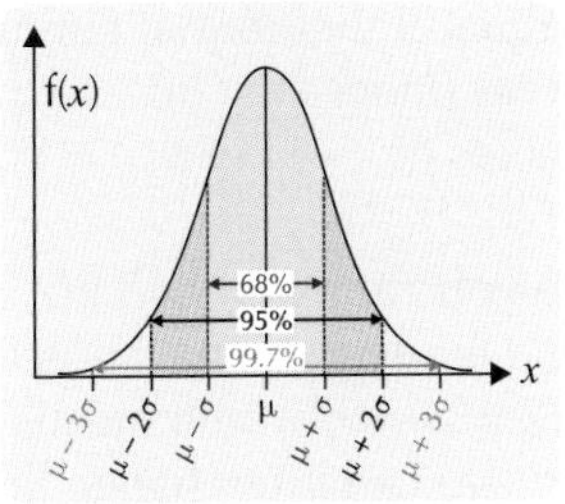

So **68%** of **observations** are within **±σ** of the mean, **95%** of **observations** are within **±2σ** of the mean and **99.7%** of **observations** are within **±3σ** of the mean.

> **Tip:** Remember... standard deviation is the square root of the variance — so it's a measure of **dispersion** (how spread out values are from the mean).

Describing a normal distribution

If a continuous random variable X is **normally** distributed with mean μ and variance σ^2, it is written like this: ⟶ $X \sim N(\mu, \sigma^2)$

'**N**' stands for '**normal**' and '~' is short for '**is distributed**'.

- So going back to our hedgehog weights on the previous page, we could define a random variable, $W \sim N(\mu, \sigma^2)$, where W represents hedgehog weight.
- Here, μ would represent the mean weight of the hedgehogs and σ would represent the standard deviation of hedgehog weights.

The most **important** normal distribution is the **standard normal distribution** Z, which has a mean of 0 and a variance of 1. There's a lot more about the standard normal distribution on the next few pages.

2. The Standard Normal Distribution, Z

Learning Objectives:

- Be able to use tables to find probabilities for the standard normal distribution, Z.
- Be able to use tables to find values for z, when given probabilities.

The most important normal distribution is the standard normal distribution. The 'special' random variable Z follows a standard normal distribution — Z is called the 'standard normal variable'. In this section you'll see how to use tables to find the probability that Z takes a value in a given range.

The standard normal distribution

The **standard normal distribution**, Z, has **mean 0** and **variance 1**. → $Z \sim N(0, 1)$

Below is a graph of the standard normal distribution. As you'd expect, the curve is **symmetrical** about the mean, **0**.

Remember that **areas under the curve** show **probabilities**. The **shaded area** here shows the probability that Z takes a value that's **less than or equal to** z. So to find this probability, we need to work out the area.

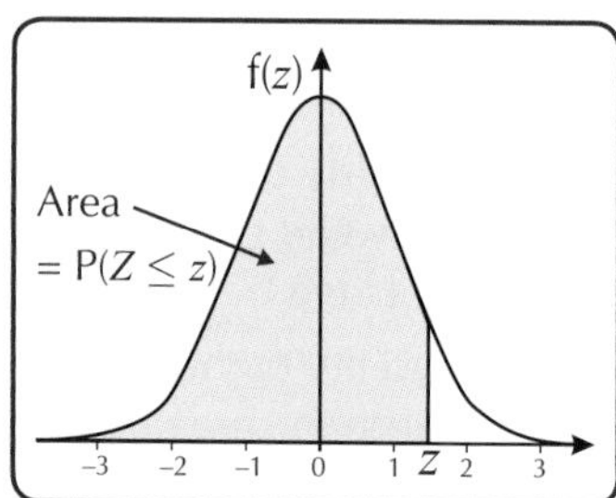

Tip: Remember from Chapter 3 (p63) that a cumulative distribution function of a random variable, X, is a function $F(x)$ which gives $P(X \leq x)$.

Working out the area under a normal distribution curve is usually difficult. But the reason why Z is **so important** is that there are **tables** that list areas under the curve for N(0, 1). The main table you'll use (see page 159) shows values of the normal **cumulative distribution function**, $\Phi(z)$. These are the **areas** under the curve to the **left of** z (the **probability** that $Z \leq z$) for different values of z — i.e. $\Phi(z) = P(Z \leq z)$.

Tip: In the formula booklet you'll be given in the exam, $\Phi(z)$ is labelled the 'Normal Distribution Function'.

Tip: The table only gives $P(Z \leq z)$ for $z \geq 0$.

So you can often find $P(Z \leq z)$ by looking up the value of z in the table and reading off the value for $\Phi(z)$. And since Z is a **continuous** distribution, $P(Z = z) = 0$, which means that $P(Z \leq z)$ and $P(Z < z)$ are the **same** thing. So you can **interchange** the ≤ and < signs — i.e. $\Phi(z) = P(Z < z)$ as well.

Tip: Remember from the previous page that if X has a normal distribution, then $P(X < k) = P(X \leq k)$ for any value of k — the standard normal variable is no exception.

Example 1

Find the following probabilities.

a) $P(Z \leq 0.64)$

This is a nice, straightforward one — all you have to do is look up $z = 0.64$ in the table for $\Phi(z)$.

So, $P(Z \leq 0.64) = 0.73891$ ← Always write down the full value from the table.

b) $P(Z < 0.1)$

Z is a continuous variable, so $P(Z < 0.1)$ is just the same as $P(Z \leq 0.1)$. So again, you just look up 0.1 in the table for $\Phi(z)$.

So, $P(Z < 0.1) = 0.53983$

Tip: The table for $\Phi(z)$ is on page 159.

To find the probability that Z is less than or equal to 0.64, you need to find the '0.6' row in the left-hand column and then go across the row until you get to the '0.04' column.

OK, so finding the probability that Z is **less than** z, where z is **positive**, is easy. And finding the probability that Z takes a value **greater than** (or greater than or equal to) z is only **slightly trickier**.

Using the fact that the **total area** under the curve is **1**, we get this definition. →

$$\mathbf{P(Z > z) = 1 - P(Z \le z) = 1 - \Phi(z)}$$

Tip: And we also get:
$P(Z \ge z) = 1 - P(Z < z)$
$= 1 - \Phi(z)$
(since $P(Z < z) = P(Z \le z)$)

Example 2

Find the following probabilities.

a) $P(Z > 0.23)$

$P(Z > 0.23) = 1 - P(Z \le 0.23)$
$= 1 - 0.59095$ ← $P(Z \le 0.23) = 0.59095$
$= 0.40905$

b) $P(Z \ge 1.15)$

$P(Z \ge 1.15) = 1 - P(Z < 1.15)$
$= 1 - 0.87493$ ← $P(Z < 1.15) = 0.87493$
$= 0.12507$

Tip: Drawing a sketch always helps to make things clearer.

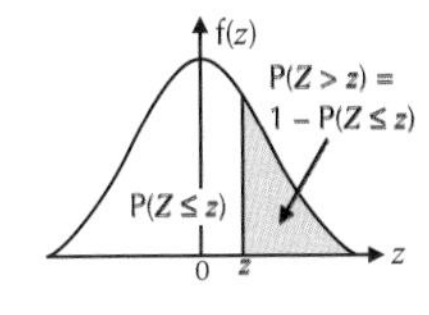

Now then, things start to get a bit **trickier** when z takes a **negative** value. To work these out, you need to use the **symmetry** of the curve. The best thing to do is to start by **drawing a sketch** and **shading** the area you want to find.

Example 3

Find the following probabilities.

a) $P(Z > -0.42)$

- **Shade** the area you want to find. →
- Because z is **negative**, you **can't look it up** in the table — so the method used in Example 2 won't work. Instead, use symmetry to shade an **area of the same size** involving a **positive** value of z.
  This is the area to the **left** of z **= +0.42**. →
- So $P(Z > -0.42) = P(Z < 0.42)$.
  And looking up 0.42 in the $\Phi(z)$ table you get:

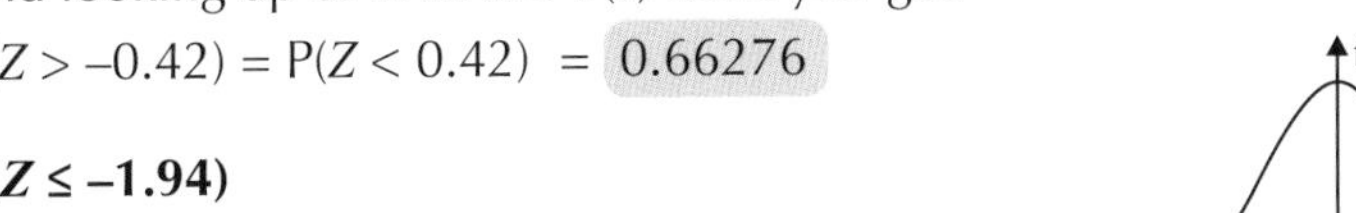

$P(Z > -0.42) = P(Z < 0.42) = 0.66276$

b) $P(Z \le -1.94)$

- **Shade** the area you want to find. →
- Again, use symmetry to shade an **area of the same size**, but involving a **positive** value of z instead of a negative one.
  This is the area to the **right** of z **= +1.94**. →

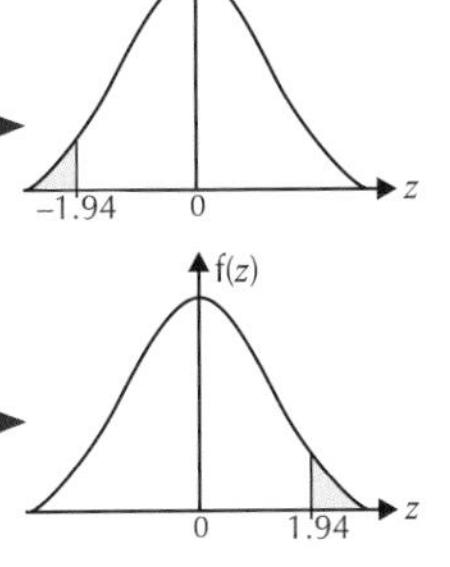

- So $P(Z \le -1.94) = P(Z \ge 1.94)$.
- You still can't get your answer from the table directly, but using the fact that the area under the curve is 1, $P(Z \ge 1.94) = 1 - P(Z < 1.94)$.

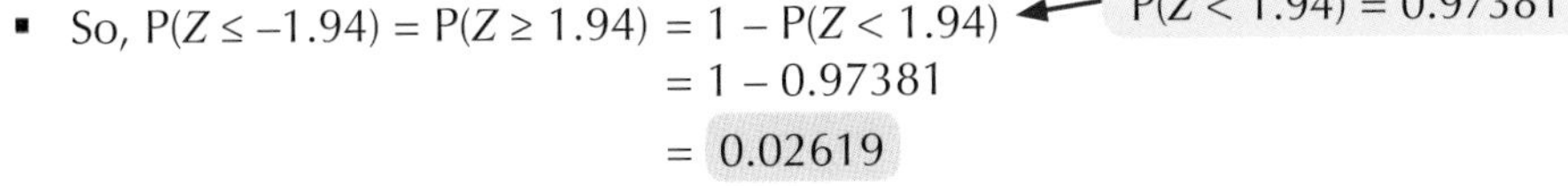

- So, $P(Z \le -1.94) = P(Z \ge 1.94) = 1 - P(Z < 1.94)$ ← $P(Z < 1.94) = 0.97381$
  $= 1 - 0.97381$
  $= 0.02619$

Tip: Remember, you're always trying to get to an area that you can look up in the table.

In the next example, you're asked to find the probability that Z takes a value **between two limits**. You can do this by **subtracting** one area from another.

Example 4

Find the probability that $0.12 < Z \leq 0.82$.

- **Shade** the area you want to find.
- To find this area, you need to find the area to the left of $z = 0.82$, then **subtract** the area to the left of $z = 0.12$. That will leave you with the area between the two values.
- So, $P(0.12 < Z \leq 0.82) = P(Z \leq 0.82) - P(Z \leq 0.12)$
$= 0.79389 - 0.54776$
$= 0.24613$

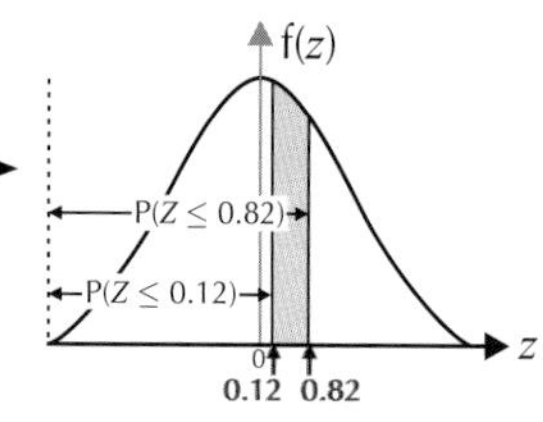

Exercise 2.1

Q1 Use the table of the normal cumulative distribution function, $\Phi(z)$, to find the following probabilities.

a) $P(Z \leq 1.87)$ b) $P(Z \leq 0.39)$ c) $P(Z < 0.99)$ d) $P(Z < 3.15)$

Q2 Use the table of the normal cumulative distribution function, $\Phi(z)$, to find the following probabilities.

a) $P(Z > 2.48)$ b) $P(Z > 0.85)$ c) $P(Z \geq 1.23)$ d) $P(Z \geq 0.14)$

Q3 By using sketches and the table of the normal cumulative distribution function, $\Phi(z)$, find the following probabilities.

a) $P(Z > -3.35)$ b) $P(Z > -0.24)$ c) $P(Z > -1.21)$

d) $P(Z < -0.62)$ e) $P(Z < -1.14)$ f) $P(Z \leq -2.06)$

Q4 Work out the following probabilities.

a) $P(1.34 < Z < 2.18)$ b) $P(0.76 < Z < 1.92)$

c) $P(-1.45 < Z < 0.17)$ d) $P(-2.14 < Z < 1.65)$

e) $P(-1.66 < Z < 1.66)$ f) $P(-0.34 < Z < 0.34)$

g) $P(-3.25 < Z < -2.48)$ h) $P(-1.11 < Z < -0.17)$

Q4 Hint: For parts g) and h), use symmetry to find an identical area for which both limits are positive.

Finding a z-value

So you know how to find **probabilities** when you've been given z, using the $\Phi(z)$ table. The other sort of question you need to be able to answer is where you're **given** a **probability**, e.g. $P(Z < z) = 0.58706$, and you have to **find** z. How you go about this depends on what sort of decimal the probability is.

The first thing to try is the **table of percentage points** of the normal distribution (see page 160).

- The **percentage-points** table gives the value of z for some probabilities, p, where $p = P(Z \leq z)$.
- So this time you **start** off with the **probability** that Z is **less** than a value of z, and look up the value of z in the table.

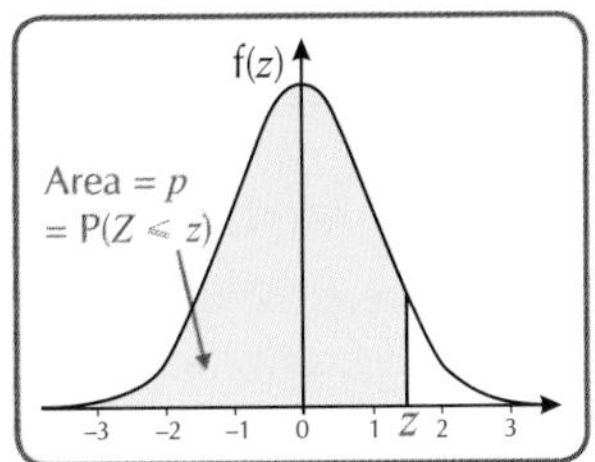

Tip: The percentage-points table just does what the cumulative distribution function table did — but in reverse.

Examples

a) If $P(Z \leq z) = 0.85$, then what is the value of z?

- Start by drawing a **sketch**, showing what you know.
- Try looking up $p = 0.85$ in the **percentage-points** table. See p160

  From the table, if $p = 0.85$, then $z = 1.0364$.

  So, if $P(Z \leq z) = 0.85$, then $z = 1.0364$

b) Find z if $P(Z < z) = 0.99$.

- Start by drawing a **sketch**, showing what you know.
- Try looking up $p = 0.99$ in the **percentage-points** table.

  From the table, if $p = 0.99$, then $z = 2.3263$.

  So, if $P(Z < z) = 0.99$, then $z = 2.3263$

Tip: Again, go down the rows to find the first decimal place of p (or the first two decimal places of p in the bottom half of the table), and then across the columns to find the second decimal place (or the third).

Tip: Remember, $<$ and $\leq$ mean the same for a continuous distribution.

Depending on the **value of p**, you might not be able to find what you want from the percentage-points table. If you're given a probability that isn't in the table of percentage points, it's usually best to see if you can find what you need in the **table for $\Phi(z)$** (the normal cumulative distribution function). But you need to read the table 'the other way round'.

Tip: The percentage-points table contains probabilities with at most 3 decimal places, so if you're given a value of p with more than 3 decimal places, you're probably going to need the table showing $\Phi(z)$.

Example

If $P(Z < z) = 0.95543$, then what is the value of z?

- 0.95543 isn't in the table of percentage points so use the table for $\Phi(z)$ instead.
- Start by drawing a **sketch**, showing what you know.
- OK, so you need to find z for which $\Phi(z) = 0.95543$.
- Using the table, read through the values of $\Phi(z)$ until you find 0.95543. $\Phi(z) = 0.95543$ for $z = 1.70$.

  So, if $P(Z < z) = 0.95543$, then $z = 1.70$

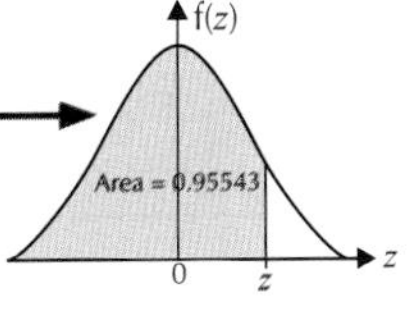

The table for $\Phi(z)$ is on p159.

Tip: Always check that the answer seems reasonable. The total probability is 1, so for an area of 0.95543, z will be positive and quite far to the right.

If **P(*Z* < *z*)** is **less than 0.5**, then z will be **negative**, and these values **aren't listed** in the tables. But you can still **use the tables** — you just need to do a bit of thinking and sketching to decide what to look up.

- The area, ***a***, to the **left of *z*** is less than 0.5. You can see from the graph that there's an area of the same size to the **right** of the value **–*z*** (where $-z$ is positive).
- Now you can draw a second graph showing the area to the **left** of **–*z***. This is the area **1 – *a***.
- The area $1 - a$ is **greater than 0.5**, so you can look it up in the table of percentage points or the $\Phi(z)$ table to find the value of **–*z***.
- Finally, multiply $-z$ by -1 to get z.

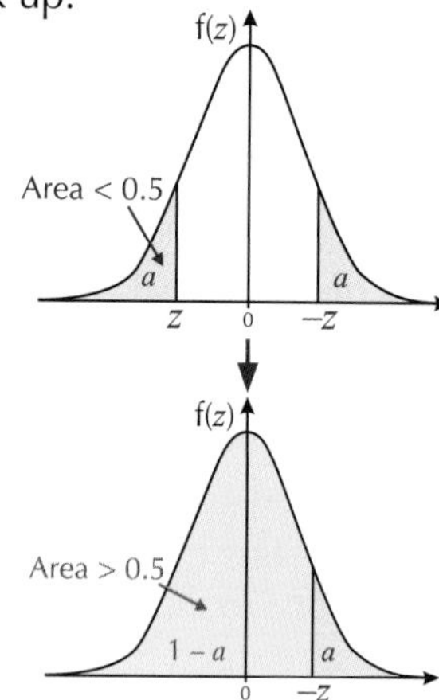

Tip: If $P(Z < z) < 0.5$, then z will be negative.

Example

If P(*Z* < *z*) = 0.26109, then what is the value of *z*?

- First, draw a **sketch**, showing what you know, and mark on the **equivalent area** to the right of $-z$.
- **Subtract** 0.26109 from 1 to get the area to the **left** of $-z$.
  $1 - 0.26109 =$ **0.73891**.
- Draw another sketch showing the new area.
- Look up $\Phi(z) = 0.73891$ in the table.
  $\Phi(z) = 0.73891$ for $z = 0.64$, so **$-z = 0.64$**.
- So, $z = \mathbf{-1 \times 0.64} = -0.64$. So, if $P(Z < z) = 0.26109$, then $z = -0.64$

Tip: Again, check the answer seems OK. $P(Z < z) < 0.5$, so z should be negative.

If **P(*Z* > *z*)** is **greater than 0.5**, you'll have the same problem — you won't be able to find z listed in the tables as it'll be negative. But you can use symmetry in a similar way to find $-z$.

Tip: If $P(Z > z) > 0.5$, then $1 - P(Z \leq z) > 0.5$ so $P(Z \leq z) < 0.5$ and so z will be negative again.

Example

If P(*Z* > *z*) = 0.76, then what is the value of *z*?

- Start by drawing a **sketch**, showing what you know.
- Since $p > 0.5$, you know that z is negative.
- So use **symmetry** to shade an area of the **same size** that you can look up in the tables.
  This is the area to the **left of –*z***.
- $p = 0.76$ is in the percentage-points table so read off the table to get $-z = 0.7063$. See p160
  So, **$-z = 0.7063$** and $z = \mathbf{-1 \times 0.7063} = -0.7063$.
- So, if $P(Z > z) = 0.76$, then $z = -0.7063$

Okay, so the **Φ(*z*)** table and the **percentage-points** table both contain values for **P(*Z* ≤ *z*)**. It really depends on what sort of decimal the **probability** is as to which table you should use to find z.

Examples

a) If P($Z < z$) = 0.9, then what is the value of z?

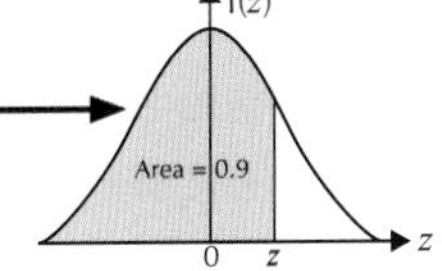

- Start by drawing a **sketch**, showing what you know.
- P($Z < z$) only has 1 decimal place, so you'll probably need to use the percentage-points table.
- P($Z < z$) = 0.9 so try looking up p **= 0.9** in the **percentage-points** table.

  From the table, if $p = 0.9$, then $z = 1.2816$.

  So, if P($Z < z$) = 0.9, then $z = 1.2816$

Tip: The $\Phi(z)$ table doesn't contain $\Phi(z) = 0.9$.

Most of the probabilities in the $\Phi(z)$ table are quite 'unpleasant looking', with 5 decimal places.

b) If P($Z < z$) = 0.05, then what is the value of z?

- This probability has only 2 decimal places, so it looks like you're going to need the percentage-points table. But you can't use it directly because P($Z < z$) < 0.5, so $z < 0$.
- Start by drawing a **sketch**, showing what you know.
- This shows that the area to the right of $-z$ is 0.05.
- **Subtract** 0.05 from 1 to get the area to the **left** of $-z$.

  1 – 0.05 = **0.95**.

  From the table, $p = 0.95$ for $z = 1.6449$.

  So, $-z$ **= 1.6449** and z = **–1 × 1.6449** = –1.6449.
- So, if P($Z < z$) = 0.05, then $z = -1.6449$

Tip: You don't always have to do a sketch if you feel you don't need to, but they do help you to avoid mistakes.

c) If P($Z > z$) = 0.0392, then what is the value of z?

- This is a fairly unpleasant decimal, so you'll need to use the table for $\Phi(z)$ this time.
- Start by drawing a **sketch**, showing what you know.
- Since P($Z > z$) = 0.0392, you know that P($Z \leq z$) = 1 – 0.0392 = 0.9608. So look this up in the **$\Phi(z)$ table**.

  From the table, $\Phi(z) = 0.9608$ for $z = 1.76$.
- So, if P($Z > z$) = 0.0392, then $z = 1.76$

The final type of example we need to go through is when you're given the **probability** that Z takes a value **between two limits**, and you're asked to **find** the **missing limit**.

Examples

a) If P($0 < Z < z$) = 0.4452, find the value of z.

- Start by drawing a **sketch**, showing what you know.
- If you find P($Z < z$), you can use the $\Phi(z)$ table to get z.

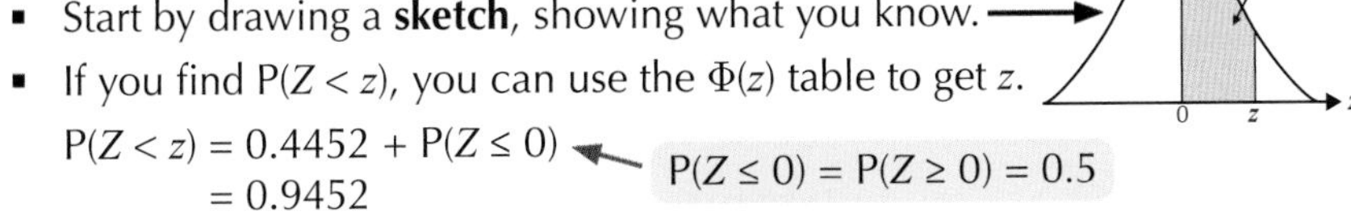

  P($Z < z$) = 0.4452 + P($Z \leq 0$)
  = 0.9452

  P($Z \leq 0$) = P($Z \geq 0$) = 0.5
- Using the table, $\Phi(z) = 0.9452$ for $z = 1.60$.
- So, if P($0 < Z < z$) = 0.4452, then $z = 1.60$

b) If P(0.8 < Z < z) = 0.19995, find the value of z.

- Start by drawing a **sketch**, showing what you know.
- If you find $P(Z < z)$, you can use the $\Phi(z)$ table to get z.

  $P(Z < z) = P(Z \leq 0.8) + P(0.8 < Z < z)$
  $= 0.78814 + 0.19995$
  $= 0.98809$ ← Using the $\Phi(z)$ table
- Using the table, $\Phi(z) = 0.98809$ for $z = 2.26$.
- So, if $P(0.8 < Z < z) = 0.19995$, then $z = 2.26$

f(z)
Area = 0.19995
0 0.8 z
z

Exercise 2.2

Q1 Use the table of the normal cumulative distribution function, $\Phi(z)$, to find z, given each of the following probabilities.

a) $P(Z < z) = 0.85769$ b) $P(Z < z) = 0.82639$

c) $P(Z < z) = 0.37828$ d) $P(Z < z) = 0.00402$

e) $P(Z > z) = 0.75804$ f) $P(Z > z) = 0.94408$

g) $P(Z > z) = 0.48006$ h) $P(Z > z) = 0.0951$

Q2 Use the percentage-points table to find z, given each of the following probabilities.

a) $P(Z < z) = 0.995$ b) $P(Z < z) = 0.8$

c) $P(Z > z) = 0.3$ d) $P(Z > z) = 0.15$

e) $P(Z > z) = 0.9$ f) $P(Z > z) = 0.85$

g) $P(Z < z) = 0.4$ h) $P(Z < z) = 0.01$

Q3 Hint: If you subtract the given area from 1 and divide by 2, you get the area $\geq z$ (and $\leq -z$). And that means you can easily find $P(Z \leq z)$.

Q3 Find the value of z, given each of the following probabilities.

a) $P(-z < Z < z) = 0.5991$ b) $P(-z < Z < z) = 0.94256$

c) $P(-z < Z < z) = 0.4$ d) $P(-z < Z < z) = 0.98$

Q4 Hint: Remember, $P(Z < 0)$ and $P(Z > 0)$ both equal 0.5.

Q4 Find the value of z, given each of the following probabilities.

a) $P(0 < Z < z) = 0.38686$ b) $P(0 < Z < z) = 0.48537$

Q5 Hint: One way of doing these is to flip the interval across the line $z = 0$.

Q5 Find the value of z, given each of the following probabilities.

a) $P(z < Z < 0) = 0.24215$ b) $P(z < Z < 0) = 0.14431$

Q6 Find the value of z, given each of the following probabilities.

a) $P(1.5 < Z < z) = 0.04062$ b) $P(0.58 < Z < z) = 0.0691$

c) $P(-1.3 < Z < z) = 0.87104$ d) $P(-0.54 < Z < z) = 0.66704$

e) $P(z < Z < 0.27) = 0.54585$ f) $P(z < Z < -1.25) = 0.09493$

3. Normal Distributions and Z-Tables

All normally distributed variables can be transformed to the standard normal variable, Z. This is really useful, because it means that you can use the Z-tables to find out information about any normal distribution.

Learning Objectives:

- Be able to transform normal variables to the standard normal variable, Z.
- Use Z-tables to find probabilities for normal variables.
- Use simultaneous equations to find the mean and variance of a normal distribution.

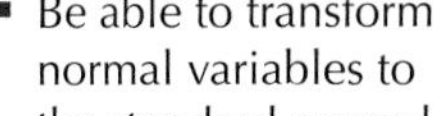

Converting to the Z distribution

Any continuous random variable, X, where $X \sim N(\mu, \sigma^2)$, can be **transformed** to the **standard normal variable**, Z, by:

- **subtracting the mean** (μ), and then
- **dividing by the standard deviation** (σ).

$$\text{If } X \sim N(\mu, \sigma^2), \text{ then } \frac{X - \mu}{\sigma} = Z, \text{ where } Z \sim N(0, 1)$$

Once you've transformed a variable like this, you can use the Z-tables.

Tip: Remember, the standard deviation is the square root of the variance.

- Here's a sketch of the distribution of X, where $X \sim N(20, 9)$. $\mu = 20$, $\sigma = 3$
- To transform X into Z, you need to transform **all values of X** (called x) into **values of Z** (called z), using the formula:

$$z = \frac{x - 20}{3}$$

- For example:

$x = 23$ becomes $z = \frac{23 - 20}{3} = 1$

- To find a **probability** for X, rewrite it as a probability for Z, then find the corresponding area under the Z curve.

f(x) $X \sim N(20, 9)$ — x: 11 14 17 **20** 23 26 29

f(z) $Z \sim N(0, 1)$ — z: –3 –2 –1 **0** 1 2 3

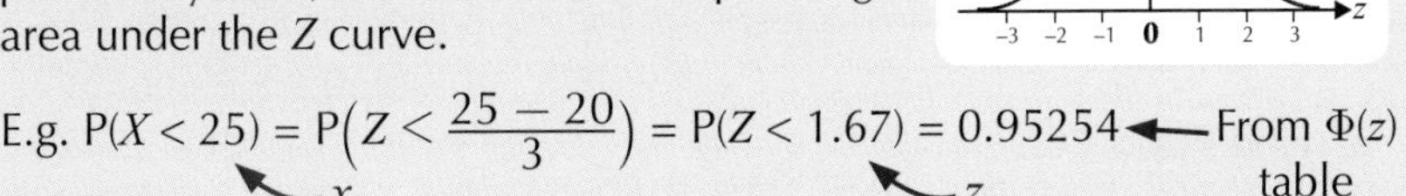

E.g. $P(X < 25) = P\left(Z < \frac{25 - 20}{3}\right) = P(Z < 1.67) = 0.95254$ ← From $\Phi(z)$ table (x ... z)

Tip: Here the z-value has been rounded to 2 decimal places so we can use the $\Phi(z)$ table. This rounding means that the probability we get isn't quite as precise as if we'd been able to use the full value.

Examples

a) If $X \sim N(5, 16)$, find $P(X < 7)$.

- Start by **transforming** X to Z. $\mu = 5$, $\sigma = \sqrt{16} = 4$

$P(X < 7) = P\left(Z < \frac{7 - 5}{4}\right) = P(Z < 0.5)$

- Draw a **sketch** showing the area you need to find.
- Look up $z = 0.5$ in the table for $\Phi(z)$. See p159

$P(Z < 0.5) = 0.69146$

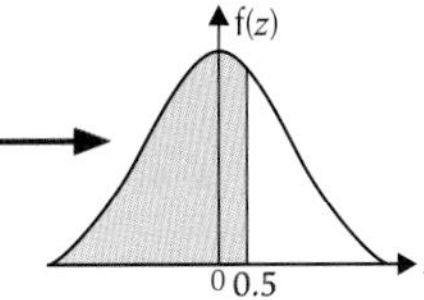

Tip: You'll usually be given the variance, which means taking the square root to find the standard deviation.

Tip: You might not need a sketch to answer this one, but it's a good habit to get into for the trickier questions.

b) If $X \sim N(5, 16)$, find $P(X > 9)$.

- Start by **transforming** X to Z.

  $P(X > 9) = P\left(Z > \frac{9-5}{4}\right) = P(Z > 1)$

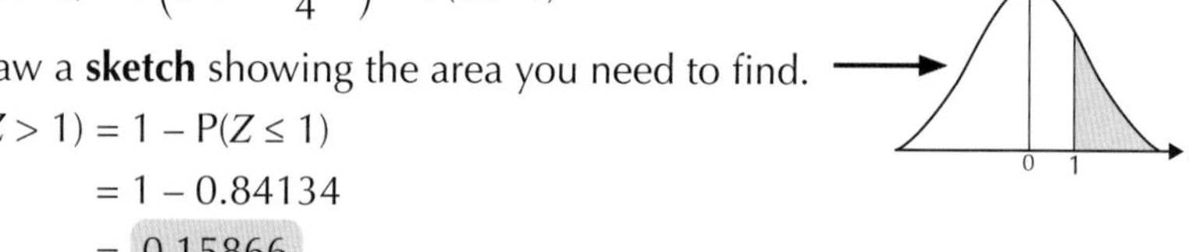

- Draw a **sketch** showing the area you need to find.

  $P(Z > 1) = 1 - P(Z \leq 1)$

  $= 1 - 0.84134$

  $= 0.15866$

c) If $X \sim N(5, 16)$, find $P(5 < X < 11)$.

- Start by **transforming** X to Z.

  $P(5 < X < 11) = P\left(\frac{5-5}{4} < Z < \frac{11-5}{4}\right) = P(0 < Z < 1.5)$

- Draw a **sketch** showing the area you need to find.

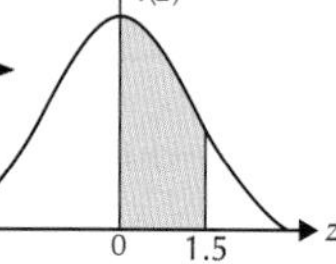

- To find this area, you need to find the area to the left of $z = 1.5$, then **subtract** the area to the left of $z = 0$.
- So, $P(0 < Z < 1.5) = P(Z < 1.5) - P(Z \leq 0)$

  $= 0.93319 - 0.5$

  $= 0.43319$

Tip: See page 93.

As you saw in the previous section, you often need to use the **symmetry** of the curve to answer questions on the normal distribution.

We'll be using the same methods here as in Section 2, but we need to do the **extra step** of transforming X to Z first.

Examples

If $X \sim N(102, 144)$:

a) Find $P(X > 78)$.

- Start by **transforming** X to Z.

  $P(X > 78) = P\left(Z > \frac{78-102}{12}\right) = P(Z > -2.0)$

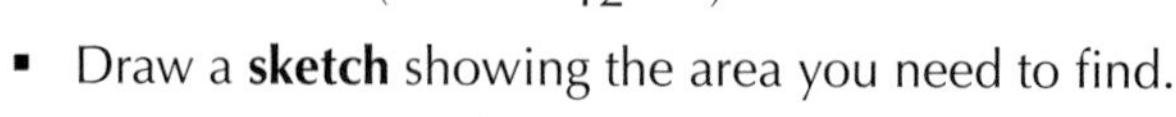

- Draw a **sketch** showing the area you need to find.

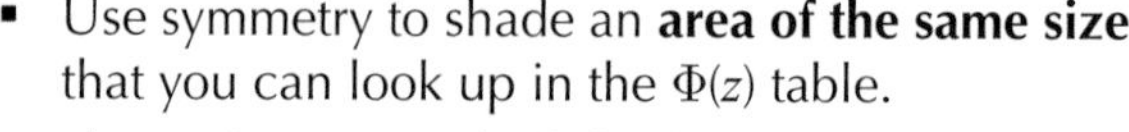

- Use symmetry to shade an **area of the same size** that you can look up in the $\Phi(z)$ table.

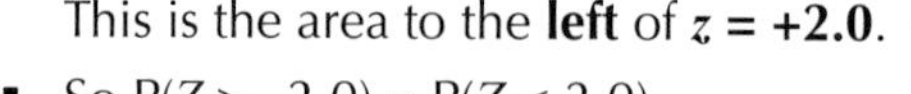

  This is the area to the **left** of $z = +2.0$.

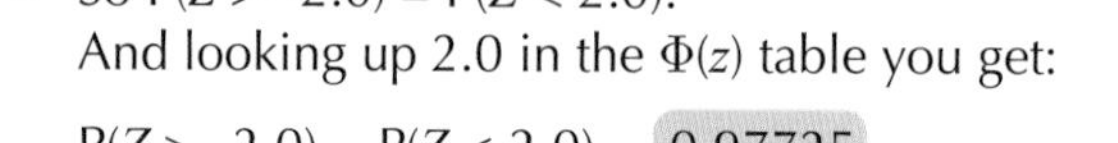

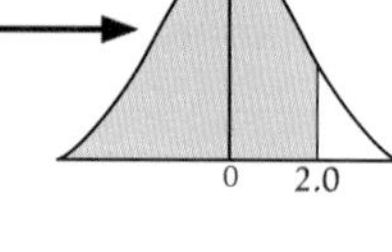

- So $P(Z > -2.0) = P(Z < 2.0)$.

  And looking up 2.0 in the $\Phi(z)$ table you get:

  $P(Z > -2.0) = P(Z < 2.0) = 0.97725$ See p159

b) Find P($X \leq 98$).

- Start by **transforming** X to Z.

  $P(X \leq 98) = P\left(Z \leq \frac{98 - 102}{12}\right) = P(Z \leq -0.33)$ ← To 2 d.p.
- Draw a **sketch** showing the area you need to find.
- You can't look up a **negative** value of z in the table, so again, use symmetry to shade an **area of the same size**. This is the area to the **right** of z = **+0.33**.

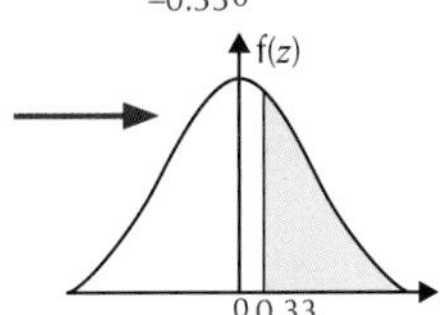

- So $P(Z \leq -0.33) = P(Z \geq 0.33)$.
- Now, $P(Z \geq 0.33) = 1 - P(Z < 0.33)$

  $= 1 - 0.62930$

  $= 0.37070$

Tip: Round z values to 2 decimal places so you can look them up in the table.

c) Find P($84 \leq X \leq 106$).

- Start by **transforming** X to Z.

  $P(84 \leq X \leq 106) = P\left(\frac{84 - 102}{12} \leq Z \leq \frac{106 - 102}{12}\right)$

  $= P(-1.5 \leq Z \leq 0.33)$
- Draw a **sketch** showing the area you need to find.

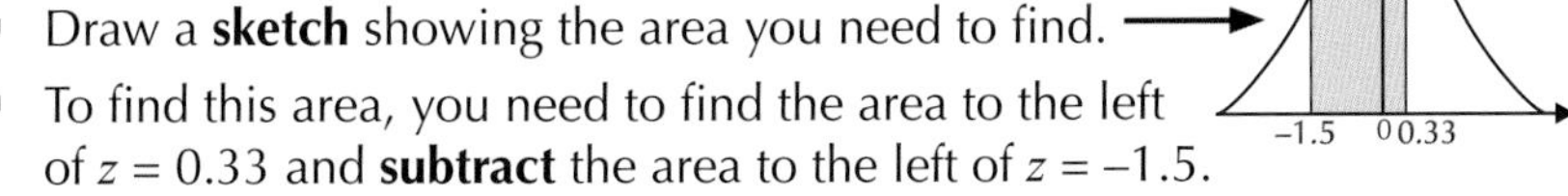

- To find this area, you need to find the area to the left of $z = 0.33$ and **subtract** the area to the left of $z = -1.5$.
- So, $P(-1.5 \leq Z \leq 0.33) = P(Z \leq 0.33) - P(Z < -1.5)$
- You can find $P(Z \leq 0.33)$ directly from the table, but $P(Z < -1.5)$ takes a bit more working out.

  $P(Z < -1.5) = P(Z > 1.5) = 1 - P(Z \leq 1.5)$

  $= 1 - 0.93319$

  $= 0.06681$
- So, $P(Z \leq 0.33) - P(Z < -1.5) = 0.62930 - 0.06681 = 0.56249$

You also need to be able to **find values**, when you're **given probabilities**.

For example, find a, given that $P(X < a) = 0.6$.

- As usual, the first step is to transform X to Z.

  If $X \sim N(\mu, \sigma^2)$, the equation $P(X < a) = 0.6$ becomes $P\left(Z < \frac{a - \mu}{\sigma}\right) = 0.6$.
- Then you use the same methods as on pages 95-98, and you end up with an equation in a to solve.

Tip: You can look up probabilities in the $\Phi(z)$ table, or the percentage-points table. See p95-98 for a reminder and some examples.

Examples

a) $X \sim N(85, 25)$. If $P(X < a) = 0.91924$, find the value of a.

- Start by **transforming** X to Z.

  $P(X < a) = P\left(Z < \frac{a - 85}{5}\right) = 0.91924$
- Draw a **sketch** to show the information.

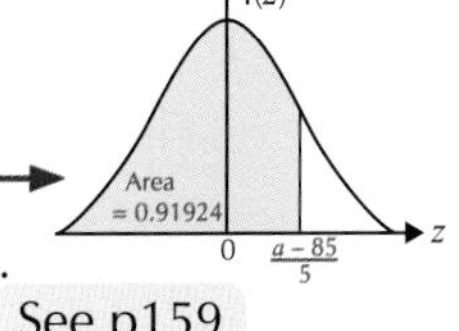

- Use the $\Phi(z)$ table to find z for which $\Phi(z) = 0.91924$. See p159

  $\Phi(z) = 0.91924$ for $z = 1.40$, so $\frac{a - 85}{5} = 1.40$ ← Equation in a.
- Now, just **solve** for a:

  $\frac{a - 85}{5} = 1.4 \Rightarrow a - 85 = 7 \Rightarrow a = 92$

b) $X \sim N(85, 25)$. If $P(X < b) = 0.01786$, find the value of b.

- Start by **transforming** X to Z.

  $P(X < b) = P\left(Z < \frac{b-85}{5}\right) = 0.01786$
- Draw a **sketch** to show the information — the area is less than 0.5, so $\frac{b-85}{5}$ must be negative. Now mark on the **equivalent area** to the right of $-\frac{b-85}{5}$.

- You can see that $P\left(Z > \frac{85-b}{5}\right) = 0.01786$.

  So $P\left(Z \leq \frac{85-b}{5}\right) = 1 - 0.01786 = 0.98214$
- Using the $\Phi(z)$ table, $\Phi(z) = 0.98214$ for $z = 2.10$, so $\frac{85-b}{5} = 2.10$.
- So **solving** for b, $\frac{85-b}{5} = 2.10 \Rightarrow 85 - b = 10.5 \Rightarrow$ $b = 74.5$

Tip: The equivalent area is to the right of $-\frac{b-85}{5}$, i.e. to the right of $\frac{85-b}{5}$.

Exercise 3.1

Hint: Round z values to 2 d.p. so you can look them up in the table.

Q2 Hint: The standard deviation doesn't have to be a whole number.

Q4 Hint: You'll often see the variance written as a number squared.

Q1 If $X \sim N(40, 25)$, find: a) $P(X < 50)$ b) $P(X < 43)$

Q2 If $X \sim N(24, 6)$, find: a) $P(X > 28)$ b) $P(X > 25)$

Q3 If $X \sim N(120, 40)$, find: a) $P(X > 107)$ b) $P(X > 115)$

Q4 If $X \sim N(17, 3^2)$, find: a) $P(X < 15)$ b) $P(X < 12)$

Q5 If $X \sim N(50, 5^2)$, find:
a) $P(52 < X < 63)$ b) $P(57 < X < 66)$

Q6 If $X \sim N(0.6, 0.04)$, find:
a) $P(0.45 < X < 0.55)$ b) $P(0.53 < X < 0.58)$

Q7 If $X \sim N(260, 15^2)$, find:
a) $P(240 < X < 280)$ b) $P(232 < X < 288)$

Q8 $X \sim N(70, 16)$
a) Find a if $P(X < a) = 0.99379$ b) Find b if $P(X < b) = 0.77337$

Q9 $X \sim N(95, 25)$
a) Find m if $P(X > m) = 0.01017$ b) Find t if $P(X > t) = 0.22965$

Q10 $X \sim N(48, 100)$
a) Find c if $P(X < c) = 0.12507$ b) Find d if $P(X < d) = 0.00964$

Q11 $X \sim N(73, 6^2)$
a) Find w if $P(X > w) = 0.91774$ b) Find k if $P(X > k) = 0.6664$

Q12 $X \sim N(18, 0.25)$. Find a if $P(18 - a < X < 18 + a) = 0.899$.

Q13 $X \sim N(170, 40^2)$. Find t if $P(170 < X < t) = 0.37698$.

Q14 $X \sim N(98, 225)$. Find v if $P(107.6 < X < v) = 0.16767$.

The normal distribution in real-life situations

Now it's time to use everything you've learnt about normal distributions to answer questions in **real-life** contexts. These are the kind of questions that usually come up in **exams**.

You always start by **defining** a **normally-distributed random variable** to represent the information you're given. Then you use the usual methods to find out what you need to know.

Tip: The first step is always to define the variable.

Example 1

A machine which fills boxes of cereal is set so that the mass of cereal going into the boxes follows a normal distribution with mean 766 g and standard deviation 8 g.

a) Find the probability that a randomly selected box of cereal contains less than 780 g of cereal.

- First, **define a random variable** to represent the mass of cereal in a box.
  If X represents the mass of cereal in g, then $X \sim N(766, 64)$. ← 8^2
- Next, turn the question into a **probability for X**.
  So you want to find, $P(X < 780)$.
- Now you can **transform** X to Z in the usual way.
  $P(X < 780) = P\left(Z < \frac{780 - 766}{8}\right)$
  $= P(Z < 1.75)$

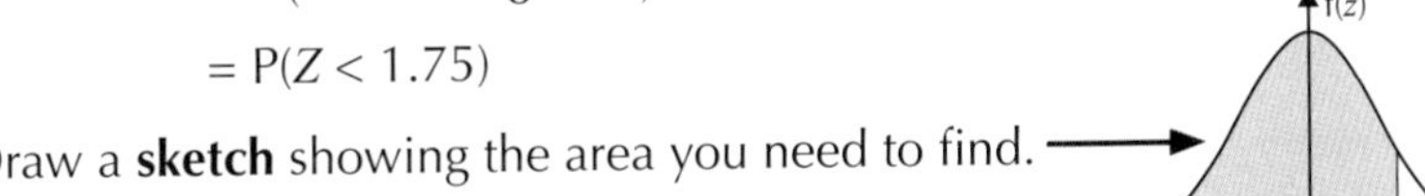

- Draw a **sketch** showing the area you need to find.
- Using the $\Phi(z)$ table, $P(Z < 1.75) = 0.95994$
- So P(a random box of cereal contains less than 780 g) = **0.95994**

Tip: So the variable here is the mass of cereal in a box.

Tip: See p159 for the $\Phi(z)$ table.

Tip: Always check the answer seems sensible. Using the rules on p91, you know that 97.5% of values are less than $2 \times \sigma$ above the mean (and $2 \times 8 + 766 = 782$). So this answer seems about right.

b) Find the probability that a randomly selected box of cereal contains between 780 g and 790 g of cereal.

- Again, turn the question into a **probability for X**.
  So you want to find, $P(780 < X < 790)$.
- Next, **transform** X to Z.
  $P(780 < X < 790) = P\left(\frac{780 - 766}{8} < Z < \frac{790 - 766}{8}\right)$
  $= P(1.75 < Z < 3.0)$
- Draw a **sketch** to help you see this area.
  This is the area to the left of 3.0, minus the area to the left of 1.75 (which you found in part a)).

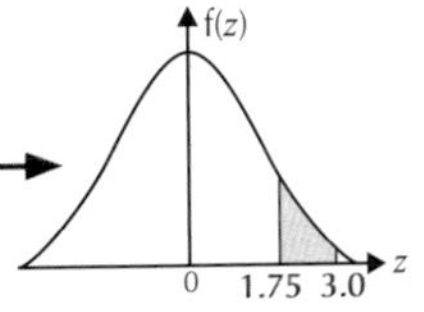

- So, $P(1.75 < Z < 3.0) = P(Z < 3.0) - P(Z \leq 1.75)$
- Using the $\Phi(z)$ table, $P(Z < 3.0) = 0.99865$.
  So, $P(Z < 3.0) - P(Z \leq 1.75) = 0.99865 - 0.95994 = 0.03871$ ← From part a)
- This means:
  P(a random box of cereal contains between 780 g and 790 g) = **0.03871**

Here's another example. In part b), we need to use the symmetry of the curve to work out what area to look up in the table.

Example 2

The times taken by a group of people to complete an assault course are normally distributed with a mean of 600 seconds and a variance of 105 seconds. Find the probability that a randomly selected person took:

a) more than 620 seconds

- Start by **defining a random variable** to represent the time taken.
  If X represents the time taken in seconds, then $X \sim N(600, 105)$.
- Next, turn the question into a **probability for X**.
  So you want to find $P(X > 620)$.
- Now you can **transform** X to Z.
  $$P(X > 620) = P\left(Z > \frac{620 - 600}{\sqrt{105}}\right)$$
  $$= P(Z > 1.95)$$
  To 2 d.p.
- Draw a **sketch** to show the information.
- So, $P(Z > 1.95) = 1 - P(Z \leq 1.95)$
  $$= 1 - 0.97441$$
  See p159
  $$= 0.02559$$
- This means:
  P(a randomly selected person took more than 620 seconds) = **0.02559**

b) fewer than 575 seconds

- Again, turn the question into a **probability for X**.
  So this time you want to find $P(X < 575)$.
- Next **transform** X to Z.
  $$P(X < 575) = P\left(Z < \frac{575 - 600}{\sqrt{105}}\right)$$
  $$= P(Z < -2.44)$$
  To 2 d.p.
- Draw a **sketch** to show the information. You can't look up a **negative** value of z in the table, so use symmetry to shade an **area of the same size**.

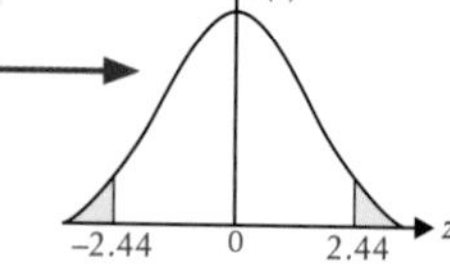

- OK so, $P(Z < -2.44) = P(Z > 2.44)$
  $$= 1 - P(Z \leq 2.44)$$
  $$= 1 - 0.99266 = 0.00734$$
- This means:
  P(a randomly selected person took fewer than 575 seconds) = **0.00734**

Real-life normal distribution questions also ask you to **find values**, when you're **given probabilities**.

Remember there are **two tables** you can use to look up probabilities — the table of the cumulative distribution function, $\Phi(z)$, and the percentage-points table.

Example

The forces needed to snap lengths of a certain type of elastic are normally distributed with μ = 13 N and σ = 1.8 N.

a) The probability that a randomly selected length of elastic is snapped by a force of less than *a* N is 0.75804. Find the value of *a*.

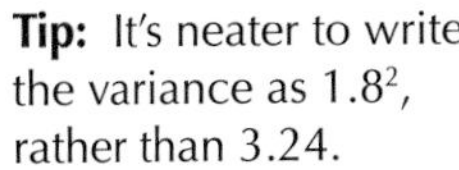

Tip: It's neater to write the variance as 1.8^2, rather than 3.24.

- Start by **defining a random variable** to represent the force needed. If F represents the force needed in N, then $F \sim N(13, 1.8^2)$.
- Next, turn the question into a **probability for F**. So you know that $P(F < a) = 0.75804$.
- Next, **transform** F to Z. $P(F < a) = P\left(Z < \frac{a-13}{1.8}\right) = 0.75804$
- Draw a **sketch** to show the information.
- Use the $\Phi(z)$ table to find z for which $\Phi(z) = 0.75804$. $\Phi(z) = 0.75804$ for $z = 0.70$, so $\frac{a-13}{1.8} = 0.70$
- Now, just **solve** for a:

$\frac{a-13}{1.8} = 0.7 \Rightarrow a - 13 = 1.26 \Rightarrow$ $a = 14.26$

Tip: Use a sensible letter for the variable — it doesn't have to be X.

Tip: $P(Z < 0.75804)$ isn't in the percentage-points table, so you'll need to use the $\Phi(z)$ table.

b) Find the range of values that includes the middle 80% of forces needed.

- It's difficult to know where to start with this one. So it's a good idea to **sketch the distribution of F**, to show the range you need to find.

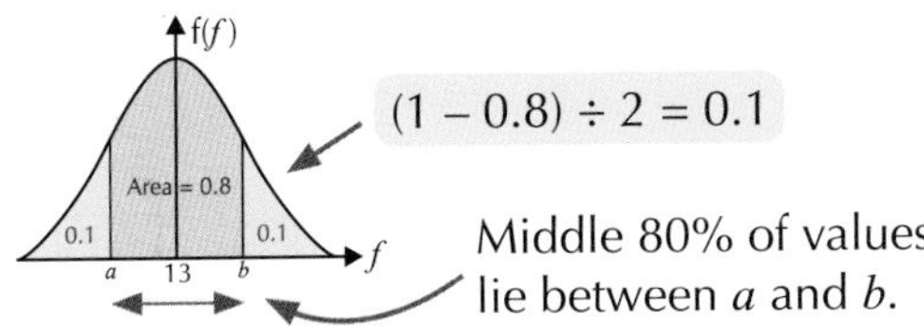

$(1 - 0.8) \div 2 = 0.1$

Middle 80% of values lie between a and b.

- Now you can write **2 probability statements** — 1 for a and 1 for b. $P(F < a) = 0.1$ and $P(F > b) = 0.1$.
- Next, **transform** F to Z.

$P(F < a) = P\left(Z < \frac{a-13}{1.8}\right) = 0.1$ and $P(F > b) = P\left(Z > \frac{b-13}{1.8}\right) = 0.1$

- Draw another **sketch** to show this information.
- So, now you need to use the **tables** to find a and b. The easiest one to start with is b, because $P\left(Z > \frac{b-13}{1.8}\right) = 0.1 \Rightarrow P\left(Z \leq \frac{b-13}{1.8}\right) = 0.9$ and you can use the **percentage-points** table to find the value of z for which $P(Z \leq z) = 0.9$.

From the table, $p = 0.9$ for $z = 1.2816$. See p160

Tip: $P(Z > z)$ is a 'nice' decimal, so you'll probably need to use the percentage-points table.

So, $\frac{b-13}{1.8} = 1.2816 \Rightarrow b = 15.31$

To 2 d.p.

- And using symmetry, $\frac{a-13}{1.8} = -1.2816 \Rightarrow a = 10.69$
- So the range of values is 10.69 N to 15.31 N

Tip: The range is symmetrical about $z = 0$, so $\frac{a-13}{1.8} = -\frac{b-13}{1.8}$.

Exercise 3.2

Q1 The lengths of worms in a certain area are found to follow a normal distribution, with mean 8.4 cm and standard deviation 3.1 cm.

a) What is the probability that a randomly selected worm is shorter than 9.5 cm?

b) What is the probability that a randomly selected worm is longer than 10 cm?

c) What is the probability that a randomly selected worm has a length of between 5 cm and 11 cm?

Q2 The lengths of time taken by a group of blood donors to replace their red blood cells are modelled by a normal distribution with a mean of 36 days and a standard deviation of 6 days.

a) It takes Edward 28 days to replace his red blood cells. Find the probability that a randomly selected donor from the group takes less time than Edward to replace their red blood cells.

b) 6.3% of the group take longer than Bella to replace their red blood cells. How long does it take Bella?

Q3 The 'personal best' times taken by athletes at a sports club to run 400 m are known to follow a normal distribution with a mean of 51 seconds and a standard deviation of 2.1 seconds.

a) Gary's 'personal best' time is 49.3 seconds. What percentage of the athletes have a slower 'personal best' time than Gary?

b) The athletes with 'personal bests' in the top 20% of times are selected for a special training programme. What time do they have to beat to be selected for the programme?

Q4 A particular type of toy car uses two identical batteries. The lifetimes of individual batteries can be modelled by a normal distribution with a mean of 300 hours and a standard deviation of 50 hours.

a) What is the probability that a battery of this type lasts less than 200 hours?

b) What is the probability that a battery of this type lasts at least 380 hours?

c) Stating any assumptions you make, find the probability that both of the batteries in a car last at least 380 hours.

d) The probability that a randomly selected battery lasts more than 160 hours, but less than h hours, is 0.97469. Find the value of h.

Q4 Hint: See p50 for a reminder of how to find probabilities of multiple events.

Q5 The masses of the eggs laid by the hens on farmer Elizabeth's farm are assumed to follow a normal distribution with mean 60 g and standard deviation 3 g.

a) The probability that a randomly selected egg has a mass of at least $60 - m$ grams is 0.95254. Find the value of m to the nearest gram.

b) Farmer Elizabeth keeps the lightest 10% of eggs for herself and uses them to make sponge cakes. Find the maximum mass of an egg that could end up in one of farmer Elizabeth's sponge cakes.

Finding the mean and standard deviation of a normal distribution

Remember that any normally distributed variable, $X \sim N(\mu, \sigma^2)$, can be **transformed** to the standard normal variable, Z, by **subtracting the mean**, μ, and **dividing by the standard deviation**, σ.

So X and Z are **linked** by the equation: $Z = \frac{X - \mu}{\sigma}$

So far you've used this relationship to find **probability facts** for X, when the mean and standard deviation have been **known**. But you can use exactly the **same approach** to find the **mean** and **standard deviation** when they're **unknown**... as long as you already know some probability facts.

Example 1

If the random variable $X \sim N(\mu, 4)$ and $P(X < 23) = 0.90147$, find μ.

- Okay, start by **transforming the probability** you're given for X into a probability for Z. The mean is unknown, so just leave it as μ for now.

  $P(X < 23) = P\left(Z < \frac{23 - \mu}{2}\right) = 0.90147$

- Draw a **sketch** to show the information.
- Now, if you use the $\Phi(z)$ table to find z for which $\Phi(z) = 0.90147$, you can form an **equation** in μ.

  From the table, $\Phi(z) = 0.90147$ for $z = 1.29$. See p159

  So, $\frac{23 - \mu}{2} = 1.29$ ← Equation in μ.

- Now **solve** this equation for μ.

  $\frac{23 - \mu}{2} = 1.29 \Rightarrow 23 - \mu = 2.58 \Rightarrow \mu = 20.42$

Tip: As always, check that the answer seems about right. You know it must be a bit lower than 23, so 20.42 seems OK.

Example 2

If the random variable $X \sim N(\mu, 4^2)$ and $P(X > 19.84) = 0.025$, find μ.

- **Transform the probability** you're given for X into a probability for Z.

  $P(X > 19.84) = P\left(Z > \frac{19.84 - \mu}{4}\right) = 0.025$

- Draw a **sketch** to show the information.
- 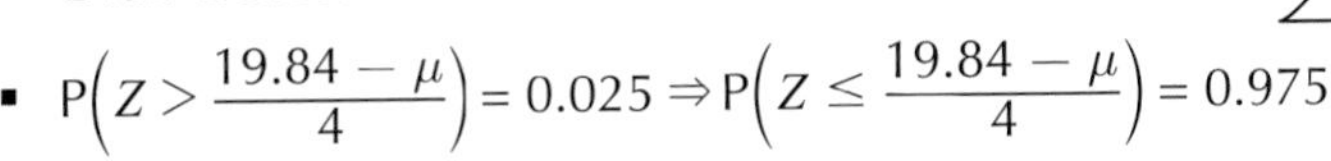

  $P\left(Z > \frac{19.84 - \mu}{4}\right) = 0.025 \Rightarrow P\left(Z \leq \frac{19.84 - \mu}{4}\right) = 0.975$

- From the percentage-points table, $p = 0.975$ for $z = 1.96$. See p160

  So, $\frac{19.84 - \mu}{4} = 1.96$

- Now **solve** this equation for μ.

  $\frac{19.84 - \mu}{4} = 1.96 \Rightarrow 19.84 - \mu = 7.84 \Rightarrow \mu = 12$

In the first two examples we found the mean, but you can find the **standard deviation** (s.d.) in exactly the same way.

Example 3

If the random variable $X \sim N(53, \sigma^2)$ and $P(X < 50) = 0.2$, find σ.

- Again, start by **transforming the probability** you're given for X into a probability for Z. The s.d. is unknown, so just leave it as σ for now.

  $P(X < 50) = P\left(Z < \frac{50 - 53}{\sigma}\right) = P\left(Z < -\frac{3}{\sigma}\right) = 0.2$

- Draw a **sketch** to show the information. The area is less than 0.5, so mark on the **equivalent area** to the right of $-\left(-\frac{3}{\sigma}\right)$. ← $-(-3/\sigma) = 3/\sigma$

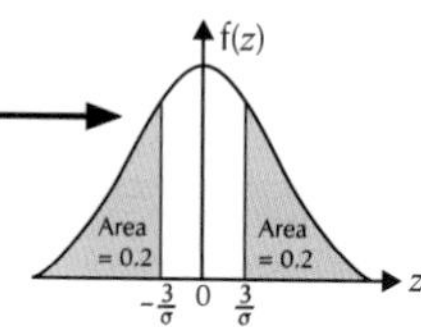

- You can see that $P\left(Z > \frac{3}{\sigma}\right) = 0.2$ so $P\left(Z \le \frac{3}{\sigma}\right) = 0.8$.

- From the percentage-points table, $p = 0.8$ for $z = 0.8416$. See p160

  So, $\frac{3}{\sigma} = 0.8416$ ← Equation in σ.

- Now **solve** this equation for σ.

  $\frac{3}{\sigma} = 0.8416 \Rightarrow \sigma = 3.56$ ← To 3 s.f.

Tip: Values of σ should always be positive.

Tip: Remember, you can solve simultaneous equations by adding or subtracting them to get rid of one unknown.

When you're asked to find the mean **and** the standard deviation, the method is a little bit **more complicated**.

You start off as usual, but instead of getting one equation in one unknown to solve, you end up with **two equations** in **two unknowns**, μ and σ. In other words, you have **simultaneous equations**, which you **solve** to find μ and σ.

Example

The random variable $X \sim N(\mu, \sigma^2)$.
If $P(X < 9) = 0.55962$ and $P(X > 14) = 0.03216$, find μ and σ.

- Let's start with the first probability for X, and **transform** it into a probability for Z.

  $P(X < 9) = P\left(Z < \frac{9 - \mu}{\sigma}\right) = 0.55962$

- Draw a **sketch** to show the information.

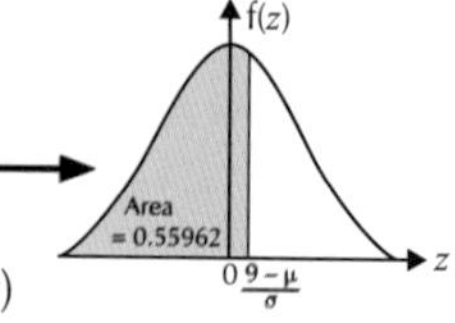

- Now, if you use the $\Phi(z)$ table to find z for which $\Phi(z) = 0.55962$, you can form an **equation** in μ and σ.

  From the table, $\Phi(z) = 0.55962$ for $z = 0.15$. See p159

  So, $\frac{9 - \mu}{\sigma} = 0.15 \Rightarrow 9 - \mu = 0.15\sigma$ ← 1st equation in μ and σ

- Now do the same thing for the second probability for X.
Transforming to Z, you get:

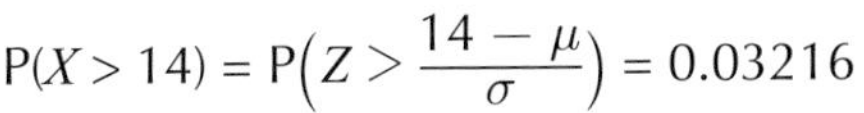

$$P(X > 14) = P\left(Z > \frac{14 - \mu}{\sigma}\right) = 0.03216$$

- Draw a **sketch** to show the information.

- You can see from the graph that:

$$P\left(Z \leq \frac{14 - \mu}{\sigma}\right) = 1 - P\left(Z > \frac{14 - \mu}{\sigma}\right) = 1 - 0.03216 = 0.96784$$

- Now use the $\Phi(z)$ table to find z for which $\Phi(z) = 0.96784$.
From the table, $\Phi(z) = 0.96784$ for $z = 1.85$.
So, $\frac{14 - \mu}{\sigma} = 1.85 \Rightarrow 14 - \mu = 1.85\sigma$ ← 2nd equation in μ and σ

Tip: $p = 0.03216$ isn't in the percentage-points table, so it might help to use a sketch.

- So now you have your **simultaneous** equations:
$9 - \mu = 0.15\sigma$ ❶
$14 - \mu = 1.85\sigma$ ❷ ← It helps to number the equations, so you can refer to them later.

- Each equation has one 'μ', so you can **subtract** them to get rid of μ, which will leave you with an **equation in σ** to solve.
❷ – ❶ gives $14 - 9 - \mu - (-\mu) = 1.85\sigma - 0.15\sigma$
$\Rightarrow 5 = 1.7\sigma$
$\Rightarrow \sigma = 2.941176... \Rightarrow \sigma = 2.94$ ← To 3 s.f.

- Finally, find μ by **substituting** $\sigma = 2.94...$ back into one of the equations.
Using equation ❶,
$9 - \mu = 0.15\sigma \Rightarrow \mu = 9 - 0.15 \times 2.94... \Rightarrow \mu = 8.56$ ← To 3 s.f.

Exercise 3.3

Q1 For each of the following, use the information to find μ.

a) $X \sim N(\mu, 6^2)$ and $P(X < 23) = 0.93319$.

b) $X \sim N(\mu, 8^2)$ and $P(X < 57) = 0.99702$.

c) $X \sim N(\mu, 100^2)$ and $P(X > 528) = 0.12924$.

d) $X \sim N(\mu, 0.4^2)$ and $P(X < 11.06) = 0.03216$.

e) $X \sim N(\mu, 0.02^2)$ and $P(X > 1.52) = 0.99379$.

Q2 $X \sim N(\mu, 3.5^2)$. If the middle 95% of the distribution lies between 6.45 and 20.17, find the value of μ.

Q2 Hint: Start by drawing a diagram showing the distribution of X.

Q3 For each of the following, use the information to find σ.

a) $X \sim N(48, \sigma^2)$ and $P(X < 53) = 0.89435$.

b) $X \sim N(510, \sigma^2)$ and $P(X < 528) = 0.77337$.

c) $X \sim N(17, \sigma^2)$ and $P(X > 24) = 0.03673$.

d) $X \sim N(0.98, \sigma^2)$ and $P(X < 0.95) = 0.30854$.

e) $X \sim N(5.6, \sigma^2)$ and $P(X > 4.85) = 0.83646$.

Q4 $X \sim N(68, \sigma^2)$. If the middle 70% of the distribution lies between 61 and 75, find the value of σ.

Q5 Hint: You need to form and solve simultaneous equations in μ and σ.

Q5 For each of the following, find μ and σ.

a) $X \sim N(\mu, \sigma^2)$, $P(X < 30) = 0.91924$ and $P(X < 36) = 0.99534$.

b) $X \sim N(\mu, \sigma^2)$, $P(X < 4) = 0.93319$ and $P(X < 4.3) = 0.99865$.

c) $X \sim N(\mu, \sigma^2)$, $P(X < 20) = 0.78814$ and $P(X < 14) = 0.0548$.

d) $X \sim N(\mu, \sigma^2)$, $P(X < 696) = 0.97128$ and $P(X < 592) = 0.24196$.

e) $X \sim N(\mu, \sigma^2)$, $P(X > 33) = 0.10565$ and $P(X > 21) = 0.95994$.

f) $X \sim N(\mu, \sigma^2)$, $P(X > 66) = 0.36317$ and $P(X < 48) = 0.34458$.

Q6 The volume of vinegar contained in bottles of vinegar is modelled by a normal distribution with a standard deviation of 5 ml. Over time, it is found that 71.9% of bottles contain less than 506 ml of vinegar.

a) Find the mean volume of vinegar contained in the bottles.

b) The label on each bottle says it contains 500 ml of vinegar. What percentage of bottles contain less than 500 ml?

Q7 The heights of a population of 17-year-old boys are assumed to follow a normal distribution with a mean of 175 cm. 80% of this population of 17-year-old boys are taller than 170 cm.

a) Find the standard deviation of the heights of the 17-year-old boys in this population.

b) One 17-year-old boy is selected from the population at random. Find the probability that his height is within 4 cm of the mean height.

Q8 In a particularly wet village, it rains almost continuously. The daily rainfall, in cm, is modelled by a normal distribution. The daily rainfall is less than 4 cm on only 10.2% of days, and it's greater than 7 cm on 64.8% of days.

Find the mean and standard deviation of the daily rainfall.

Review Exercise — Chapter 4

Q1 Find the probability that:

a) $Z < 0.84$
b) $Z < 2.95$
c) $Z > 0.68$
d) $Z \geq 1.55$
e) $Z < -2.10$
f) $Z \leq -0.01$
g) $Z > 0.10$
h) $Z \leq 0.64$
i) $Z > 0.23$
j) $0.10 < Z \leq 0.50$
k) $-0.62 \leq Z < 1.10$
l) $-0.99 < Z \leq -0.74$

Q2 Find the value of z if:

a) $P(Z < z) = 0.91309$
b) $P(Z < z) = 0.58706$
c) $P(Z > z) = 0.03593$
d) $P(Z > z) = 0.01$
e) $P(Z \leq z) = 0.40129$
f) $P(Z \geq z) = 0.995$
g) $P(-z < Z < z) = 0.5035$
h) $P(0.25 < Z < z) = 0.39165$

Q3 If $X \sim N(50, 16)$ find:

a) $P(X < 55)$ b) $P(X < 42)$ c) $P(X > 56)$ d) $P(47 < X < 57)$

Q4 If $X \sim N(5, 7^2)$ find:

a) $P(X < 0)$ b) $P(X < 1)$ c) $P(X > 7)$ d) $P(2 < X < 4)$

Q5 $X \sim N(80, 15)$

a) If $P(X < a) = 0.99$, find a.
b) If $P(|X - 80| < b) = 0.8$, find b.

Q5 Hint: $|X - 80| < b$ means that X is 'within b' of 80.

Q6 The mass of items produced by a factory is normally distributed with a mean of 55 grams and a standard deviation of 4.4 grams. Find the probability of a randomly chosen item having a mass of:

a) less than 55 grams b) less than 50 grams c) more than 60 grams

Q7 The mass of eggs laid by an ostrich is normally distributed with a mean of 1.4 kg and a standard deviation of 300 g. If 88.3% of the eggs laid by this ostrich have a mass of less than a kg, find the value of a.

Q8 $X \sim N(\mu, 10)$ and $P(X < 8) = 0.89251$. Find μ.

Q9 $X \sim N(\mu, 8^2)$ and $P(X > 221) = 0.30854$. Find μ.

Q10 $X \sim N(11, \sigma^2)$ and $P(X < 13) = 0.6$. Find σ.

Q11 $X \sim N(108, \sigma^2)$ and $P(X \leq 110) = 0.96784$. Find σ.

Q12 The random variable $X \sim N(\mu, \sigma^2)$.
If $P(X < 15.2) = 0.97831$ and $P(X > 14.8) = 0.10565$, then find μ and σ.

Exam-Style Questions — Chapter 4

1 The exam marks for 1000 candidates can be modelled by a normal distribution with mean 50 marks and standard deviation 15 marks.

a) One candidate is selected at random. Find the probability that they scored less than 30 marks on this exam.
(3 marks)

b) The pass mark is 41.
Estimate the number of candidates who passed the exam.
(3 marks)

c) Find the mark needed for a distinction if the top 10% of the candidates achieved a distinction.
(3 marks)

2 The random variable X follows a normal distribution with mean μ and standard deviation 6. The probability that X takes a value of less than 50 is 0.12302.

a) Find the mean of this distribution.
(4 marks)

b) Find $P(X > 71)$.
(3 marks)

c) Find the value of a such that $P(\mu - a < X < \mu + a) = 0.8$.
(4 marks)

3 The lifetimes of a particular type of battery are normally distributed with mean μ and standard deviation σ. A student using these batteries finds that 40% last less than 20 hours and 80% last less than 26 hours.

a) Find μ and σ.
(7 marks)

b) Find the probability that a randomly selected battery of this type has a lifetime of at least 15 hours.
(3 marks)

4 The random variable X has a normal distribution with mean 120 and standard deviation 25.

a) Find $P(X > 145)$. *(3 marks)*

b) Find the value of j such that $P(120 < X < j) = 0.46407$ *(4 marks)*

5 The diameters of the pizza bases made at a restaurant are normally distributed. The mean diameter is 12 inches, and 5% of the bases measure more than 13 inches.

a) Write down the median diameter of the pizza bases. *(1 mark)*

b) Find the standard deviation of the diameters of the pizza bases. *(4 marks)*

Any pizza base with a diameter of less than 10.8 inches is considered too small and is discarded.

c) If 100 pizza bases are made in an evening, approximately how many would you expect to be discarded due to being too small? *(3 marks)*

Three pizza bases are selected at random.

d) Find the probability that at least one of these bases is too small. *(3 marks)*

6 A garden centre sells bags of compost. The volume of compost in the bags is normally distributed with a mean of 50 litres.

a) If the standard deviation of the volume is 0.4 litres, find the probability that a randomly selected bag will contain less than 49 litres of compost. *(3 marks)*

b) If 1000 of these bags of compost are bought, find the expected number of bags containing more than 50.5 litres of compost. *(5 marks)*

A different garden centre sells bags of similar compost. The volume of compost, in litres, in these bags is described by the random variable Y, where $Y \sim N(75, \sigma^2)$. It is found that 10% of the bags from this garden centre contain less than 74 litres of compost.

c) Find σ. *(3 marks)*

Chapter 5 **Estimation**

1. Populations and Samples

Learning Objectives:
- Know what is meant by a population and a sample.
- Know what is meant by simple random sampling, and why it is used.
- Know the difference between a population parameter and a statistic.

One of the main aims of the subject of statistics is to take a small amount of information, and say as much as you can with it... but without saying too much. This is the idea when using sample data to say something about a population.

Populations

In any statistical investigation, there will be a **group** of something that you want to **find out about** — it could be people, items, animals... or anything else.

The **whole group** that you want to investigate, consisting of **every single** person/item/animal etc., is called a **population**. This could be:

- All the students in a maths class
- All the penguins in Antarctica
- All the chocolate puddings produced by a company in a year

To collect information about your population, you can carry out a **survey**. This will involve **questioning** the people or **examining** the items.

You could collect information from **every single member** of the population. But that's usually difficult, expensive and time-consuming — so it's more common to gather information from a **sample** instead.

Sampling

You can find out about a population by questioning or examining just a **selection** of the people or items. This selected group is called a **sample**.

- Data collected from a sample is usually used to draw conclusions about the **whole population**, so it's important that the sample is as much like the population as possible in all the ways that matter for your study. In other words, it must be a **representative sample**.
- If a sample is not representative, it is **biased**. A biased sample is one which doesn't **fairly represent** the population.

Tip: Remember... using a sample is just a means to an end — what you're actually interested in finding out about is the **population**.

It's usually **impossible** to be 100% certain that a sample is genuinely representative (you wouldn't be able to tell unless you **already knew** quite a lot about the population). But there are certain things you can do to help **avoid** introducing bias unnecessarily.

Follow these steps to get an unbiased sample:

- Select from the **correct population** and make sure none of the population is **excluded**.

  For example, if you want to find out the views of residents from a particular street, your sample should:
  - include **only** residents from that street,
  - be chosen from a **complete list** of all the residents.

- Choose the members of your sample **at random**.

  Non-random sampling methods include, for example:
  - asking friends — who may all give similar answers, or
  - asking for volunteers — who may all have strong views.

- Make sure **all** your sample members **respond**.

  If some of your sampled residents are out when you go to interview them, it's important that you go back and get their views another time.

One really important kind of random sample is the '**simple random sample**'.

A 'simple random sample of size n' is one where n members of the population are chosen **at random** from a **full list** of the population.

- Each selection is **independent** of every other selection.
- **Every** member of the population has an **equal chance** of being selected.
- Every possible **sample** is **equally likely**.

One disadvantage of using a sample is that there will be **variability** between samples — each possible sample will give **different** results. So you could select one which just happens **not to accurately reflect** the population.

- For example, in a survey to determine the average height of the residents in a street, a random sample of 10 **could** in theory consist of the 10 tallest people, or the 10 shortest. This would mean you'd get the wrong idea about the average height of residents in the rest of the street.
- But if you choose your sample of 10 people **at random**, then the probability of getting a **really** unrepresentative sample should be **very small**. And by using a bigger sample size, you can make this probability even smaller.

Tip: Getting a full list of the population is relatively easy if the population is 'residents in a particular street'.

But if your population is, say, 'all the people living in a particular country', then it's usually impossible to find an accurate list of everyone because, for example:

- a country's population changes all the time,
- some people won't want to be recorded as resident in a country,

...and so on.

Tip: If you don't make sure people in your sample respond, then the sample isn't truly random.

Tip: The reasons why randomness is so important will become clear.

Tip: Using a random sample means there will be no 'systematic' (non-random) bias in your sample, but you could still end up with a biased sample due to **chance**.

Statistics

Before going any further, you'll need to know a couple of definitions:

- **Parameters** are quantities that describe the characteristics of a **population** — e.g. the **mean** (μ), **variance** (σ^2), or **proportion** with a particular characteristic.
- **Greek letters** like μ and σ are often used for parameters.

In a statistical investigation, you're often trying to find the values of certain parameters of a population. These parameters can be **estimated** using **statistics**. There's an important difference between a parameter and a statistic.

- A quantity that is calculated using only **observations** from a **sample** is called a **statistic**.
- **Latin letters** likes m and s are often used for statistics.

2. Statistics

Learning Objectives:

- Be able to state whether a quantity is a statistic.
- Be able to find unbiased estimates of a population mean and variance.

This is where the real statistics fun begins. Simple random sampling should give you an unbiased sample from a population — now you'll learn how to use this sample to estimate characteristics of the population.

The sampling distribution of a statistic

You met the basic idea of a **statistic** on the previous page.
Here's a more mathematical description:

- Suppose a **random sample** of observations (X_1, ..., X_n) is taken from a population.
- A quantity that is calculated only from these **known observations** is called a **statistic**.
- A statistic is a **random variable** — it takes different values for **different samples**.

It's important that you can recognise what's a statistic and what's not.

Example

A random sample of 10 observations (X_1, ..., X_{10}) is taken from a population with unknown mean, μ. State whether or not the following are statistics:

a) $X_{10} - X_1$

Yes. This quantity can be calculated using only the known observations X_{10} and X_1.

Tip: The values of n and X_i depend only on your sample data.

b) $\frac{\sum X_i}{n}$

Yes. This quantity can be calculated using only the known observations X_1, ..., X_{10} and the sample size n (= 10).
This is actually the **sample mean**, usually written $\overline{X}$.

c) $\sum X_i^2 - \mu$

No. You'd need the unknown mean μ to work out this quantity, so it cannot be calculated using only known observations.

Tip: $\frac{\sum(X_i - \overline{X})^2}{n-1}$ is known as the sample variance, S^2. See page 118.

d) $\frac{\sum(X_i - \overline{X})^2}{n-1}$

Yes. This quantity can be calculated using only the known observations X_1, ..., X_{10}, the sample mean $\overline{X}$ (which is itself a statistic and so can be calculated from known observations) and the sample size n.

e) $\frac{\sum|X_i - \mu|}{n}$

No. This quantity depends on the unknown mean μ.

In the previous example, the 10 observations (X_1, ..., X_{10}) are independent **random variables** — each of them takes a random value from the population, and these values will be different for different samples.

This means a **statistic** calculated from these observations is also a **random variable**, and will also be different for different samples.

Now then... if a statistic is a random variable, it must have a **probability distribution**. The **probability distribution** of a statistic is called its **sampling distribution**:

> If a statistic Y is calculated from a **sample** of a population, then the **sampling distribution** of Y gives all the possible values, y, that Y can take, along with their probabilities, $P(Y = y)$.

For example, if a random sample of **size n** (X_1, ..., X_n) is taken from a population with an **unknown mean** μ, the **sample mean**, $\overline{X}$, is given by:

$$\overline{X} = \frac{\sum X_i}{n}$$

If you were to plot a graph showing the **possible values** of $\overline{X}$ on the horizontal axis and the **probability** of these values on the vertical axis, you'd probably end up with a graph that looks a bit like the one on the right.

This shows the **sampling distribution** of $\overline{X}$.

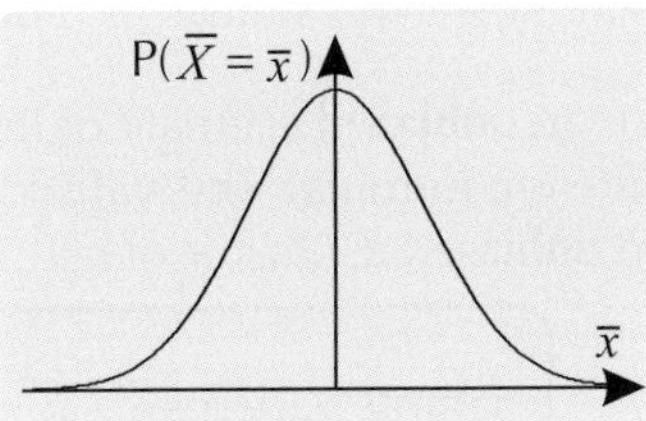

Tip: If you took a sample of observations and calculated a particular statistic, then kept taking other samples and calculating the same statistic, you'd end up with lots of values of the same statistic.

Tip: There's more about probability distributions in Chapter 3.

Tip: Remember...

- $\overline{X}$ (with a capital X) is just the 'name' of the random variable.
- The possible values that $\overline{X}$ can take are written $\overline{x}$ (with a small x).

Tip: There's more about the sampling distribution of $\overline{X}$ on p120.

Estimating a population mean (μ)

Remember... the **population mean** (μ) is a **parameter** that you're trying to estimate using a **statistic** worked out from your **sample data**.

It turns out that a really good statistic to use is the **sample mean**, $\overline{X}$.

- This is because observed values of $\overline{X}$ are **much more likely** to be close to the value of μ than far away.
- In fact, the expected value (or mean) of $\overline{X}$ equals μ.

$$E(\overline{X}) = \mu$$

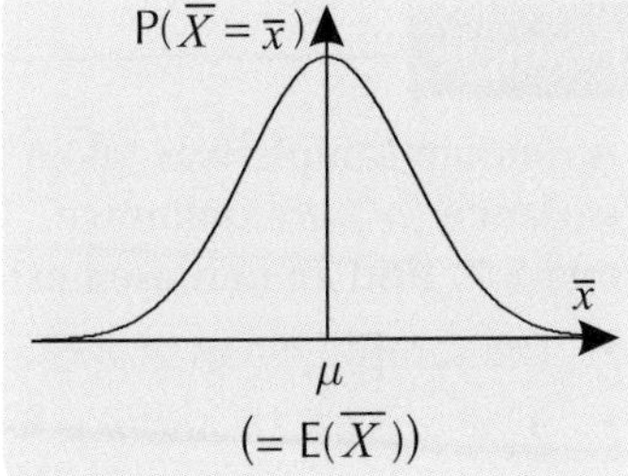

Here, we're using the statistic $\overline{X}$ to **estimate** the value of μ.

- The sample mean $\overline{X}$ is called an **estimator** of μ.
- And because $E(\overline{X}) = \mu$, the sample mean is an **unbiased** estimator of μ.

> An estimator is **unbiased** if its expected value equals the parameter it is trying to estimate.

Tip: Remember... the expected value of a symmetrical distribution is in the middle.

Tip: You'll see that the sampling distribution of the sample mean will very often have a graph like this one — centred around μ and falling away quite quickly as you get further from μ — **as long as** you pick your sample **at random**.

This is the reason why taking a random sample is so important. If you used a non-random sample, you couldn't be sure how the values of $\overline{X}$ were distributed.

Example

A random sample was taken from a population whose mean (μ) is unknown. If the observed values were 5.6, 5.8, 5.5, 5.8 and 5.7, find an unbiased estimate of μ.

- The sample mean ($\bar{x}$) will give an unbiased estimate of the population mean (μ).

$$\sum x = 28.4, \text{ so } \bar{x} = \frac{\sum x}{n} = \frac{28.4}{5} = 5.68$$

Tip: Remember... the observations $X_1, ..., X_n$ are written as capitals in this formula because they're random variables representing the observations from **any** random sample.

When you know the actual values from a **particular** sample, then you'd write the observations $x_1, ..., x_n$.

Estimating a population variance (σ^2)

Not all estimators are **unbiased**.

For example, the formula on the right is the formula for **population variance**.

$$\frac{\sum(X_i - \overline{X})^2}{n} = \frac{\sum X_i^2}{n} - \left(\frac{\sum X_i}{n}\right)^2$$

However, when you use this formula with **sample data**, you find that its **expected value** does **not** equal σ^2, the population variance. That means this statistic is a **biased** estimator of the population variance.

For an **unbiased** estimate of the population variance, you need to use a different formula. The statistic S^2 is called the **sample variance**, and is an **unbiased** estimator of σ^2.

Tip: The first expression for S^2 is in the formula book you'll be given in the exam...

...but the bottom ones are more useful — remember them as:

'the mean of the squares minus the square of the mean, all multiplied by $\frac{n}{n-1}$'.

$$\text{Sample variance: } S^2 = \frac{\sum(X_i - \overline{X})^2}{n-1}$$
$$= \frac{n}{n-1}\left[\frac{\sum X_i^2}{n} - \left(\frac{\sum X_i}{n}\right)^2\right] = \frac{n}{n-1}\left[\frac{\sum X_i^2}{n} - \overline{X}^2\right]$$

The **sample standard deviation** (S) is the square root of the sample variance.

$$\text{Sample standard deviation: } S = \sqrt{\text{sample variance}}$$

Tip: S^2 is an unbiased estimator of σ^2, so: $E(S^2) = \sigma^2$

Example

A random sample was taken from a population whose mean (μ) and variance (σ^2) are unknown. If the observed values were 5.6, 5.8, 5.5, 5.8 and 5.7, find an unbiased estimate of σ^2.

- The sample mean of these numbers is $\bar{x} = 5.68$ (see previous example).
- $\sum x^2 = 161.38$ and $n = 5$.
- So the sample variance (s^2) is: $s^2 = \frac{n}{n-1}\left[\frac{\sum x^2}{n} - \left(\frac{\sum x}{n}\right)^2\right]$

$$= \frac{n}{n-1}\left[\frac{\sum x^2}{n} - \bar{x}^2\right]$$
$$= \frac{5}{4}\left[\frac{161.38}{5} - 5.68^2\right] = 0.017$$

Tip: Remember... $\frac{\sum x}{n} = \bar{x}$.

If your data's **grouped**, you need to use **class mid-points**.

Example

The table summarises how many pets 95 students picked at random from a school have. Find unbiased estimates for the mean number of pets and the variance for the whole school.

Number of pets	0	1	2	3	4	5–6	7-8	9-10
Frequency, f	4	13	24	17	15	11	5	6

- First add some **extra rows** to the table, showing the class mid-points (x), as well as fx, x^2 and fx^2.

Class mid-point, x	0	1	2	3	4	5.5	7.5	9.5
fx	0	13	48	51	60	60.5	37.5	57
x^2	0	1	4	9	16	30.25	56.25	90.25
fx^2	0	13	96	153	240	332.75	281.25	541.5

- Then you can work out the following totals.

$$\sum f = 95 = n, \sum fx = 327 \text{ and} \sum fx^2 = 1657.5$$

- Now you can find the **sample mean** $\overline{x}$ (which is your unbiased estimate of the population mean μ). This is:

$$\overline{x} = \frac{\sum fx}{n} = \frac{327}{95} = 3.44 \text{ (to 3 sig. fig.)}$$

- Now work out the **sample variance** s^2 (which is your unbiased estimate of the population variance σ^2). This is:

$$s^2 = \frac{n}{n-1}\left[\frac{\sum fx^2}{n} - \left(\frac{\sum fx}{n}\right)^2\right]$$

$$= \frac{95}{94}\left[\frac{1657.5}{95} - \left(\frac{327}{95}\right)^2\right] = 5.66 \text{ (to 3 sig. fig.)}$$

Tip: For more about finding the mean and variance of grouped data, see pages 12 and 20.

Tip: Remember... $n = \sum f$

Tip: With grouped data, the formula for sample variance (S^2) becomes:

$$\frac{n}{n-1}\left[\frac{\sum fX_i^2}{n} - \left(\frac{\sum fX_i}{n}\right)^2\right]$$

or $\frac{n}{n-1}\left[\frac{\sum fX_i^2}{n} - \overline{X}^2\right]$

Exercise 2.1

Q1 Heights of South African giraffes are known to follow a normal distribution with unknown mean μ and unknown standard deviation σ. 10 giraffes are measured and their heights are X_1 to X_{10}. Which of the following are statistics?

a) $\frac{\sum X_i}{10}$ b) $\frac{\sum (X_i - \mu)^2}{10}$ c) $X_1 + X_2$ d) $\sum (X_i - \sigma)$

Q2 A random sample was taken from a population whose mean (μ) and variance (σ^2) are unknown.
The values in the sample were: 24, 25, 24, 23, 26, 27, 22, 23, 21, 25.
Calculate unbiased estimates of μ and σ^2.

Q3 The table below summarises the marks scored in a test by 30 pupils picked at random from a population of 200.

Marks	31-40	41-50	51-60	61-70	71-80	81-90
Frequency (f)	2	4	5	8	6	5

a) Find an unbiased estimate of the population mean mark μ.

b) Find an unbiased estimate of the population variance σ^2.

3. Confidence Intervals

Learning Objectives:

- Be able to calculate the standard error of a sample mean if the population variance is known.
- Be able to find a confidence interval for the mean of a normally distributed population if the population variance is known.
- Be able to comment on the validity of a claim made about a population mean.

Confidence intervals are a way to give an estimate of a population parameter in a more 'helpful and informative' way. To work out a confidence interval you need to know a statistic's sampling distribution.

The standard error of $\overline{X}$

So far you've used statistics to estimate the population mean and variance. The rest of this chapter is about estimating a population mean, but in a slightly different way — using a **confidence interval**. A confidence interval is a **range** of values, and allows you to estimate the population mean while being very specific about **how uncertain** you are.

The key to finding a confidence interval for the population mean (μ) is being able to find the **sampling distribution** of the sample mean ($\overline{X}$).

- You already know that the **expected value** of $\overline{X}$ is the population mean (μ).
- The next thing you need to know is the **standard deviation** of $\overline{X}$, also known as its **standard error**.

The **standard deviation** of a statistic's sampling distribution gives you an idea of how much you can expect the statistic to **vary** between samples. It's so important that it even gets its own special name — the **standard error** of the statistic.

Tip: Think of the standard error as a measure of the 'reliability' of a statistic.

The smaller a statistic's standard error, the less it will vary between samples.

The **standard error** of a statistic is the standard deviation of the sampling distribution of that statistic.

The **sample mean** is a statistic, and you can easily work out its standard error. It depends on the population's **standard deviation** (σ) and the **sample size** (n).

The standard error of the sample mean = $\frac{\sigma}{\sqrt{n}}$

The sampling distribution of $\overline{X}$ if $X \sim N(\mu, \sigma^2)$

Tip: This is a **really** important result.

Notice that $E(\overline{X}) = \mu$.

And $Var(\overline{X}) = \frac{\sigma^2}{n}$ — i.e. the standard deviation of $\overline{X}$ (or the standard error of the mean) is $\frac{\sigma}{\sqrt{n}}$.

Tip: Another way of stating this result is that:

$$\frac{\overline{X} - \mu}{\sigma / \sqrt{n}} \sim N(0, 1)$$

If a population is **normally** distributed, you can say **exactly** what the distribution of $\overline{X}$ will be.

- If a **population** is **normally distributed**, then the **sampling distribution** of the sample mean also follows a **normal distribution**.

If $X \sim N(\mu, \sigma^2)$, then $\overline{X} \sim N\left(\mu, \frac{\sigma^2}{n}\right)$.

Example

The random variable X is normally distributed with $X \sim N(170, 40)$. A sample of size 10 is taken from the distribution of X.

a) State the sampling distribution of the sample mean $\overline{X}$.

- Here, the random variable X represents members of the population. So this population has a mean of 170 and a variance of 40, and is **normally distributed**. This means $\overline{X}$ is also normally distributed.
- The sample size (n) is 10, so the sample mean $\overline{X}$ must follow the distribution $\overline{X} \sim N(170, \frac{40}{10}) = N(170, 4)$.

b) On the same axes, sketch the normal curves for X and $\overline{X}$.

- Both normal curves will have the same mean ($= \mu = 170$), so they'll both be centred on 170.
- The only difference is in the variance — the variance of $\overline{X}$ is a lot smaller, so this graph will be thinner but taller.

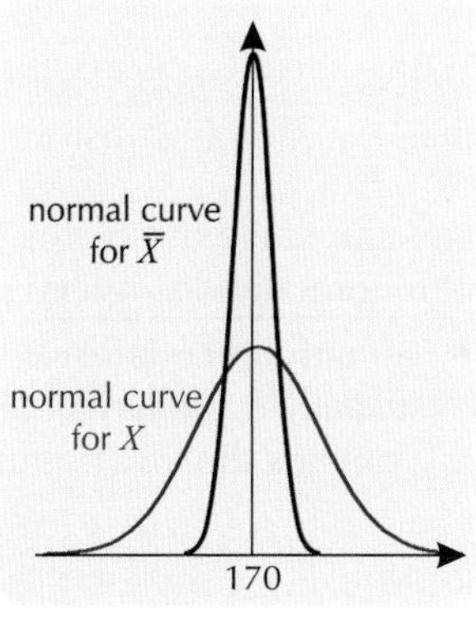

Tip: This is why a bigger sample means a much better estimate of the population mean.

The **bigger** the sample size, the **smaller** the variance of the sampling distribution of $\overline{X}$ ... so the closer an observation of $\overline{X}$ is likely to be to the population mean.

c) Find P($\overline{X}$ < 165).

- $\overline{X}$ is a normally distributed random variable, and you know its mean and variance.
- So to find P($\overline{X}$ < 165), convert this to a probability involving the standard normal variable Z, and use your normal tables.

$$\begin{aligned} P(\overline{X} < 165) &= P\left(Z < \frac{165 - 170}{2}\right) \\ &= P(Z < -2.5) \\ &= P(Z > 2.5) \\ &= 1 - P(Z \leq 2.5) \\ &= 1 - 0.99379 = 0.00621 \end{aligned}$$

Tip: Var($\overline{X}$) = 4, so the standard deviation of $\overline{X}$ is 2.

Tip: As long as you can find the sampling distribution of $\overline{X}$, you can be very specific about the probability of the sample mean falling within a particular range of values.

Exercise 3.1

Q1 Random samples of size 20 are taken from a population with variance 32.5.

Calculate the standard error of the sample mean.

Q2 A certain type of rubber ball has a height of bounce which is normally distributed with a standard deviation of 2 cm. A random sample of 60 such balls is tested and the height the balls bounce to is measured. Find the standard error of the sample mean.

Q3 The heights of a large number of female students form a normally distributed population of mean 164 cm and variance 57 cm^2. Random samples of 30 heights are taken.

a) Write down the distribution of the sample mean.

b) If 100 such samples are taken, how many would you expect to have a mean of less than 162 cm?

Q4 The volume of milk in a particular type of bottle follows a normal distribution with mean 500 ml and standard deviation 2.63 ml. The volumes in a random sample of 10 bottles are measured and the mean volume ($\overline{X}$) calculated.

a) State the sampling distribution of $\overline{X}$.

b) What is the probability that $\overline{X}$ exceeds 501 ml?

Confidence intervals for μ if $X \sim N(\mu, \sigma^2)$

You've seen that if a population is **normally distributed** and follows $N(\mu, \sigma^2)$, then the sampling distribution of the sample mean ($\overline{X}$) is $\overline{X} \sim N\left(\mu, \frac{\sigma^2}{n}\right)$.

You can make use of this fact to calculate a **confidence interval** for the mean of a normally distributed population with a **known variance**.

- A **confidence interval** for the mean of a population is a **range** of values (usually symmetrical about your sample mean) that you're 'fairly sure' contains the true population mean. Look at this example:

(11.2, 14.4) is a 95% confidence interval for μ

- This means that there's a **probability of 95%** that the interval (11.2, 14.4) includes the true value of μ.
- Remember... the value of μ is **fixed** (but unknown) — it's the **confidence interval** that will change depending on your sample.

Here's the formula for a confidence interval for μ if X is **normally distributed**.

Tip: This formula just says a confidence interval for the population mean extends a distance 'z × **standard error of the sample mean**' from your sample mean (in both directions).

Let $\overline{X}$ be the mean of a random sample from a **normally distributed** population $N(\mu, \sigma^2)$, where the value of σ is **known**.

A **confidence interval** for the **population mean** is: $\left(\overline{X} - z\frac{\sigma}{\sqrt{n}}, \overline{X} + z\frac{\sigma}{\sqrt{n}}\right)$

where n is the **sample size** and the value of z depends on the 'level of confidence' you need. For example:

- for a 95% confidence interval, choose z so that $P(-z < Z < z) = 0.95$,
- for a 98% confidence interval, choose z so that $P(-z < Z < z) = 0.98$.

Tip: The case when the population variance is unknown is dealt with (for a large sample) on p129.

For example, suppose you take a random sample of size 25 from a normally distributed population with an **unknown mean** but **known variance** of $\sigma^2 = 9$. You find that your sample mean is $\overline{X} = 147$, and you're after a 95% confidence interval for μ.

Tip: You'll need to use the 'percentage-points' table (on p160) to solve equations of the form $P(Z < z) = 0.975$. See Chapter 4 for more information.

- You find your value of z for a 95% confidence interval by solving $P(-z < Z < z) = 0.95$.
- You're only going to need to find confidence intervals that are **symmetrical** about the **sample mean**.

  So to solve $P(-z < Z < z) = 0.95$, use your tables to solve $P(Z < z) = 0.975$. This gives a value of $z = 1.9600$.

f(z)
95%
2.5%
2.5%
z
z = –1.96
z = 1.96

Tip: This formula relies on the sampling distribution of $\overline{X}$ following a **normal distribution**. (But because X follows a normal distribution, you know $\overline{X}$ must also follow a normal distribution—see p120.)

- The standard error of the sample mean is $\frac{\sigma}{\sqrt{n}} = \frac{\sqrt{9}}{\sqrt{25}} = \frac{3}{5} = 0.6$.
- So your confidence interval is:

$$\left(\overline{X} - z\frac{\sigma}{\sqrt{n}}, \overline{X} + z\frac{\sigma}{\sqrt{n}}\right) = (147 - 1.9600 \times 0.6,\ 147 + 1.9600 \times 0.6)$$

$$= \mathbf{(145.824,\ 148.176)\ (to\ 3\ d.p.)}$$

Example

A machine makes chocolate bars with weights that are normally distributed with a standard deviation of 8.2 grams. A random sample of 10 bars is chosen, with weights (in grams) as follows:
251.3 257.2 249.5 254.3 252.6 256.1 254.7 255.3 254.8 252.6.

a) Calculate the sample mean $\overline{x}$.

$\overline{x}$ = (251.3 + 257.2 + 249.5 + 254.3 + 252.6 + 256.1 + 254.7 + 255.3 + 254.8 + 252.6) ÷ 10 = 253.84 g

b) Calculate a 95% confidence interval for the mean weight of all the bars made by the machine.

- This is a 95% confidence interval, so you need to find z with $P(-z < Z < z) = 0.95$. So use your percentage-points table and look up $P(Z < z) = 0.975$ — this gives $z = 1.9600$.
- So your confidence interval is:

$$\left(\overline{x} - z\frac{\sigma}{\sqrt{n}}, \overline{x} + z\frac{\sigma}{\sqrt{n}}\right)$$
$$= \left(253.84 - 1.9600 \times \frac{8.2}{\sqrt{10}}, 253.84 + 1.9600 \times \frac{8.2}{\sqrt{10}}\right)$$
$$= (248.76\text{ g}, 258.92\text{ g}) \text{ (to 2 d.p.)}$$

c) Calculate a 99% confidence interval for the mean weight of all the bars made by the machine.

- This is a 99% confidence interval, so this time you need to find z such that $P(-z < Z < z) = 0.99$. So use your percentage-points table and look up $P(Z < z) = 0.995$ — this gives $z = 2.5758$.
- So your confidence interval is:

$$\left(\overline{x} - z\frac{\sigma}{\sqrt{n}}, \overline{x} + z\frac{\sigma}{\sqrt{n}}\right)$$
$$= \left(253.84 - 2.5758 \times \frac{8.2}{\sqrt{10}}, 253.84 + 2.5758 \times \frac{8.2}{\sqrt{10}}\right)$$
$$= (247.16\text{ g}, 260.52\text{ g}) \text{ (to 2 d.p.)}$$

Tip: Notice that the 99% confidence interval is wider than the 95% confidence interval.

The more certain you want to be that the true value of μ is in your confidence interval, the wider your confidence interval will need to be.

You'll often have to use a confidence interval to comment on the probable **validity** of a **claim** someone has made.

Example 1

Jack fits satellite dishes. The times it takes him to fit a dish are normally distributed with a standard deviation of 2 minutes. In a random sample of 100 fittings, the installation times have a mean ($\overline{x}$) of 90.8 minutes.

a) Construct a 95% confidence interval for the mean time (in minutes) it takes Jack to fit a dish.

- This is a 95% confidence interval. So you need to find z such that $P(-z < Z < z) = 0.95$, which means that $z = 1.96$.
- So your confidence interval is:

$$\left(90.8 - 1.96 \times \frac{2}{\sqrt{100}}, 90.8 + 1.96 \times \frac{2}{\sqrt{100}}\right) = (90.408\text{ mins}, 91.192\text{ mins})$$

b) Jack claims that, on average, it takes him 91 minutes to fit each dish. Comment, with justification, on his claim.

- Since 91 is within this confidence interval, the claim seems to be valid. In other words, these results provide no evidence to doubt the claim.

Tip: If Jack had claimed it took him 90 minutes on average to fit each dish, then the claim would **not** be supported by these results.

This is because 90 minutes falls **outside** the confidence interval.

Example 2

The lengths (in cm) of a gardener's crop of cucumbers are normally distributed with a variance of 9. The mean length of the cucumbers in a random sample of 20 is 35.8 cm.

a) Construct a 90% confidence interval for the population mean.

- For a 90% confidence interval, you need to find z such that $P(-z < Z < z) = 0.90$, which means that $z = 1.6449$.
- So your confidence interval is:

$$\left(35.8 - 1.6449 \times \frac{3}{\sqrt{20}}, 35.8 + 1.6449 \times \frac{3}{\sqrt{20}}\right) = \text{(34.70 cm, 36.90 cm)}$$

b) The gardener claims that the mean length of the entire crop of cucumbers is less than 37 cm. Comment on this claim.

- The **whole** confidence interval is less than 37 cm, so this claim seems valid based on this evidence.

c) Find the probability that the mean length of the cucumbers falls in the interval (34.07 cm, 37.53 cm).

- Solve $\bar{x} - z\frac{\sigma}{\sqrt{n}} = 34.07$, i.e. $35.8 - z\frac{3}{\sqrt{20}} = 34.07$
  This gives $z = 2.58$ (to 2 d.p.).
- So you need to find $P(-2.58 < Z < 2.58)$.
  This is $P(Z < 2.58) - P(Z \le -2.58) = P(Z < 2.58) - P(Z \ge 2.58)$
  $= P(Z < 2.58) - (1 - P(Z < 2.58)) = 2 \times P(Z < 2.58) - 1$
  $= 2 \times 0.99506 - 1 =$ 0.990 (to 3 sig. fig.)

Tip: Remember... to find z with $P(-z < Z < z) = 0.90$, use your tables to look up the value of z with $P(Z \le z) = 0.95$.

Tip: If the confidence interval **contained** 37, then you would **not** have evidence that the mean length of the cucumbers is less than 37 cm.

Tip: In c), solving $\bar{x} + z\frac{\sigma}{\sqrt{n}} = 37.53$ gives the same value for z.

Exercise 3.2

Q1 A depot uses a mechanical shovel to load grit onto lorries. The weight of grit in one scoop of the mechanical shovel follows a normal distribution with unknown mean (μ) and a standard deviation (σ) of 20 kg. A random sample of 30 scoops has a mean weight of 510 kg.

a) Construct a 95% confidence interval for μ.

b) It is claimed that the shovel collects more than 500 kg on average. Comment on the claim.

Q2 A company is testing the breaking strength of cables. The breaking strengths (in newtons, N) are normally distributed with a variance of 3600. In a random sample of 50 cables, the mean breaking strength is 1600 N.

a) Construct a 98% confidence interval for the mean breaking strength.

b) With what probability does the mean breaking strength lie in the interval (1585 N, 1615 N)?

Q3 The lives (in hours, h) of a certain brand of light bulb are normally distributed with known variance σ^2. A 95% confidence interval for the mean life based on results from a random sample of 36 bulbs is (1023.3 h, 1101.7 h), and is symmetrical about the sample mean.

a) Calculate the sample mean.

b) Find the standard error of the sample mean.

c) Find the population standard deviation (σ).

d) Construct a 99% confidence interval for the population mean.

e) The manufacturer of the light bulbs claims that he is 99% certain that the average life is more than 1020 hours. Comment on this claim.

4. Large Samples and the Central Limit Theorem

So far you've seen how to find a confidence interval for a population mean where the population follows a normal distribution.
But the Central Limit Theorem means that for large samples, the same method still works even if the population isn't normally distributed.

Learning Objective:

- Be able to use the Central Limit Theorem to find a confidence interval for the mean of a population that does not follow a normal distribution, based on a large sample.

The Central Limit Theorem

The formula for a confidence interval for μ on p122 depends on the sampling distribution of $\overline{X}$ following a **normal distribution** with variance $\frac{\sigma^2}{n}$.
If X is normally distributed then this is fine, because you saw on p120 that:

> If $X \sim \mathrm{N}(\mu, \sigma^2)$, then $\overline{X} \sim \mathrm{N}\left(\mu, \frac{\sigma^2}{n}\right)$.

But what if X is **not** normally distributed?
Well... this is why the **Central Limit Theorem** is so important.

The Central Limit Theorem tells you pretty much **all** you could want to know about the sampling distribution of $\overline{X}$ — even if you know nothing about the distribution of X **except** its mean (μ) and variance (σ^2).

> **The Central Limit Theorem**
>
> Suppose you take a **random sample** of n readings from **any** distribution with mean μ and variance σ^2.
>
> - For **large *n***, the distribution of the sample mean $\overline{X}$ is **approximately normal**: $\overline{X} \sim \mathrm{N}\left(\mu, \frac{\sigma^2}{n}\right)$.
> - The **bigger** n is, the **better** this approximation will be. (For $n > 30$ it's pretty good.)

Tip: Notice that this relies on the sample being selected **at random**.

This means that as long as you have a **large random sample**, you can do the following for **any** distribution:

- calculate the **probability** that a sample mean will fall within a particular range, assuming you know μ and σ,
- calculate **confidence intervals** for the population mean μ if μ is unknown.

Tip: Remember... if X is **normally** distributed, then the sampling distribution of the mean ($\overline{X}$) is **exactly** normal — and you **don't** need to use the Central Limit Theorem.

Here's an example showing how you'd use the Central Limit Theorem to find the probability of $\overline{X}$ falling in a particular range, assuming you know the values of both μ and σ.

Tip: In this section, you'll always be told the population variance (or population standard deviation).

In the next section, you'll see that a large sample is important for another reason too — when you have to **estimate** the population variance.

Example

A random sample of size 50 is taken from a population with mean 60 and variance 10. Find the probability that the sample mean is less than 59.

- This question doesn't say anything about the distribution of the population except its mean and variance. But since n (= 50) is quite large, you can use the Central Limit Theorem.
- Here $\overline{X} \sim \mathrm{N}\left(60, \frac{10}{50}\right) = \mathrm{N}(60, 0.2)$ (approximately), and you need to find $\mathrm{P}(\overline{X} < 59)$.

Tip: As always... if you need to, draw a sketch:

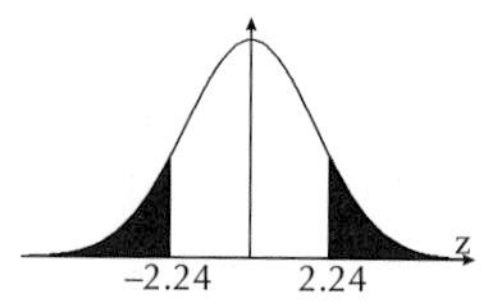

- Since $\overline{X}$ has an (approximately) normal distribution, you can standardise it and use tables for Z. So subtract the mean (= 60) and divide by the standard deviation (= $\sqrt{0.2}$):

$$P(\overline{X} < 59) \approx P\left(Z < \frac{59 - 60}{\sqrt{0.2}}\right) = P(Z < -2.24)$$

- Now you can use your normal-distribution tables (see p159).

$P(Z < -2.24) = P(Z > 2.24) = 1 - P(Z \leq 2.24)$
$= 1 - 0.98745 = 0.01255$

Exercise 4.1

Q1 A random sample of size 80 is taken from a population which has a mean of 55 and variance 12.

a) What is the sampling distribution of the sample mean? Explain why you need to use the Central Limit Theorem.

b) Find the probability that the sample mean is greater than 54.

Q2 A random sample of size 80 is taken from a population that follows a normal distribution with mean 55 and variance 12.

What is the sampling distribution of the sample mean?
Explain why you do **not** need to use the Central Limit Theorem here.

Confidence intervals for μ — with a large sample and known variance

Here's the formula for a confidence interval for μ for **any** distribution with known variance σ^2, based on a **large sample**.

Tip: This formula depends on the sampling distribution of the mean following a **normal distribution**.

As long as the sample size is large, the Central Limit Theorem tells you that this will be the case.

Let $\overline{X}$ be the mean of a **large** random sample ($n > 30$) from **any** population with known variance σ^2.

A **confidence interval** for the **population mean** is: $\left(\overline{X} - z\frac{\sigma}{\sqrt{n}}, \overline{X} + z\frac{\sigma}{\sqrt{n}}\right)$

where n is the sample size and the value of z depends on the 'level of confidence' you need.

So as long as you know its variance (or its standard deviation), you can use the Central Limit Theorem to find **confidence intervals** for the mean of **any** population... as long as the sample is large enough.

Example 1

A random sample of size 40 is taken from a population with variance 25.

a) Find a 95% confidence interval for the population mean if the sample mean ($\overline{x}$) is 116.

- The sample size is large here and the variance is known, so use the confidence-interval formula above.
- For a 95% confidence interval, you need to find z such that $P(-z < Z < z) = 0.95$, which means using your tables to look up $P(Z < z) = 0.975$. This gives $z = 1.9600$.

- So your confidence interval is:

$$\left(\bar{x} - z\frac{\sigma}{\sqrt{n}}, \bar{x} + z\frac{\sigma}{\sqrt{n}}\right)$$
$$= \left(116 - 1.9600 \times \frac{\sqrt{25}}{\sqrt{40}}, 116 + 1.9600 \times \frac{\sqrt{25}}{\sqrt{40}}\right)$$
$$= (114.45, 117.55) \text{ (to 2 d.p.)}$$

b) It is claimed that the mean of this population is 116. Comment on this claim.

- The claim seems valid based on this evidence, since 116 falls inside the confidence interval.

c) State the probability that the population mean falls outside this confidence interval.

- This is a 95% confidence interval, so the probability that the population mean falls outside these limits must be 0.05.

Example 2

The scheduler of a tennis tournament needs an idea of how long matches can be expected to last, on average. The data he finds about the lengths of 30 randomly selected previous matches is shown in the table below.

Length in minutes	**40-60**	**60-80**	**80-100**	**100-120**	**120-140**	**140-160**
Frequency (f)	**3**	**8**	**7**	**8**	**3**	**1**

a) It is known that the variance of the lengths of all matches is 29 minutes. Find an approximate 95% confidence interval for the mean length (μ) of a match.

- Your data is grouped, so you'll need to estimate the sample mean ($\bar{x}$) using the class mid-points. It's best to add some rows to the table.

Length in minutes	40-60	60-80	80-100	100-120	120-140	140-160
Frequency (f)	3	8	7	8	3	1
Class mid-point (x)	50	70	90	110	130	150
fx	150	560	630	880	390	150

- $\sum f = 30$ and $\sum fx = 2760$, which gives an estimated sample mean of:

$$\bar{x} = \frac{\sum fx}{\sum f} = \frac{2760}{30} = 92 \text{ minutes}$$

- Again, for a 95% confidence interval, you need to find z with $P(-z < Z < z) = 0.95$, which means that $z = 1.9600$.

- So your confidence interval is:

$$\left(\bar{x} - z\frac{\sigma}{\sqrt{n}}, \bar{x} + z\frac{\sigma}{\sqrt{n}}\right)$$
$$= \left(92 - 1.9600 \times \frac{\sqrt{29}}{\sqrt{30}}, 92 + 1.9600 \times \frac{\sqrt{29}}{\sqrt{30}}\right)$$
$$= (90.1 \text{ mins}, 93.9 \text{ mins}) \text{ (to 3 sig. fig.)}$$

Tip: You can only find an **approximate** confidence interval here, because the data is **grouped** (and so you don't have the exact data values).

b) One player claims that the mean length of a match is more than 90 minutes, while another player claims it is more than 93 minutes. Comment on each of these claims.

- The **whole** of the confidence interval lies above 90 minutes, so the claim that the mean length of a match is more than 90 minutes seems **justified**, based on this evidence.
- Part of the confidence interval lies below 93 minutes, so the claim that the mean length of a match is more than 93 minutes does **not** seem justified, based on this evidence.

Exercise 4.2

Q1 It is known that the standard deviation of the masses of bags of sugar produced by a particular supplier is 4.1 g. Eighty bags of sugar were randomly selected and their mean mass was found to be 513 g.

Find a 99% confidence interval for the mean mass of all the bags of sugar produced by this supplier.

Q2 A number of random samples of the same size (n) are taken from a population with mean 30 and variance 10. It is found that in 2% of the samples the mean of the sample exceeded 30.5.

Find the probable sample size n, given that it is known to be large.

Q3 The table below summarises the ages (in years) of a random sample of 80 people who visit a gym.

Age (years)	15-19	20-24	25-29	30-39	40-49	50-69
Frequency (f)	12	17	17	10	14	10

a) Estimate the sample mean $\bar{x}$.

b) It is known that the variance of all the gym members' ages is 184. Find an approximate 95% confidence interval for the mean age (μ) of a gym member.

5. Large Samples and Estimating the Standard Error

You've seen how to work out confidence intervals for:
(i) the mean of a normally distributed population, and
(ii) the mean of any population when you have a large sample.
But you've always known the population variance (or standard deviation).

Learning Objectives:

- Be able to estimate the standard error of the sample mean.
- Be able to find confidence intervals for a population mean when the population variance is unknown but the sample size is large.

Estimating the standard error

You saw on p125 that a **large sample size** is important, because it allows you to use the Central Limit Theorem.

But a large sample size is important for another reason too.

- Up till now, you've always **known** the population standard deviation (σ), so you've been able to work out the **standard error** of the sample mean ($\frac{\sigma}{\sqrt{n}}$), and then use this to find a confidence interval.
- However, in practice you often have to **estimate** the standard error using the estimator below.

> The **estimator** of the standard error ($\frac{\sigma}{\sqrt{n}}$) is: $\frac{S}{\sqrt{n}}$
> where S is the sample standard deviation.

- For **large n**, this estimate of the standard error should be pretty good.
- So a large sample size means you don't have to be **told** the population variance or standard deviation to be able to work out the standard error of the sample mean. If n is large, you can **estimate** this standard error pretty well using your sample data.

Tip: See p118 for more about the sample standard deviation.

Here's an example showing how you'd go about estimating the standard error of the mean.

Example

The weights in grams of a random sample of 80 newts were measured, and the summary statistics below calculated. Estimate the sample mean's standard error.

$$\sum x = 7238, \sum x^2 = 684\,688$$

- First work out the sample variance (s^2).

$$s^2 = \frac{n}{n-1}\left[\frac{\sum x^2}{n} - \left(\frac{\sum x}{n}\right)^2\right]$$

$$= \frac{80}{79}\left[\frac{684\,688}{80} - \left(\frac{7238}{80}\right)^2\right] = 377.594...$$

- Now you can work out an estimate of the mean's **standard error**.

$$\frac{s}{\sqrt{n}} = \frac{\sqrt{377.594...}}{\sqrt{80}} = 2.17\text{ g (to 3 sig. fig.)}$$

Exercise 5.1

Q1 A candle-maker is testing the precision with which his machine produces candles of a certain length. The lengths (x, in cm) of a random sample of 50 candles are measured, with the following results:

$$\sum x = 506 \text{ and } \sum x^2 = 5460.$$

Estimate the standard error of the sample mean.

Q2 The lengths, measured to the nearest centimetre, of 46 worms from a garden are summarised in the following frequency table:

Length in cm	5-6	7-8	9-10	11-12	13-14
Frequency (f)	6	9	14	10	7

Calculate an estimate of the standard error of the sample mean.

Confidence intervals for μ — with large n but unknown σ^2

Tip: Again, this formula for a confidence interval only works when the sample mean $\overline{X}$ is **normally distributed**.

But because the sample size is large, the Central Limit Theorem tells you that $\overline{X}$ **will be** approximately normally distributed.

(Although if the population itself (X) is normally distributed, then from p120 you know that $\overline{X}$ will be **exactly** normally distributed, and you don't need the Central Limit Theorem.)

Now you can work out a confidence interval for the population mean even if the population variance (σ^2) is unknown... as long as the sample size is large enough.

Here's the formula for a confidence interval for μ for any distribution, where the population variance is unknown but the sample size is large.

Let $\overline{X}$ be the mean of a random sample of size n (where n is **large**) from a population with **unknown variance**.
Let S be the sample standard deviation.

A **confidence interval** for the **population mean** is: $\left(\overline{X} - z\frac{S}{\sqrt{n}}, \overline{X} + z\frac{S}{\sqrt{n}}\right)$

where z depends on the 'level of confidence' you need.

Example 1

A random sample of size 50 is taken from a population with an unknown standard deviation and an unknown mean. If $\sum x = 80$ and $\sum x^2 = 192$, find a 95% confidence interval for the population mean.

- The sample size is large ($n = 50$) but the population standard deviation is unknown, so use the confidence interval formula above.
- First, you need to find the **sample mean**.

$$\overline{x} = \frac{\sum x}{n} = \frac{80}{50} = 1.6$$

- Now you need to find the **sample standard deviation** (s). Start by finding the sample variance (s^2).

$$s^2 = \frac{n}{n-1}\left[\frac{\sum x^2}{n} - \left(\frac{\sum x}{n}\right)^2\right]$$
$$= \frac{50}{49}\left[\frac{192}{50} - \left(\frac{80}{50}\right)^2\right]$$
$$= \frac{1}{49}[192 - 128] = \frac{64}{49}$$

So the sample standard deviation is $s = \sqrt{\frac{64}{49}} = \frac{8}{7}$

- This is a 95% confidence interval, so $z = 1.96$.
- This gives you a **confidence interval** of:

$$\left(\overline{x} - z\frac{s}{\sqrt{n}}, \overline{x} + z\frac{s}{\sqrt{n}}\right) = \left(1.6 - 1.96 \times \frac{8}{7\sqrt{50}}, 1.6 + 1.96 \times \frac{8}{7\sqrt{50}}\right)$$
$$= (1.28, 1.92) \text{ (to 2 d.p.)}$$

Example 2

A random sample of 188 batteries was tested to see how long they lasted. The times are summarised in the table below.

Time (hours)	**0-20**	**20-40**	**40-60**	**60-80**	**80-100**
Frequency	**90**	**46**	**28**	**14**	**10**

a) Estimate the sample mean and variance of the batteries' lives.

- Here, you only have grouped data, so you'll need to estimate the sample mean ($\overline{x}$) and the sample variance (s^2) using the class mid-points. It's best to add some rows to the table.

Time (hours)	0-20	20-40	40-60	60-80	80-100
Frequency	90	46	28	14	10
Class mid-point (x)	10	30	50	70	90
fx	900	1380	1400	980	900
x^2	100	900	2500	4900	8100
fx^2	9000	41400	70000	68600	81000

$\sum f = 188, \sum fx = 5560$ and $\sum fx^2 = 270\,000$

- So your estimate of the sample mean will be:

$$\overline{x} = \frac{\sum fx}{\sum f} = \frac{5560}{188} = 29.57... = 29.6 \text{ hours (to 3 sig. fig.)}$$

- And your estimate of the sample variance will be:

$$s^2 = \frac{n}{n-1}\left[\frac{\sum fx^2}{\sum f} - \overline{x}^2\right] = \frac{188}{187}\left[\frac{270\,000}{188} - 29.5744...^2\right]$$
$$= 564.523... = 565 \text{ (to 3 sig. fig.)}$$

b) Calculate an estimate of the standard error of the sample mean.

- Use the formula:

$$\frac{s}{\sqrt{n}} = \frac{\sqrt{564.523...}}{\sqrt{188}} = 1.732... = 1.73 \text{ hours (to 3 sig. fig.)}$$

c) Find an approximate 99% confidence interval for the mean lifetime (μ) of the entire population of batteries.

- You need to find z with $P(-z < Z < z) = 0.99$.
  So use your normal tables to find z with $P(Z < z) = 0.995$.
  This gives $z = 2.5758$.
- So your 99% confidence interval is:

$$\left(\overline{x} - z\frac{s}{\sqrt{n}}, \overline{x} + z\frac{s}{\sqrt{n}}\right)$$
$$= (29.57... - 2.5758 \times 1.732..., 29.57... + 2.5758 \times 1.732...)$$
$$= (25.1 \text{ hours}, 34.0 \text{ hours}) \text{ (to 3 sig. fig.)}$$

d) Indicate, with a reason, whether you have made use of the Central Limit Theorem.

- Yes. The battery lives do not necessarily follow a normal distribution, but because the sample size was large the Central Limit Theorem tells us that the sampling distribution of the mean approximately follows a normal distribution, which is necessary when using the above confidence-interval formula.

Example 3

Some Trading Standards officers checked the masses (x, in g) of 50 randomly selected bags of potatoes that were said to contain 1000 g. Their data is summarised below.

$$\sum x = 49655 \qquad \sum(x - \overline{x})^2 = 28920.5$$

a) Find values for the sample mean ($\overline{x}$) and sample standard deviation (s).

- $\overline{x} = \frac{\sum x}{n} = \frac{49655}{50} = 993.1\text{g}$
- $s = \sqrt{\frac{\sum(x - \overline{x})^2}{n - 1}} = \sqrt{\frac{28920.5}{49}} = 24.294...... = 24.29 \text{ g (to 4 sig. fig.)}$

b) Use your answers to a) to find a 98% confidence interval for the mean mass (in grams) of a bag of potatoes.

- You need to find z with $P(-z < Z < z) = 0.98$.
  So use your normal tables to look up $P(Z < z) = 0.99$, which gives $z = 2.3263$.
- So your 99% confidence interval is:

$$\left(\overline{x} - z\frac{s}{\sqrt{n}}, \overline{x} + z\frac{s}{\sqrt{n}}\right)$$
$$= \left(993.1 - 2.3263 \times \frac{24.294...}{\sqrt{50}}, 993.1 + 2.3263 \times \frac{24.294...}{\sqrt{50}}\right)$$
$$= (985.1, 1001.1) \text{ (to 1d.p.)}$$

c) Do the Trading Standards officers have evidence that the mean mass of potatoes in the bags is less than 1000 g?

- No, since 1000 g is contained within this confidence interval.

Exercise 5.2

Q1 A random sample of 70 gym members had their pulses taken for 30 seconds after they had done 10 minutes on a running machine. The mean was 63 beats with a sample standard deviation of 5.

a) Find a 95% confidence interval for the mean number of beats during 30 seconds for all the gym members' pulses after 10 minutes on the running machine. State whether or not you are using the Central Limit Theorem, explaining your reasons.

b) Find a 99% confidence interval for the population mean.

Q2 The numbers of sweets (x) in a random sample of 100 tins of sweets are counted. The results are:

x	82	83	84	85	86	87
f	6	9	19	27	22	17

a) Work out an unbiased estimate of the population mean.

b) Calculate an unbiased estimate for the population variance.

c) Construct a 98% confidence interval for the population mean.

Q3 A scientist wants to know the length of worms in his wormery. He measures the lengths (x cm) of 50 randomly selected worms, and obtains the results below.

$$\sum x = 634, \quad \sum x^2 = 8356$$

a) Find unbiased estimates of the population mean and variance.

b) Construct a 99% confidence interval for the mean length of the worms.

c) The scientist claims that the mean length of worms in the wormery is greater than 11.5 cm. Comment on this claim.

Q4 Some decorative mugs are hand-painted. One of the painters records the times it takes her to paint the mugs (x, in minutes). In a random sample of 60 mugs the following results are obtained:

$$\sum x = 1884, \quad \sum (x - \bar{x})^2 = 57\,200$$

a) Calculate the sample mean and the sample variance for these times.

b) Construct a 95% confidence interval for the population mean (μ minutes).

c) On average, the company expects no longer than 30 minutes to be spent painting a mug. Comment on this painter's performance.

d) In constructing the confidence interval, state why the use of the Central Limit Theorem was necessary.

Review Exercise — Chapter 5

Q1 The manager of a tennis club wants to know if members are happy with the facilities provided. She decides to ask the views of a sample of members.

a) Identify the population the manager is interested in.

b) Explain how the manager could avoid systematic bias in her sample.

Q2 What is a simple random sample?

Q3 The weights of a population of jars of pickled onions have unknown mean μ and standard deviation σ. A random sample of 50 weights (X_1, ..., X_{50}) are recorded. For each of the following, say whether or not it's a statistic:

a) $\frac{X_{25} + X_{26}}{2}$ b) $\sum X_i - \sigma$ c) $\sum X_i^2 + \mu$ d) $\frac{\sum X_i}{50}$

Q4 A random sample was taken from a population whose mean (μ) and variance (σ^2) are unknown.

Find unbiased estimates of μ and σ^2 if the sample values were:

8.4, 8.6, 7.2, 6.5, 9.1, 7.7, 8.1, 8.4, 8.5, 8.0.

Q5 A random sample of size 15 (X_1,..., X_{15}) is taken from a normally-distributed population with mean 7.2 and standard deviation 5.

a) Calculate the standard error of the sample mean.

b) Write down the sampling distribution of the sample mean.

c) Find $P(\overline{X} < 7.5)$.

Q6 A random sample of size 80 is taken from a population with mean 18 and standard deviation 4.

a) What can you say about the sampling distribution of the sample mean? Explain your answer fully.

b) Find $P(\overline{X} > 19)$.

Q7 A random sample of size 25 is taken from a normally-distributed population with standard deviation 0.4.

Find a 99% confidence interval for the population mean if the sample mean is 18.2.

Q8 A random sample of size 120 is taken from a population with standard deviation 3.

Find a 95% confidence interval for the population mean if the sample mean is 33.8. State clearly any assumptions you make.

Q9 A random sample of size 100 was taken from a population. The following statistics were then calculated: $\sum x = 104$ and $\sum x^2 = 122.1$

Estimate the standard error of the sample mean.

Q10 A sample of size 80 was taken from a population with an unknown mean. The following statistics were then calculated: $\sum x = 24.2$ and $\sum x^2 = 41.3$

Find a 95% confidence interval for the population mean. State clearly any assumptions you make.

Exam-Style Questions — Chapter 5

1 A random sample of 50 sunflowers is selected. Their heights are measured.
The results are summarised in the table below.

Height, h (cm)	0-40	40-80	80-100	100-140	140-160
Frequency, f	5	8	11	19	7

Calculate an unbiased estimate of:

a) the mean height of the population, *(1 mark)*

b) the variance of the population heights. *(2 marks)*

2 The weights of a population of marsh frogs are normally distributed with a standard deviation of 8.5 grams. The weights of a random sample of 30 marsh frogs are measured.
The total weight of all 30 frogs is found to be 3.84 kg.

a) Calculate the mean weight in grams of the frogs in this sample. *(1 mark)*

b) Calculate the standard error in grams of the sample mean weight. *(2 marks)*

c) Construct a 95% confidence interval for the mean weight (in grams) of this population of marsh frogs. *(3 marks)*

d) Within what range would you expect approximately 99% of individual marsh frogs' weights to fall? *(3 marks)*

3 A sample of 60 racing snails sold by a business was selected at random.
The distance covered (x metres) in 10 minutes by each of the 60 snails was measured.
The following statistics were then calculated: $\sum x = 184$ and $\sum x^2 = 620$

a) Estimate the sample mean's standard error. *(4 marks)*

b) Construct a 98% confidence interval for the population mean.
State clearly any assumptions you make. *(5 marks)*

c) The manager of the business claims that, on average, its snails can cover over 3 metres in 10 minutes. Comment on this claim. *(2 marks)*

4 The number of minutes (X) taken by Ravi to travel to work each day may be modelled by a normal distribution with unknown mean μ and standard deviation σ.
The value of X was measured on 40 days. The results are summarised below.

$$\sum x = 1676 \text{ and } \sum (x - \bar{x})^2 = 1382$$

a) Find an unbiased estimate of the population variance. *(1 mark)*

b) Construct a 99% confidence interval for the population mean. *(4 marks)*

c) Ravi claims it takes him, on average, 42 minutes to travel to work.
His manager believes the mean time is actually over 46 minutes.
Comment on each of these claims. *(2 marks)*

5 The times spent in a queue at a local post office by a random sample of 80 customers were recorded. The results are summarised in the table below.

Time (in seconds)	Number of customers
$0 \le t \le 30$	33
$30 < t \le 60$	17
$60 < t \le 90$	20
$90 < t \le 120$	7
$120 < t \le 150$	2
$150 < t \le 180$	1

a) Calculate estimates for the sample mean and the sample standard deviation. *(4 marks)*

b) Are the waiting times normally distributed? Explain your answer. *(1 mark)*

c) The mean time spent in a queue by the customers in this sample is denoted $\overline{X}$.
Explain why the distribution of $\overline{X}$ will be approximately normal. *(1 mark)*

d) Write down estimates for:

(i) the population mean waiting time (μ) *(1 mark)*

(ii) the standard error of $\overline{X}$ *(2 marks)*

e) The mean waiting time for all customers is μ seconds.
Calculate an approximate 95% confidence interval for μ. *(3 marks)*

Chapter 6 Correlation and Regression

1. Correlation

Correlation is all about how closely two quantities are linked.
For example, as one quantity grows, the other might grow as well.
Or it might shrink. Or there might be no pattern at all to what it does.

Learning Objectives:

- Be able to plot scatter diagrams using paired observations of two variables.
- Be able to tell from a scatter diagram whether two variables are positively correlated, negatively correlated, or not correlated.
- Be able to calculate and interpret a product moment correlation coefficient.
- Be able to use linear scaling to simplify the calculation of correlation coefficients.

Scatter diagrams and correlation

Sometimes variables are measured in **pairs** — maybe because you want to investigate whether they're linked.

These pairs of variables might be things like:

- 'my age' and 'length of my feet',
- 'temperature' and 'number of accidents on a stretch of road'.

Data made up of pairs of values (x, y) is called **bivariate data**. You can plot bivariate data on a **scatter diagram** — where each variable is plotted along one of the axes. The pattern of points on a scatter diagram can tell you something about the data.

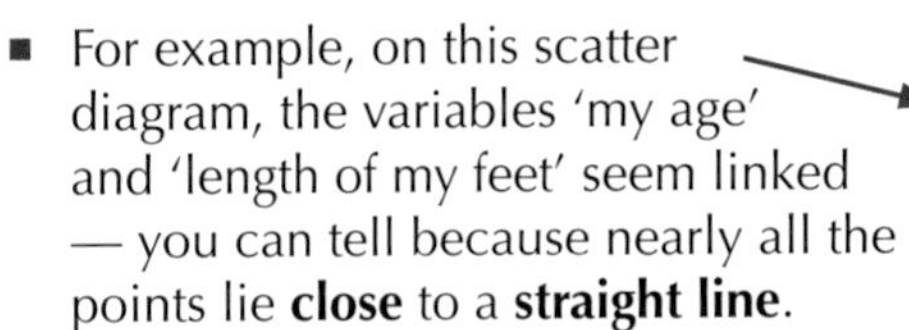

- For example, on this scatter diagram, the variables 'my age' and 'length of my feet' seem linked — you can tell because nearly all the points lie **close** to a **straight line**.

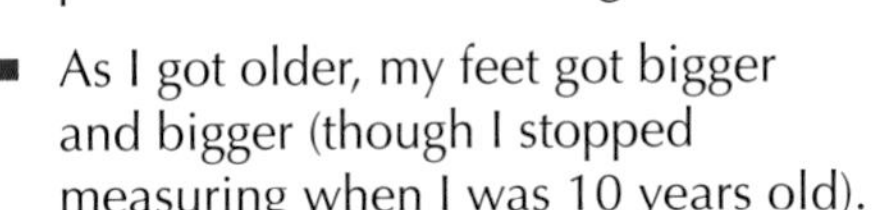

- As I got older, my feet got bigger and bigger (though I stopped measuring when I was 10 years old).

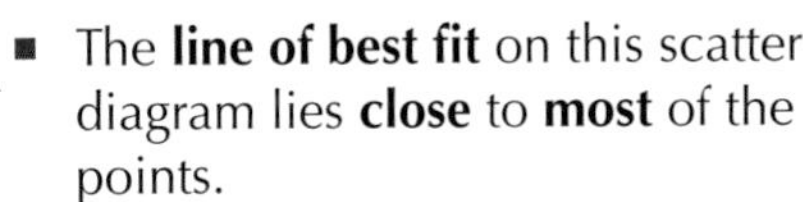

- The **line of best fit** on this scatter diagram lies **close** to **most** of the points.

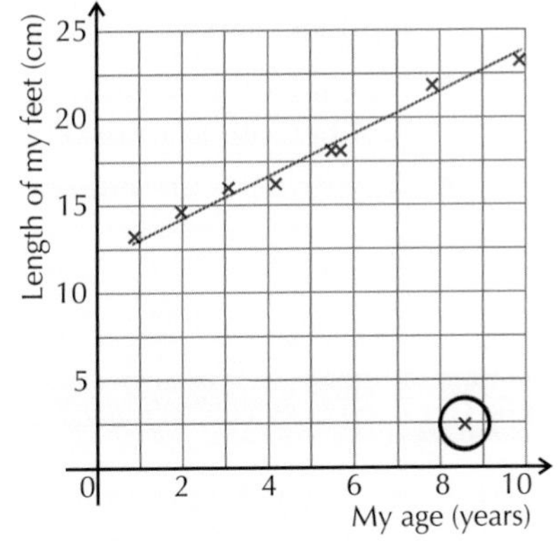

- The circled point doesn't fit the pattern of the rest of the data at all — so the line of best fit doesn't need to pass close to it. A point like this could show a measurement error (like here), or just a 'freak' observation.

Tip: The line of best fit doesn't need to actually **pass through** any of the data points — it just needs to be **near** to them.

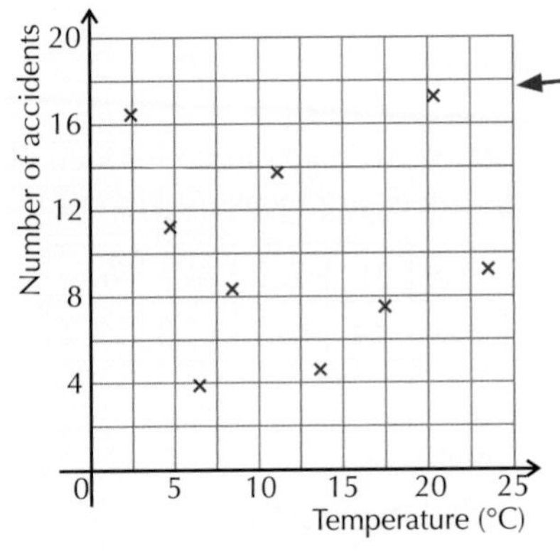

- It's a lot harder to see any connection between the variables 'temperature' and 'number of accidents' on this scatter diagram — the data seems scattered pretty much everywhere.
- You can't draw a line of best fit for this data — there isn't a line that lies close to **most** of the points. (It would be hard to draw a line lying close to more than about half the points.)

Correlation is all about whether points on a scatter diagram lie close to a **straight line**.

- Sometimes, as one variable gets bigger, the other one also gets bigger — in this case, the scatter diagram might look like this.
- Here, a line of best fit would have a **positive gradient**.
- The two variables are **positively correlated**.

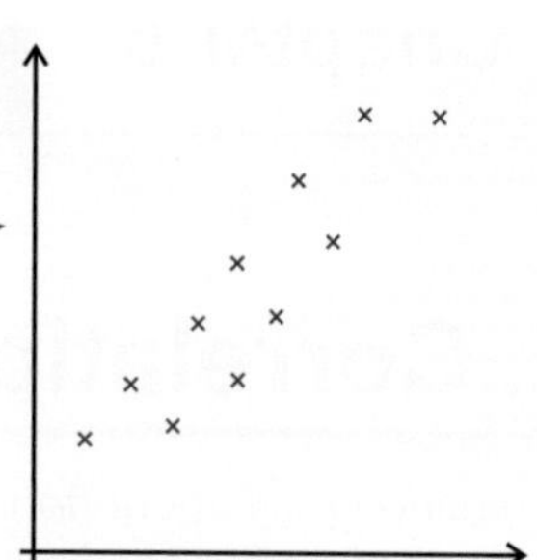

Tip: Or you can say there's a **positive correlation** between them.

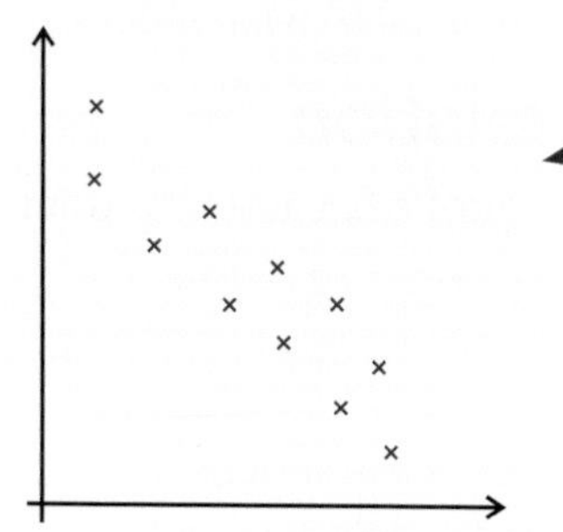

- But if one variable gets smaller as the other one gets bigger, then the scatter diagram would look like this.
- In this case, a line of best fit would have a **negative gradient**.
- The two variables are **negatively correlated**.

Tip: Or you can say there's a **negative correlation** between them.

- And if the two variables are **not** linked at all, you'd expect a **random scattering** of points.
- It's impossible to draw a line of best fit close to most of the points.
- The variables are **not correlated**.

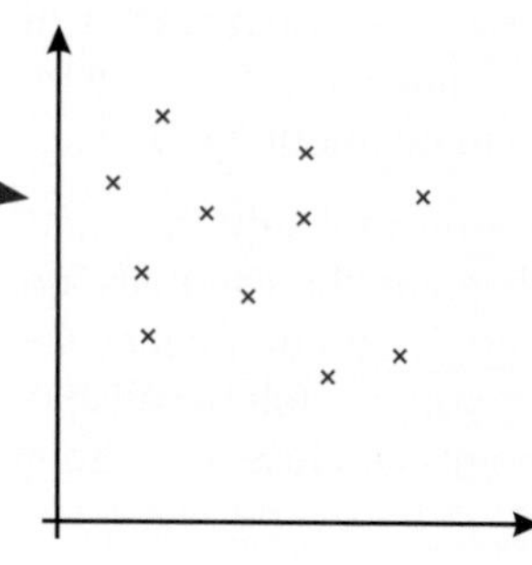

Tip: Or you can say there's **no correlation** between them.

Exercise 1.1

Q1 Owen asked a group of people how far from the town centre they live, and how many visits they made to the cinema in the previous year. The table shows his results.

Distance from centre (km)	0.6	7.0	1.4	16.8	10.4	3.6	9.2
Cinema visits	14	15	21	3	10	18	11

a) Plot a scatter diagram to show this data.

b) Describe the type of correlation shown.

Q2 This table shows the average length and the average circumference of eggs for several species of bird. (All distances are measured in cm.)

Length	6.2	2.1	3.4	5.7	11.9	10	7.2	4.5	6.8
Circumference	14	6.3	7.1	7.4	3.5	24	18.7	11.3	18.4

a) Plot a scatter diagram to show this data.

b) Describe the type of correlation shown.

c) One of the measurements was recorded incorrectly. Use your scatter diagram to determine which one.

S_{xx}, S_{yy} and S_{xy}

Suppose you've got a set of **bivariate** data written as n pairs of values (x, y).

The formula for the **variance** of the x-values can be written: $\text{variance}_x = \frac{S_{xx}}{n}$

where $S_{xx} = \sum(x - \bar{x})^2 = \sum x^2 - \frac{(\sum x)^2}{n}$

Similarly, the **variance** of the y-values can be written: $\text{variance}_y = \frac{S_{yy}}{n}$

where $S_{yy} = \sum(y - \bar{y})^2 = \sum y^2 - \frac{(\sum y)^2}{n}$

There's also a similar quantity S_{xy} that involves **both** x and y.

$$S_{xy} = \sum(x - \bar{x})(y - \bar{y}) = \sum xy - \frac{\sum x \sum y}{n}$$

To get a feel for what S_{xy} means, look at the scatter diagrams below. The dotted lines show the value of $\bar{x}$ (the mean of the x-values) and $\bar{y}$ (the mean of the y-values).

- This scatter diagram shows a pair of variables (x and y) that are **positively correlated** — so most of the values fall in the shaded squares.
- For each point in the **top-right** square, $(x - \bar{x})(y - \bar{y}) > 0$ (since $x > \bar{x}$ and $y > \bar{y}$).
- Similarly, for each point in the **bottom-left** square, $(x - \bar{x})(y - \bar{y}) > 0$ (since $x < \bar{x}$ and $y < \bar{y}$).
- This means that for **positively correlated** variables, $S_{xy} = \sum(x - \bar{x})(y - \bar{y})$ will be **positive**.

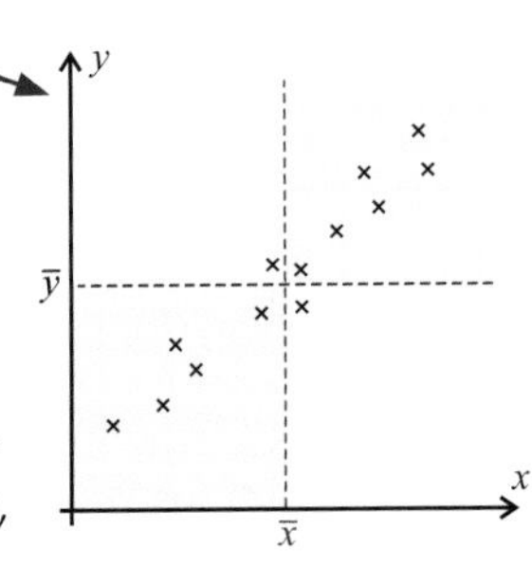

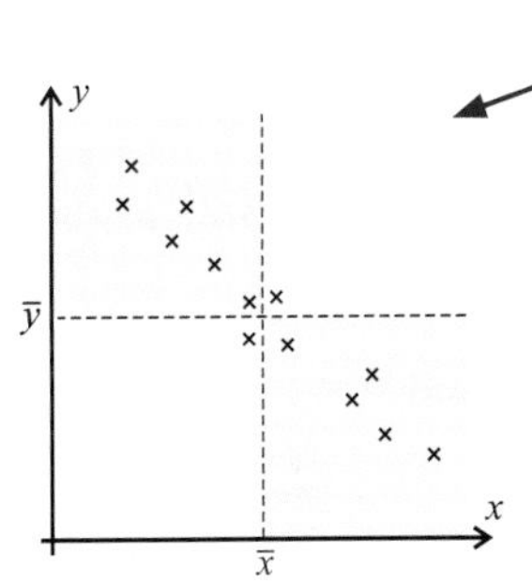

- In this scatter diagram, x and y are **negatively correlated**. Again, most values fall in the shaded squares.
- For each point in the **top-left** square, $(x - \bar{x})(y - \bar{y}) < 0$ (since $x < \bar{x}$ but $y > \bar{y}$).
- And for each point in the **bottom-right** square, $(x - \bar{x})(y - \bar{y}) < 0$ (since $x > \bar{x}$ but $y < \bar{y}$).
- So for **negatively correlated** variables, $S_{xy} = \sum(x - \bar{x})(y - \bar{y})$ will be **negative**.

- In this scatter diagram, x and y are **not correlated**.
- In this case, about half the points give a positive value for $(x - \bar{x})(y - \bar{y})$, while the other half give a negative value.
- So $S_{xy} = \sum(x - \bar{x})(y - \bar{y})$ ends up close to zero.

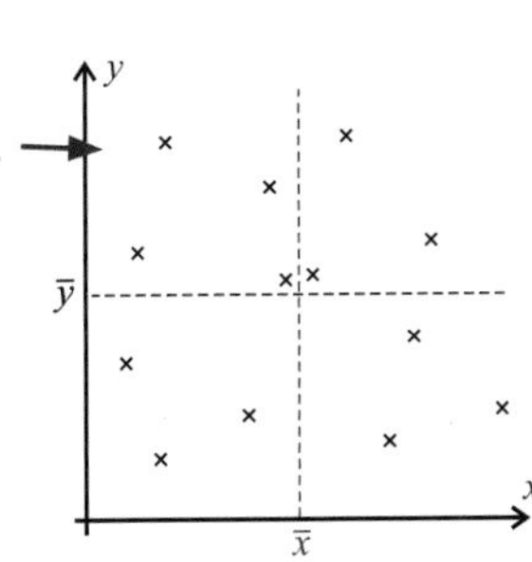

Tip: The formula for variance on page 18 is: $\text{variance} = \frac{\sum(x - \bar{x})^2}{n}$

Tip: The forms $S_{xx} = \sum x^2 - \frac{(\sum x)^2}{n}$ and $S_{yy} = \sum y^2 - \frac{(\sum y)^2}{n}$ are easier to use.

Tip: The form $S_{xy} = \sum xy - \frac{\sum x \sum y}{n}$ is easier to use.

Tip: The formulas for S_{xx}, S_{yy} and S_{xy} will be important for the rest of this chapter.

Tip: On the graph, there are two points for which $(x - \bar{x})(y - \bar{y})$ is negative, but there are far more for which $(x - \bar{x})(y - \bar{y})$ is positive.

So overall, S_{xy} is positive.

Tip: There are two points for which $(x - \bar{x})(y - \bar{y})$ is positive, but there are far more for which $(x - \bar{x})(y - \bar{y})$ is negative.

Overall, S_{xy} is negative.

Tip: The positive and negative values of $(x - \bar{x})(y - \bar{y})$ largely cancel each other out.

What's left after all this cancelling will be close to zero.

Tip: The formulas for S_{xy}, S_{xx} and S_{yy} are on the formula sheet you'll be given in the exam.

Tip: Always draw a table — it'll help you avoid mistakes.

Tip: Remember... n is the number of pairs of data values.

Example 1

Find S_{xy}, S_{xx} and S_{yy} for the data on the right.

x	1.1	1.5	2.3	2.9	3.1	3.8
y	5	8	11	16	17	24

- You're going to need to find $\sum x$, $\sum y$, $\sum x^2$, $\sum y^2$ and $\sum xy$.

  So add rows to the table showing x^2, y^2 and xy.
  And add an extra column to show the total of each row.

x	1.1	1.5	2.3	2.9	3.1	3.8	$\sum x = 14.7$
y	5	8	11	16	17	24	$\sum y = 81$
x^2	1.21	2.25	5.29	8.41	9.61	14.44	$\sum x^2 = 41.21$
y^2	25	64	121	256	289	576	$\sum y^2 = 1331$
xy	5.5	12	25.3	46.4	52.7	91.2	$\sum xy = 233.1$

- Now you can use the formulas for S_{xy}, S_{xx} and S_{yy}.

$$S_{xy} = \sum xy - \frac{\sum x \sum y}{n} = 233.1 - \frac{14.7 \times 81}{6} = 34.65$$

$$S_{xx} = \sum x^2 - \frac{(\sum x)^2}{n} = 41.21 - \frac{14.7^2}{6} = 5.195$$

$$S_{yy} = \sum y^2 - \frac{(\sum y)^2}{n} = 1331 - \frac{81^2}{6} = 237.5$$

You won't always be given the 'raw' data like above.

You could just be given 'summarised data' — in the form of the summations $\sum x$, $\sum y$, $\sum x^2$, $\sum y^2$ and $\sum xy$.

This actually makes your job slightly easier.

Example 2

Use the following summations to find S_{xy}, S_{xx} and S_{yy}.

$\sum x = 15.7$, $\sum y = 36$, $\sum x^2 = 45.55$, $\sum y^2 = 278$, $\sum xy = 93.2$, $n = 5$

- $S_{xy} = \sum xy - \frac{\sum x \sum y}{n} = 93.2 - \frac{15.7 \times 36}{5} = -19.84$

- $S_{xx} = \sum x^2 - \frac{(\sum x)^2}{n} = 45.55 - \frac{15.7^2}{5} = -3.748$

- $S_{yy} = \sum y^2 - \frac{(\sum y)^2}{n} = 278 - \frac{36^2}{5} = 18.8$

Exercise 1.2

Q1 For the data shown in the table on the right:

x	11	6	9	4	8	2	5
y	24	13	18	5	19	1	12

a) Calculate $\sum x$, $\sum y$, $\sum xy$, $\sum x^2$ and $\sum y^2$.

b) Use your summations to calculate S_{xy}, S_{xx} and S_{yy}.

Q2 Find S_{xy}, S_{xx} and S_{yy} in each case below.

a) $\sum x = 29$ $\quad \sum y = 109$ $\quad \sum x^2 = 167$
$\sum y^2 = 2031$ $\quad \sum xy = 589$ $\quad n = 5$

b) $\sum x = 206$ $\quad \sum y = 50$ $\quad \sum x^2 = 4504$
$\sum y^2 = 326$ $\quad \sum xy = 1013$ $\quad n = 10$

c) $\sum x = 115$ $\quad \sum y = 114$ $\quad \sum x^2 = 2383$
$\sum y^2 = 2762$ $\quad \sum xy = 1880$ $\quad n = 6$

Product moment correlation coefficient

The **product moment correlation coefficient** (PMCC, or r for short) measures the strength of the correlation between two variables. It basically tells you how close to a straight line the points on a scatter diagram lie.

The formula for the PMCC involves S_{xy}, S_{xx} and S_{yy}:

$$r = \frac{S_{xy}}{\sqrt{S_{xx}S_{yy}}}$$

The PMCC is always between +1 and –1.

- If all your points lie **exactly on a straight line** with a **positive** gradient (perfect positive correlation), $\boldsymbol{r = +1}$.
- If all your points lie **exactly on a straight line** with a **negative** gradient (perfect negative correlation), $\boldsymbol{r = -1}$.
- If $\boldsymbol{r = 0}$ (or more likely, pretty close to 0), that would mean the variables **aren't correlated.**

These graphs give you an idea of 'what different values of r look like'.

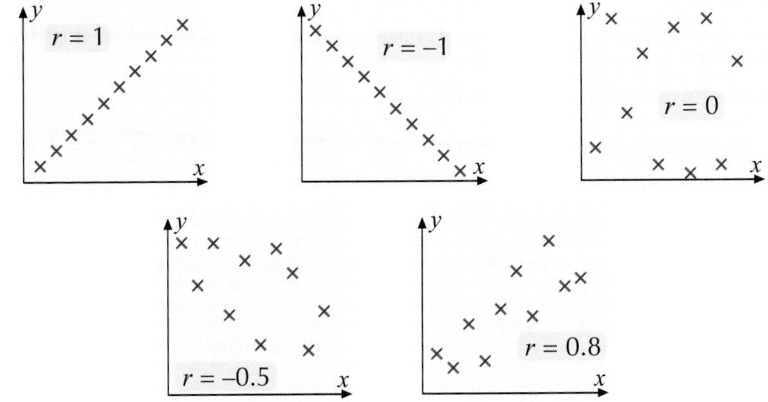

Tip: In reality, you'd never expect to get a PMCC of +1 or –1 — your scatter diagram points might lie pretty close to a straight line, but it's unlikely they'd all be on it.

Tip: The closer the value of r to +1 or –1, the stronger the correlation between the two variables. (Values close to +1 mean a strong positive correlation, and values close to –1 mean a strong negative correlation.)

Values of r close to zero mean there is only a weak correlation (but see p146).

Example 1

The following data show the score (x) of 10 students in a reading test, and the time in seconds (y) it took them to run 40 metres.

	A	B	C	D	E	F	G	H	I	J
x	3.5	5.5	6.1	4.2	2.7	1.9	5.5	3.8	5.1	3.7
y	9.8	4.7	8.4	8.4	5.8	8.4	7.6	8.2	8.9	5.4

Illustrate the data with a scatter diagram, and find the product moment correlation coefficient (r) between the variables x and y.

- The **scatter diagram's** the easy bit — just plot and label the points.

- Now for the **correlation coefficient.** From the scatter diagram, the points look pretty randomly scattered — so you'd expect a correlation coefficient fairly close to zero.

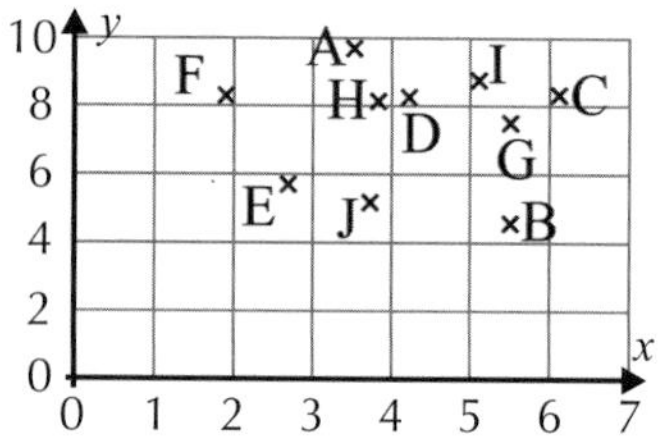

- You need to find S_{xy}, S_{xx} and S_{yy}, so add a few extra rows to your table.

x	3.5	5.5	6.1	4.2	2.7	1.9	5.5	3.8	5.1	3.7	$\sum x = 42$
y	9.8	4.7	8.4	8.4	5.8	8.4	7.6	8.2	8.9	5.4	$\sum y = 75.6$
x^2	12.25	30.25	37.21	17.64	7.29	3.61	30.25	14.44	26.01	13.69	$\sum x^2 = 192.64$
y^2	96.04	22.09	70.56	70.56	33.64	70.56	57.76	67.24	79.21	29.16	$\sum y^2 = 596.82$
xy	34.3	25.85	51.24	35.28	15.66	15.96	41.8	31.16	45.39	19.98	$\sum xy = 316.62$

- This gives: $S_{xy} = \sum xy - \frac{\sum x \sum y}{n} = 316.62 - \frac{42 \times 75.6}{10} = -0.9$

$$S_{xx} = \sum x^2 - \frac{(\sum x)^2}{n} = 192.64 - \frac{42^2}{10} = 16.24$$

$$S_{yy} = \sum y^2 - \frac{(\sum y)^2}{n} = 596.82 - \frac{75.6^2}{10} = 25.284$$

- Now use the formula for r: $r = \frac{S_{xy}}{\sqrt{S_{xx}S_{yy}}}$

$$= \frac{-0.9}{\sqrt{16.24 \times 25.284}} = -0.044 \text{ (to 3 d.p.)}$$

Tip: This is very close to zero — there seems to be little (if any) correlation between these two variables.

Example 2

A scientist collects data on the percentage water content (x) of 8 different brands of ham, and its price in pounds (y) per 100 g.
The results are summarised below.

$\sum x = 152$ $\quad \sum y = 7.73$ $\quad \sum x^2 = 3492$ $\quad \sum y^2 = 8.0169$ $\quad \sum xy = 130.41$

a) Calculate the product moment correlation coefficient (r).

- Here, $S_{xy} = \sum xy - \frac{\sum x \sum y}{n} = 130.41 - \frac{152 \times 7.73}{8} = -16.46$

$$S_{xx} = \sum x^2 - \frac{(\sum x)^2}{n} = 3492 - \frac{152^2}{8} = 604$$

$$S_{yy} = \sum y^2 - \frac{(\sum y)^2}{n} = 8.0169 - \frac{7.73^2}{8} = 0.5477875$$

Tip: Don't round your answers yet — you're going to use these values to calculate r.

- So $r = \frac{S_{xy}}{\sqrt{S_{xx}S_{yy}}} = \frac{-16.46}{\sqrt{604 \times 0.5477875}} = -0.905$ (to 3 d.p.)

b) Give an interpretation of this value of *r*.

- This is a very high negative value for r (it's very close to –1).
- This means that for the brands of ham tested, a higher percentage water content generally means a lower price.

Tip: When you're asked to interpret a value of r, always give your answer in the context of the question (so here, talk about ham, price and water content).

Exercise 1.3

Q1 Use the information below to find the product moment correlation coefficient (r) between x and y.

$\sum x = 313$ $\sum y = 75$ $\sum x^2 = 6875$

$\sum y^2 = 473$ $\sum xy = 1515$ $n = 15$

Q2 The table below shows the heights and weights of 8 teenage boys.

	A	B	C	D	E	F	G	H
Height in cm, x	180	171	182	184	166	180	173	167
Weight in kg, y	70	67	66	59	61	75	65	56

a) Plot this data on a scatter diagram.

b) Calculate the values of S_{xy}, S_{xx} and S_{yy}.

c) Find the value of the product moment correlation coefficient (r) for x and y.

Q3 For the data shown in this table:

x	13	9	15	10	8	11	12	14
y	5	7	2	4	3	8	1	2

a) Calculate $\sum x$, $\sum y$, $\sum x^2$, $\sum y^2$ and $\sum xy$.

b) Use your summations to calculate S_{xy}, S_{xx} and S_{yy}.

c) Find the value of the product moment correlation coefficient (r) for x and y.

Q4 The lengths and widths (in cm) of 8 leaves from a tree were measured. The results are shown below.

Length, x	4.6	7.2	5.1	8.3	2.4	6.4	5.7	3.3
Width, y	3.1	5.2	3.6	5.6	1.7	4.7	4.0	2.5

a) Calculate S_{xy}, S_{xx} and S_{yy}.
(You may use $\sum x^2 = 258$, $\sum y^2 = 128.2$, $\sum xy = 181.75$)

b) Calculate the correlation coefficient r.

c) Give an interpretation of your value for r.

Q5 Without carrying out any calculations, estimate the product moment correlation coefficient for the data plotted on these scatter diagrams.

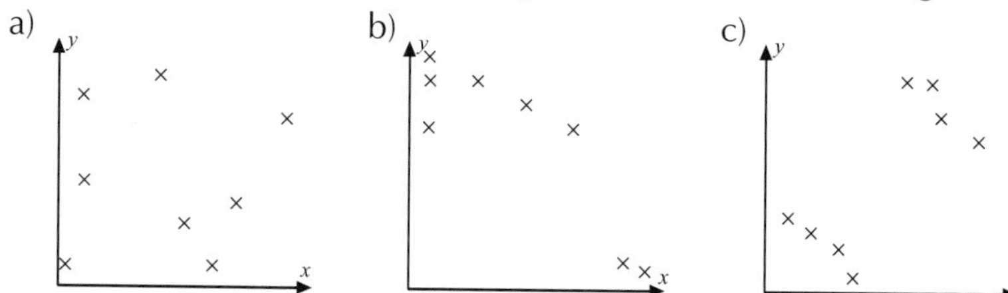

Tip: If your data consists of really huge numbers, you could use linear scaling to produce smaller, more manageable numbers.

But if your data values are tiny, you'd use linear scaling to produce larger numbers. And so on.

Linear scaling

You've seen the idea of linear scaling before (see p24).
The idea is to transform numbers so they're **less fiddly** to work with, or to convert your data to **different units**.

You can use linear scaling with **one** or **both** of the variables.

- The transformations you'll need to be able to use are of the form: $x = \frac{u - a}{b}$

  where u is an **original** data value, x is the corresponding data value after the transformation, and a and b are numbers to be chosen.

- Because this is a **linear transformation**, a graph of x against u would be a straight line.

Using a linear scaling generally **doesn't affect** the value of the product moment correlation coefficient at all — r for the transformed data is **exactly the same** as the value of r for the original data.

Tip: The reason why the correlation coefficient isn't affected is because using a **linear transformation** on a set of values doesn't change the pattern of points on a scatter diagram. The effect is the same as relabelling one of the scatter diagram's axes.

The only time linear scaling **would** affect a correlation coefficient is when the value of b is negative for **one** of the variables — then a positive correlation coefficient would become negative (and vice versa).

Example

The table below shows the annual salaries (s, in £) of six shipping clerks, along with the number of years experience (x) they have.

Experience, x	**2**	**4**	**5**	**7**	**8**	**10**
Salary, s	**23 000**	**24 000**	**24 500**	**26 000**	**26 700**	**29 000**

The values of s are to be scaled using $y = \frac{s - 20\,000}{1000}$.

a) Calculate the value of the product moment correlation coefficient between x and y.

- Make a new table of values which includes the scaled data values y. Also include the values of x^2, y^2 and xy — you'll need them to work out S_{xx}, S_{yy} and S_{xy}.

Experience, x	2	4	5	7	8	10	$\sum x = 36$
Salary, s	23 000	24 000	24 500	26 000	26 700	29 000	
Scaled salary, y	3	4	4.5	6	6.7	9	$\sum y = 33.2$
x^2	4	16	25	49	64	100	$\sum x^2 = 258$
y^2	9	16	20.25	36	44.89	81	$\sum y^2 = 207.14$
xy	6	16	22.5	42	53.6	90	$\sum xy = 230.1$

Tip: The values of 20 000 and 1000 were chosen so that the transformed data ended up less than 10. (Dividing by 100 would also have been sensible — the numbers would have been bigger but you wouldn't have any decimals.)

- This gives: $S_{xy} = \sum xy - \frac{\sum x \sum y}{n} = 230.1 - \frac{36 \times 33.2}{6} = 30.9$

$$S_{xx} = \sum x^2 - \frac{(\sum x)^2}{n} = 258 - \frac{36^2}{6} = 42$$

$$S_{yy} = \sum y^2 - \frac{(\sum y)^2}{n} = 207.14 - \frac{33.2^2}{6} = 23.4333...$$

- So $r = \frac{S_{xy}}{\sqrt{S_{xx}S_{yy}}} = \frac{30.9}{\sqrt{42 \times 23.4333...}} = 0.985$ (to 3 d.p.)

Tip: This is the correlation coefficient between x and y, but it must also be the correlation coefficient between x and s.

b) Hence write down the value of the product moment correlation coefficient between x and s. Explain your answer.

- Since s and y are related by a linear scaling (with a positive value of b), the product moment correlation coefficient between x and s must also be 0.985 (to 3 d.p.).

Exercise 1.4

Q1 Find the product moment correlation coefficient for u and v in the table below using linear scaling, where $x = u - 20$ and $y = v - 60$.

u	23	27	22	29	21	25
v	64	61	68	67	63	66

Q1 Hint: The transformation $x = u - 20$ is of the form $x = \frac{u - \text{a}}{\text{b}}$, but with b = 1.

Q2 Find the product moment correlation coefficient for u and v in the table below using linear scaling, where $x = \frac{u}{100}$ and $y = 10v$.

u	400	600	500	300	200	900	1100	800
v	0.7	2.1	0.9	1.3	1.9	1.5	2	1.6

Q2 Hint: The transformation $x = \frac{u}{100}$ is of the form $x = \frac{u - \text{a}}{\text{b}}$, but with a = 0.

Similarly, the transformation $y = 10v$ is of the form $y = \frac{v - \text{a}}{\text{b}}$, with a = 0 and b = $\frac{1}{10}$.

Q3 Find the product moment correlation coefficient for s and t in the table below using linear scaling, where $x = \frac{s - 120}{5}$ and $y = 10(t - 5)$.

s	120	125	130	135	140	145	150	155	160
t	8.2	7.5	7.1	6.7	5.7	6.2	5.8	5.4	5.2

Q4 The weights (w) in kg of a number of athletes were recorded, along with the number of seconds (s) they each took to run 100 m. The data is shown in the following table.

Weight in kg, w	76	64	80	79	67	72	69	74
Time in secs, s	11.4	12.3	13.2	11.8	12.7	11.5	13.8	13.3

Find the product moment correlation coefficient for w and s using linear scaling, where $x = w - 60$ and $y = 10(s - 11)$.

Q5 Use linear scaling to find the product moment correlation coefficient for u and v in the table below.

u	4008	4010	4011	4015	4018	4021
v	100	400	800	300	700	200

Limitations of the PMCC

Correlation is <u>not</u> the same as causation

Correlation and **causation** are often confused, but they're not the same thing at all.

- A high correlation coefficient doesn't necessarily mean that a change in one factor **causes** a change in the other.

  For example, the number of televisions sold in Japan and the number of cars sold in the USA may be correlated, but that doesn't mean that high TV sales in Japan cause high car sales in the USA (or the other way round).

- And the graph on the right shows the number of tooth-fillings a sample of 100 adults have, plotted against their salary. The graph shows that there's a positive correlation between 'fillings' and 'salary'. As the number of fillings goes up, so generally does a person's salary.

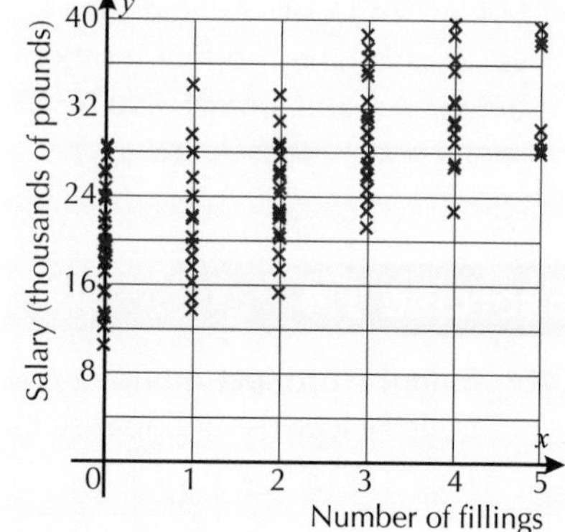

- But... that doesn't mean fillings cause someone to earn more, or that earning more causes fillings.
- The likely explanation is that both the number of fillings and a person's salary are linked to another quantity — age. As people get older, they tend to get paid more, and the number of fillings they have also tends to increase.
- Similarly, the TV sales in Japan and the car sales in the USA are probably both related to the overall strength of the global economy.

The PMCC only shows <u>linear</u> relationships

The product moment correlation coefficient (PMCC) is only a measure of a **linear** relationship between two variables (i.e. how close they'd be to a **straight line** if you plotted a scatter diagram).

- In the diagram on the right, the PMCC would be pretty low, but the two variables definitely look linked.
- It looks like the points lie close to a parabola (the shape of an x^2 curve) — not a straight line.
- This is why it's a good idea to draw a scatter diagram of your data **before** you start to calculate the PMCC — it can help you spot a **non-linear** relationship between the variables.

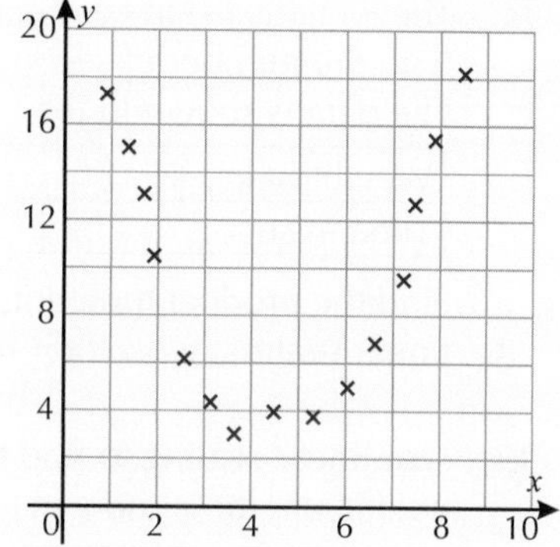

Tip: A scatter diagram will also help you spot any **outliers** (data points that lie far away from the rest of the data).

Outliers can have a big effect on the PMCC between two variables... and in some circumstances you'd be better off just ignoring them (e.g. if they're due to measurement errors).

2. Linear Regression

Linear regression is all about finding the best line of best fit on a scatter diagram. Lines of best fit are really useful — you can use them to predict how one of the quantities will be affected by a change in the other one.

Learning Objectives:

- Be able to determine which variable is the explanatory variable and which is the response variable.
- Be able to find the equation of a regression line.
- Be able to use a regression line to predict values of the response variable.
- Be aware of the problems involved with extrapolating beyond the existing data.
- Be able to transform a regression equation relating scaled variables to an equation relating the original variables.

Explanatory and response variables

When you draw a scatter diagram, you always have **two** variables.
For example, this scatter diagram shows the load on a lorry, x (in tonnes), and the fuel efficiency, y (in km per litre).

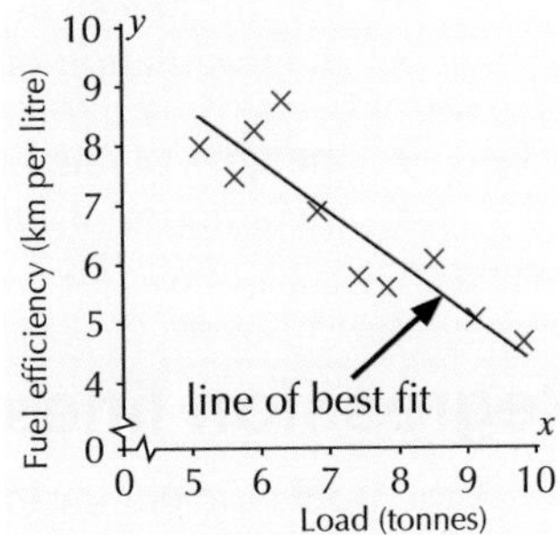

- The two variables are negatively correlated.
- In fact, all the points lie reasonably close to a straight line — the **line of best fit**.
- If you could find the equation of this line, then you could use it as a **model** to describe the relationship between x and y.

Linear regression is a method for finding the equation of a line of best fit on a scatter diagram. Or you can think of it as a method for **modelling** the relationship between two variables.

Before carrying out a linear regression, you first have to decide which variable is the **explanatory variable**, and which is the **response variable**.

- The **explanatory variable** (or **independent variable**) is the variable you can directly control, or the one that you think is **affecting** the other. In the above example, 'load' is the explanatory variable. The explanatory variable is always drawn along the **horizontal axis**.
- The **response variable** (or **dependent variable**) is the variable you think is **being affected**. In the above example, 'fuel efficiency' is the response variable. The response variable is always drawn up the **vertical axis**.

Examples

For each situation below, explain which quantity would be the explanatory variable, and which would be the response variable.

a) A scientist is investigating the relationship between the amount of fertiliser applied to a tomato plant and the eventual yield.

- The scientist can directly control the amount of fertiliser she gives each plant — so 'amount of fertiliser' is the explanatory variable.
- She then measures the effect this has on the plant's yield — so 'yield' is the response variable.

b) A researcher is examining how a town's latitude and the number of days last year when the temperature rose above 10 °C are linked.

- Although the researcher can't control the latitude of towns, it would be the difference in latitude that **leads to** a difference in temperature, and not the other way around.
- So the explanatory variable is 'the town's latitude', and the response variable is 'the number of days last year when the temperature rose above 10 °C'.

Tip: A place's latitude is an angle showing how far north or south of the equator it lies.

The latitude of the North Pole is 90° north, while the latitude of the South Pole is 90° south.

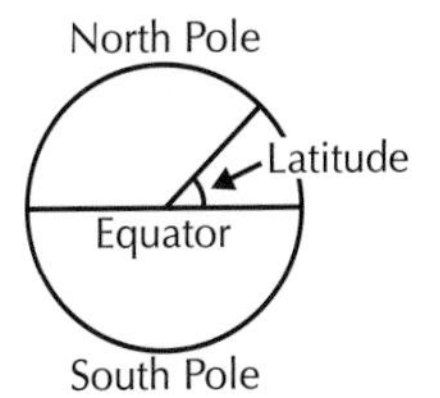

Exercise 2.1

For each situation below, explain which quantity would be the explanatory variable, and which would be the response variable.

Q1
- the time spent practising the piano each week
- the number of mistakes made in a test at the end of the week

Q2
- the age of a second-hand car
- the value of a second-hand car

Q3
- the number of phone calls made in a town in a week
- the population of a town

Q4
- the growth rate of a plant in an experiment
- the amount of sunlight falling on a plant in an experiment

Tip: b is the **gradient** of the regression line, and a is its **intercept** on the vertical axis.

Tip: Outliers can have a **dramatic** effect on the equation of a regression line, and drag it **far away** from the rest of the data values.

In the graphs below, the **circled** value is an outlier.

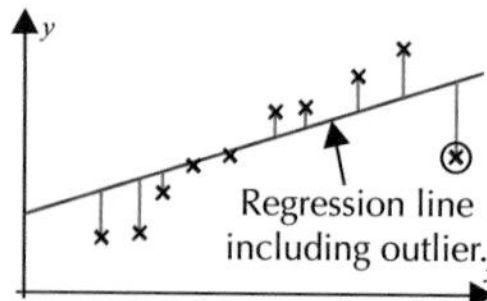

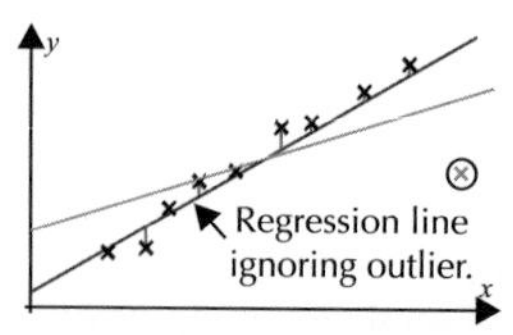

Tip: This is why this kind of regression is sometimes called **least-squares regression**.

Tip: Remember:

$$S_{xy} = \sum xy - \frac{\sum x \sum y}{n}$$

$$S_{xx} = \sum x^2 - \frac{(\sum x)^2}{n}$$

Regression lines

Here's the 'fuel efficiency v load' scatter diagram from the previous page.

- The **regression line** (which is what I'm going to call the 'line of best fit' from now on) is marked on again. The equation of this regression line is $\boldsymbol{y = \mathrm{a} + \mathrm{b}x}$, where a and b are numbers to be found.
- There are also some dotted lines showing the vertical distance between each data value and the regression line.

  Each of these small distances is called a **residual** (e_i).

  The residuals show the **errors** in the model (the regression line) — they show how the real-life observations differ from what the model predicts.

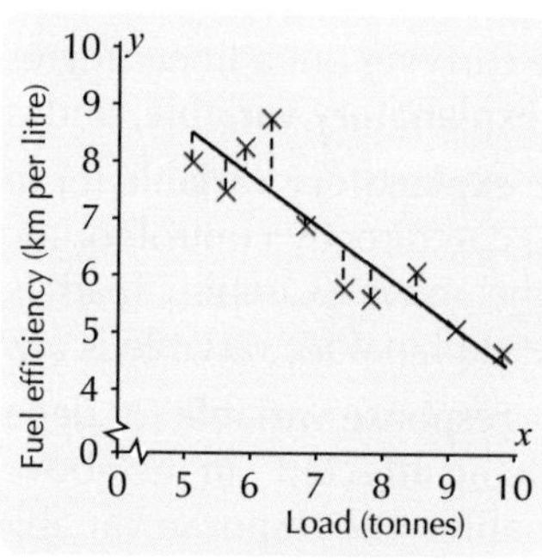

Residual	=	Observed y-value	–	Estimated y-value
e_i	=	y_i	–	$(\mathrm{a} + \mathrm{b}x_i)$

- **Linear regression** involves finding the equation of the line that minimises the sum of the squares of the residuals, $\sum e_i^2$.

  This will mean the regression line is as close as possible to your points.

The formulas below tell you how to find the **regression line of $\boldsymbol{y}$ on $\boldsymbol{x}$** (the '**...of $\boldsymbol{y}$ on $\boldsymbol{x}$**' part means that x is the explanatory variable, and y is the response variable).

The equation of the regression line of y on x is: $y = \mathrm{a} + \mathrm{b}x$

where: $\mathrm{b} = \dfrac{S_{xy}}{S_{xx}}$

and: $\mathrm{a} = \bar{y} - \mathrm{b}\bar{x}$

Example 1

The data below shows the load on a lorry, x (in tonnes), and the fuel efficiency, y (in km per litre).

a) Find the equation of the regression line of y on x.

x	5.1	5.6	5.9	6.3	6.8	7.4	7.8	8.5	9.1	9.8
y	8	7.5	8.3	8.8	6.9	5.8	5.6	6.1	5.1	4.7

Tip: This is the data used to draw the graphs on pages 147 and 148.

- First, you need to find S_{xy} and S_{xx}.

  Start by working out the four summations $\sum x$, $\sum y$, $\sum x^2$, and $\sum xy$. It's best to draw a table.

x	5.1	5.6	5.9	6.3	6.8	7.4	7.8	8.5	9.1	9.8	$\sum x = 72.3$
y	8	7.5	8.3	8.8	6.9	5.8	5.6	6.1	5.1	4.7	$\sum y = 66.8$
x^2	26.01	31.36	34.81	39.69	46.24	54.76	60.84	72.25	82.81	96.04	$\sum x^2 = 544.81$
xy	40.8	42	48.97	55.44	46.92	42.92	43.68	51.85	46.41	46.06	$\sum xy = 465.05$

Tip: Loads of calculators will work out regression lines for you if you type in the pairs of data values (x, y).

But you still need to know this method, since in the exam you might be given just the summations $\sum x$, $\sum y$, $\sum x^2$ and $\sum xy$, rather than the individual data values.

- Then: $S_{xy} = \sum xy - \frac{\sum x \sum y}{n} = 465.05 - \frac{72.3 \times 66.8}{10}$
  $= -17.914$

  And: $S_{xx} = \sum x^2 - \frac{(\sum x)^2}{n} = 544.81 - \frac{72.3^2}{10}$
  $= 22.081$

- So the **gradient** of the regression line is b, where:

  $b = \frac{S_{xy}}{S_{xx}} = \frac{-17.914}{22.081} = -0.81128... = -0.811$ (to 3 sig. fig.)

- And the **intercept** of the regression line is a, where:

  $a = \bar{y} - b\bar{x} = \frac{\sum y}{n} - b\frac{\sum x}{n} = \frac{66.8}{10} - (-0.81128...) \times \frac{72.3}{10}$
  $= 12.54559... = 12.5$ (to 3 sig. fig.).

Tip: Remember, $\bar{x} = \frac{\sum x}{n}$ and $\bar{y} = \frac{\sum y}{n}$.

- This means that the regression line of y on x is: $y = 12.5 - 0.811x$

b) Plot your regression line on a scatter diagram.

- A regression line always goes through the point $(\bar{x}, \bar{y})$.

  Here, $\bar{x} = \frac{\sum x}{n} = \frac{72.3}{10} = 7.23$ and $\bar{y} = \frac{\sum y}{n} = \frac{66.8}{10} = 6.68$.

  So the regression line must go through the point (7.23, 6.68).

- By putting $x = 0$ into the equation, you can see the line must also go through the point (0, 12.5).

- So draw the regression line through these two points.

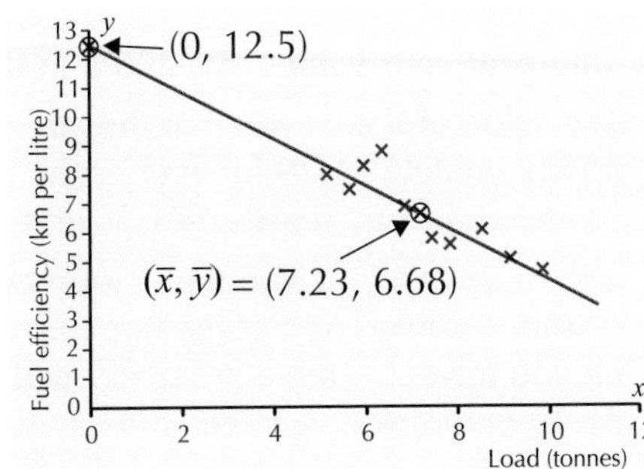

Tip: You don't have to use the point $(\bar{x}, \bar{y})$.

To plot a regression line you can choose any two points to plot. Or you can draw the line using the y-intercept and the gradient.

It's a good idea to make the points you're plotting for the regression line look different from your actual data points.

Tip: A **positive** residual means the data point is **above** the regression line for that value of x.
A **negative** residual means the data point is **below** the regression line.

c) Calculate the residuals for: (i) $x = 5.6$, (ii) $x = 6.3$.

- (i) When $x = 5.6$, the residual = observed y-value – estimated y-value
= 7.5 – (12.54559... – 0.81128... × 5.6)
= –0.502 (to 3 sig. fig.)
- (ii) When $x = 6.3$, the residual = observed y-value – estimated y-value
= 8.8 – (12.54559... – 0.81128... × 6.3)
= 1.37 (to 3 sig. fig.)

In the above example, the regression line was $y = 12.5 - 0.811x$, where x was the load (in tonnes) and y was the fuel efficiency (in km per litre).

These values for a (= 12.5) and b (= –0.811) tell you:

- for every extra tonne carried, you'd expect the lorry's fuel efficiency to fall by 0.811 km per litre (since when x increases by 1, y falls by 0.811).
- with no load ($x = 0$), you'd expect the lorry to do 12.5 km per litre of fuel (assuming it's reasonable to use the line down to $x = 0$ — see p151).

Example 2

A taxi company analyses the fares charged by a rival. It looks at 20 different journeys and records the distance (x, in miles) of the journey and the fare charged (y, in pounds). The summary statistics are shown below.

$$\sum x = 210.1,\ \sum y = 354.8,\ \sum x^2 = 2953.53,\ \sum xy = 4619.2$$

a) Calculate the equation of the regression line of y on x.

- First you need to find S_{xy} and S_{xx}.
- $S_{xy} = \sum xy - \frac{\sum x \sum y}{n} = 4619.2 - \frac{210.1 \times 354.8}{20} = 892.026$
- $S_{xx} = \sum x^2 - \frac{(\sum x)^2}{n} = 2953.53 - \frac{210.1^2}{20} = 746.4295$
- So the gradient of the regression line is b, where:
$\text{b} = \frac{S_{xy}}{S_{xx}} = \frac{892.026}{746.4295} = 1.1950... = 1.20$ (to 3 sig.fig.)
- And the intercept of the regression line is a, where:
$\text{a} = \bar{y} - \text{b}\bar{x} = \frac{\sum y}{n} - \text{b}\frac{\sum x}{n}$
$= \frac{354.8}{20} - (1.1950...) \times \frac{210.1}{20} = 5.19$ (to 3 sig. fig.).
- So the equation of the regression line is: $y = 5.19 + 1.20x$

b) Interpret your values of a and b in this context.

- The value of **b** tells you that the fare will increase by approximately £1.20 for every extra mile travelled (since when x increases by 1, y increases by 1.20).
- The value of **a** tells you that a journey of 0 miles costs £5.19 — this is a fixed part of the fare that doesn't depend on how far you travel (so the taxi's meter will show approximately £5.19 before you've even gone anywhere).

Tip: Make sure you give your explanations in the context of the question — so here you need to talk about taxis, distances and fares.

Exercise 2.2

Q1 Calculate the equation of the regression line of y on x for the data shown in the table below.

x	2	3	5	7	10	12	15
y	6	9	11	14	20	25	30

(You may use $S_{xx} = 139.4$ and $S_{xy} = 254.9$.)

Q2 The latitude (x, measured in degrees) and the mean annual temperature (y, in °C) were recorded for a number of locations. The data is shown below.

Latitude, x	8	30	19	41	64	12	60	25	52	39
Mean annual temp., y	27	16	24	10	4	27	5	22	9	12

a) Draw a scatter diagram of the data.

b) Calculate the equation of the regression line of y on x.

c) Interpret your values of a and b in this context.

d) Calculate the residuals when: (i) $x = 19$ (ii) $x = 41$

Q3 The HR department of a large company recorded the salary (y, in thousands of pounds) of a sample of 10 of its graduate employees, along with the number of years' experience (x) they had working for the company. The summary statistics are shown below.

$\sum x = 92$, $\sum y = 264$, $\sum x^2 = 1072$, $\sum y^2 = 7082$, $\sum xy = 2596$

a) Calculate the equation of the regression line $y = \text{a} + \text{b}x$.

b) Give an interpretation of the values of a and b in this context.

Interpolation and extrapolation

You can use a regression line to predict values of your **response variable**. There are two forms of this — **interpolation** and **extrapolation**.

Tip: You can only use a regression line to predict a value of the response variable — **not** the explanatory variable.

This scatter diagram shows the data from the lorry example on page 149 — with the fuel efficiency of a lorry plotted against different loads.

In the original data, the values of x were between 5.1 and 9.8 — the yellow part of the graph.

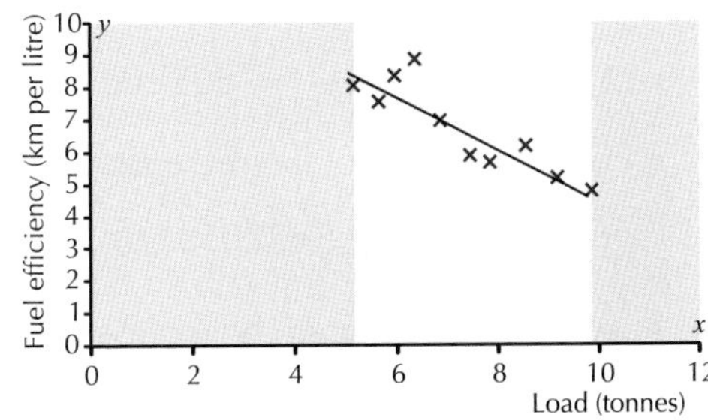

- When you use values of x within this range (i.e. values of x in the yellow part of the graph) to predict corresponding values of y, this is called **interpolation**. It's okay to do this — the predicted value should be reliable.
- When you use values of x **outside** the range of your original data (i.e. values of x in the grey part of the graph) to predict values of y, this is called **extrapolation**. It's best **not** to do this, or at least be very **cautious** about it — your prediction may be very unreliable. So here, you'd need to be very careful about using a value of x less than 5.1 or greater than 9.8.
- This is because you don't have any evidence that the relationship described by your regression line is true for values of x less than 5.1 or greater than 9.8 — and if the relationship turns out **not** to hold, then your prediction could be wildly wrong.

Tip: It's a good idea to find the residuals as a **percentage** of the response variable values because:

- Residuals of 1 unit (e.g. 1 cm, 1 kg etc.) when the values of the response variable are around 100 units or so (e.g. 100 cm, 100 kg etc.) are very small errors.
- Residuals of 1 unit when the values of the response variable are around 2 units or so are very large errors.

If you find a particularly large residual, then that might mean the data value is an **outlier**.

Checking residuals

When you're using your regression line to make a prediction, you should also check the **size** of your **residuals** (**ignoring** the plus or minus signs), as this will give you an idea of how well your regression line predicts the value of the response variable. There are **two ways** you can do this:

- You can just look at the **size** of the residuals.
- You can find the residual as a **percentage** of the response variable.

Then you have to make a judgement:

- If your residuals (or percentage residuals) are generally **small**, then any prediction based on your regression line should be fairly **reliable**.
- If your residuals (or percentage residuals) are generally **quite large**, then any prediction based on your regression line could easily be **unreliable**.

Example

The length of a spring (y, in cm) when loaded with different masses (x, in g) is shown in the table below.

Mass, x	**200**	**250**	**300**	**400**	**450**	**500**
Length, y	**9.8**	**10.7**	**10.8**	**11.8**	**12.4**	**13.2**

a) Calculate the equation of the regression line of y on x.

- Extend the table to include x^2 and xy, so that you can find S_{xy} and S_{xx}.

Mass, x	200	250	300	400	450	500	$\sum x = 2100$
Length, y	9.8	10.7	10.8	11.8	12.4	13.2	$\sum y = 68.7$
x^2	40000	62500	90000	160000	202500	250000	$\sum x^2 = 805000$
xy	1960	2675	3240	4720	5580	6600	$\sum xy = 24775$

- $S_{xy} = \sum xy - \frac{\sum x \sum y}{n} = 24775 - \frac{2100 \times 68.7}{6} = 730$

  $S_{xx} = \sum x^2 - \frac{(\sum x)^2}{n} = 805000 - \frac{2100^2}{6} = 70000$

- So the gradient of the regression line is b, where:

  $b = \frac{S_{xy}}{S_{xx}} = \frac{730}{70000} = 0.010428... = 0.01043$ (to 4 sig. fig.)

- And the intercept of the regression line is a, where:

  $a = \bar{y} - b\bar{x} = \frac{\sum y}{n} - b\frac{\sum x}{n}$

  $= \frac{68.7}{6} - (0.010428...) \times \frac{2100}{6} = 7.8$

- So the equation of the regression line is: $y = 7.8 + 0.01043x$

b) Use your regression line to estimate the length of the spring when loaded with a mass of: (i) 370 g (ii) 670 g

- (i) $x = 370$, so $y = 7.8 + 0.01043 \times 370 =$ 11.7 cm (to 1 d.p.).
- (ii) $x = 670$, so $y = 7.8 + 0.01043 \times 670 =$ 14.8 cm (to 1 d.p.).

c) Given that all the residuals lie between –0.17 and 0.29, comment on the reliability of your estimates in part b).

- The residuals and the percentage residuals are quite small, so the model appears to be fairly reliable for this range of values of x.
- $x = 370$ falls within the range of the original data for x, so this is an interpolation. This means this result should be fairly reliable.
- But $x = 670$ falls outside the range of the original data for x, so this is an extrapolation. This means the regression line may not be valid, and we need to treat this result with caution.

Exercise 2.3

Q1 The equation of the regression line of y on x is $y = 1.67 + 0.107x$.

a) Which variable is the response variable?

b) Find the predicted value of y corresponding to:
(i) $x = 5$ (ii) $x = 20$

Q1 Hint: For part a), use the fact that this is the regression line **of** ***y*** **on** ***x***. (And see page 148 if necessary.)

Q2 The regression line of y on x for a set of data in which x takes values between 2 and 15 is $y = 103 - 4.57x$.

The residuals vary between –2 and 2.

For each value of x below, estimate the corresponding value of y and comment on your estimate.

a) $x = 4$ b) $x = 20$ c) $x = 7$

Q3 Data on a large sample of new drivers aged between 17 and 35 was collected. It was found that the number of lessons taken (y) before passing their driving test could be described by the regression equation $y = 1.4x + 7$, where x is the driver's age in years.
The residuals were found to vary between –8 and 14.

a) Use the equation to estimate the number of lessons a typical 20-year-old could expect to take before they pass their driving test. Comment on your answer.

b) Use the equation to estimate the number of lessons a typical 50-year-old could expect to take before they pass their driving test. Comment on your answer.

Q4 A pharmaceutical company is testing a product to eliminate acne. A volunteer counted the number of spots (y) on an area of skin after x days of treatment with the product, where x took the values 2, 6, 10, 14, 18 and 22.

The equation of the regression line of y on x was found to be $y = 58.8 - 2.47x$, with residuals ranging from –1.2 to 0.9.

a) Estimate the number of spots the volunteer had on day 7. Comment on the reliability of your answer.

b) She forgot to count how many spots she had before starting to use the product. Estimate this number. Comment on your answer.

c) The volunteer claims that the regression equation must be wrong, because it predicts that after 30 days she should have a negative number of spots. Comment on this claim.

Regression and linear scaling

You could be asked to find a regression line for data that has been transformed using **linear scaling**. Once you've found it, you can easily transform it into a regression line for the original data.

Tip: Remember, the idea behind linear scaling is to make the numbers easier to work with.

Example 1

A company collects data on the age (g) and salary (s) of its senior managers. The data is scaled in the following way:

$$x = g - 50 \qquad y = \frac{s - 50\,000}{1000}$$

If the regression line of y on x is given by $y = 1.24x + 5.44$, find the regression line of s on g.

- Substitute the expressions defining x and y into the equation of the regression line for y on x. This gives you an equation involving just s and g.

$$\frac{s - 50\,000}{1000} = 1.24(g - 50) + 5.44$$

- Rearrange this so it is in the form $s = a + bg$, where a and b are constants. This is the regression line of s on g.

$$s - 50\,000 = 1240g - 62\,000 + 5440$$

$$s = 1240g - 6560$$

Example 2

The annual heating bill (h, in £) for 8 office buildings is shown below, along with the total floor area (f, in m²) of each building.

f	600	1000	1500	1800	2400	3400	4400	4900
h	1500	2600	3100	3400	3900	5500	5900	6100

These results were scaled in the following way:

$$x = \frac{f - 2500}{100} \qquad y = \frac{h - 4000}{100}$$

Tip: If you work out the means of these variables, you'll find that $\bar{f} = 2500$ and $\bar{h} = 4000$. These are the numbers that have been subtracted in the linear scaling. This will make some of the terms disappear when you do the calculations.

a) Find the equation of the regression line of y on x.

- First make a table of the transformed data, along with extra rows for x^2 and xy. Include the total for each row as well.

x	–19	–15	–10	–7	–1	9	19	24	$\sum x = 0$
y	–25	–14	–9	–6	–1	15	19	21	$\sum y = 0$
x^2	361	225	100	49	1	81	361	576	$\sum x^2 = 1754$
xy	475	210	90	42	1	135	361	504	$\sum xy = 1818$

Tip: $\sum x = \sum y = 0$

This is a result of subtracting the means of the original variables when choosing how to transform the data.

- $S_{xy} = \sum xy - \frac{\sum x \sum y}{n} = 1818 - \frac{0 \times 0}{8} = 1818$

  $S_{xx} = \sum x^2 - \frac{(\sum x)^2}{n} = 1754 - \frac{0^2}{8} = 1754$

- So the gradient of the regression line of y on x is b, where:

  $b = \frac{S_{xy}}{S_{xx}} = \frac{1818}{1754} = 1.036488... = 1.036$ (to 4 sig. fig.)

- And the intercept is a, where $a = \bar{y} - b\bar{x} = \frac{\sum y}{n} - b\frac{\sum x}{n} = 0$

- So the equation of the regression line of y on x is: $y = 1.036x$

Tip: a = 0 as a result of subtracting the means of the original variables when choosing how to transform the data.

b) Hence find the equation of the regression line of h on f.

- Substitute the expressions defining x and y into your regression equation.

$$y = 1.036x$$

$$\frac{h - 4000}{100} = 1.036 \times \frac{f - 2500}{100}$$

- Then rearrange into the form $h = c + df$.

$$h - 4000 = 1.036f - (1.036 \times 2500)$$

So $h = 1410 + 1.036f$

Tip: c and d are the coefficients for the regression line of h on f. They'll be different from a and b — the coefficients for the regression line of y on x.

Exercise 2.4

Q1 A set of bivariate data (x, y) has been scaled using $p = x - 7$ and $q = y - 50$. The regression line of q on p is given by $q = 40 + 2p$. Find the equation of the regression line of y on x.

Q2 The regression line of q on p is given by the equation $q = -0.9 + 0.1p$. Find the equation of the regression line of y on x if the following linear scaling has been used: $p = \frac{x - 20}{2}$ and $q = 10y - 3$.

Q3 An experiment was carried out to see whether people's weight affected how long they could hold their breath for. Each person's weight (w, in kg) was scaled using the equation $x = w - 60$. The number of seconds they could hold their breath for (t) was scaled using $y = t - 45$.

The regression line for the scaled data has equation $y = 17.4 - 0.78x$. Find the equation of the regression line of t on w.

Q4 Mrs Brown put out different amounts of birdseed (s, in grams) each day, and then counted the number of birds (v) in her garden at noon. She scaled her data in the following way:

$x = \frac{s}{100} - 2$ and $y = v - 7$

The summary statistics for the scaled data are as follows:
$\sum x = 28$, $\sum y = 124$, $\sum x^2 = 140$, $\sum xy = 618$ and $n = 10$.

a) Find the equation of the regression line of y on x.

b) Hence find the equation of the regression line of v on s.

Q5 The time (t, in hours) that seedlings could survive in water containing different concentrations of salt (s, in mg per litre) was recorded.

The results were scaled such that $x = \frac{s}{10}$ and $y = t - 29$.

The transformed data is in the table below.

x	1	2	3	5	7	10
y	19	11	9	–1	–14	–24

a) Find the equation of the regression line of y on x.

b) Hence find the equation of the regression line of t on s.

Review Exercise — Chapter 6

Q1 The table below shows the results of some measurements concerning alcoholic cocktails. Here, x = total volume in ml, and y = percentage alcohol concentration by volume.

x	90	100	100	150	160	200	240	250	290	300
y	40	35	25	30	25	25	20	25	15	7

a) Draw a scatter diagram representing this information.

b) Calculate the product moment correlation coefficient (PMCC) of these values.

c) What does the PMCC tell you about these results?

Q2 For each pair of variables below, state which would be the explanatory variable and which would be the response variable.

a) • the annual number of volleyball-related injuries
• the annual number of sunny days

b) • the annual number of rainy days
• the annual number of Monopoly-related injuries

c) • a person's disposable income
• a person's spending on luxuries

d) • the number of trips to the loo per day
• the number of cups of tea drunk per day

e) • the number of festival tickets sold
• the number of pairs of Wellington boots bought

Q3 The radius in mm, x, and the weight in grams, y, of 10 randomly selected blueberry pancakes are given in the table below.

x	48.0	51.0	52.0	54.5	55.1	53.6	50.0	52.6	49.4	51.2
y	100	105	108	120	125	118	100	115	98	110

a) Find: (i) $S_{xx} = \sum x^2 - \frac{(\sum x)^2}{n}$, (ii) $S_{xy} = \sum xy - \frac{\sum x \sum y}{n}$

The regression line of y on x has equation $y = a + bx$.

b) Find b, the gradient of the regression line.

c) Find a, the intercept of the regression line on the y-axis.

d) Write down the equation of the regression line of y on x.

e) Use your regression line to estimate the weight of a blueberry pancake of radius 60 mm.

f) Comment on the reliability of your estimate, giving a reason for your answer.

Q4 The variables P and Q are defined as $P = x - 5$ and $Q = \frac{y}{8}$, where x and y are as used in Question 3.

Find the regression line of Q on P.

Exam-Style Questions — Chapter 6

1 Values of two variables x and y are recorded in the table below.

x	1	2	3	4	5	6	7	8
y	0.50	0.70	0.10	0.82	0.50	0.36	0.16	0.80

a) Represent this data on a scatter diagram. *(2 marks)*

b) Calculate the product moment correlation coefficient (PMCC) of the two variables. *(4 marks)*

c) What does this value of the PMCC tell you about these variables? *(1 mark)*

2 The following times (in seconds) were taken by eight different runners to complete distances of 20 metres and 60 metres.

Runner	A	B	C	D	E	F	G	H
20-metre time (x)	3.39	3.20	3.09	3.32	3.33	3.27	3.44	3.08
60-metre time (y)	8.78	7.73	8.28	8.25	8.91	8.59	8.90	8.05

a) Plot a scatter diagram to represent the data, labelling each of the data points. *(2 marks)*

b) Find the equation of the regression line of y on x, and plot it on your scatter diagram. *(8 marks)*

c) Use the equation of the regression line to estimate the value of y when:
(i) $x = 3.15$, (ii) $x = 3.88$.
Comment on the reliability of your estimates, given that the residuals range from -0.56 to 0.32. *(4 marks)*

d) Find the residuals for:
(i) $x = 3.32$ (ii) $x = 3.27$.
Illustrate them on your scatter diagram. *(4 marks)*

3 A journalist at British Biking Monthly recorded the distance in miles, x, cycled by 20 different cyclists in the morning and the number of calories, y, eaten at lunch. The following summary statistics were provided:

$$S_{xx} = 310\,880 \qquad S_{yy} = 788.95 \qquad S_{xy} = 12\,666$$

a) Use these values to calculate the product moment correlation coefficient. *(2 marks)*

b) Give an interpretation of your answer to part (a). *(1 mark)*

A Swedish cycling magazine calculated the product moment correlation coefficient of the data after converting the distances to km.

c) State the value of the product moment correlation coefficient in this case. *(1 mark)*

4 The equation of the regression line for a set of data is $y = 211.599 + 9.602x$.

a) Use the equation of the regression line to estimate the value of y when:
(i) $x = 12.5$ (ii) $x = 14.7$.
(2 marks)

b) Calculate the residuals if the respective observed y-values were $y = 332.5$ and $y = 352.1$.
(2 marks)

5 Ten athletes all trained for the same 10 000 m race. On the day before the race, they each ran different distances. The distance (d, in km) each athlete ran the day before the race, and the time (t, in seconds) that each athlete recorded in the race itself were recorded.

The results were then scaled using $x = d$ and $y = t - 2367$.
The values of x and y are shown in the table below.

x	1	2	4	5	6	6	8	8	10	15
y	–219	189	315	105	–141	–333	9	177	–357	255

a) Calculate S_{xy}, S_{xx} and S_{yy}.
(You may use $\sum x^2 = 571$, $\sum y^2 = 548\,586$ and $\sum xy = 843$.)
(6 marks)

b) Find the product moment correlation coefficient between x and y.
(2 marks)

c) Write down the value of the product moment correlation coefficient between d and t. Explain your answer.
(2 marks)

d) Use your answer to part (c) to comment on how the length of a run on the day before a race affects the performance of the athletes.
(2 marks)

6 A scientist is investigating the link between the fat content of different brands of burgers and the price. She measures the amount of fat (x, in grams) in 100 g of each type of burger (when raw), and calculates the price for 100 g of each burger (y, in pence).
Her data is shown in this table.

Brand	A	B	C	D	E	F	G	H
x	5	8	10	12	16	19	20	25
y	106	94	82	81	79	42	38	22

($\sum x^2 = 1975$ and $\sum xy = 6446$)

a) Draw a scatter diagram showing this data.
(2 marks)

b) Calculate S_{xy} and S_{xx} for this data.
(5 marks)

c) The scientist models the relationship between x and y with the equation $y = \text{a} + \text{b}x$. Use linear regression to find the values of a and b.
(4 marks)

d) Draw the regression line on your scatter diagram.
(2 marks)

e) Use the scatter diagram to say which brand of burger appears to be overpriced. Explain your answer.
(2 marks)

S1 Statistical Tables

The normal distribution function

This table gives the probability, p, that the random variable $Z \sim N(0, 1)$ is less than or equal to z.

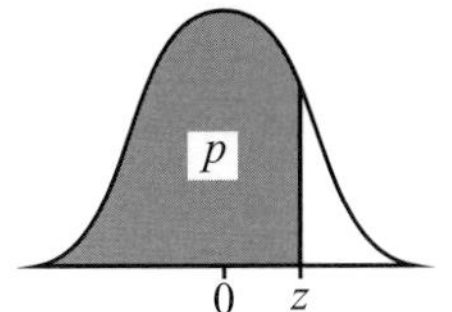

z	0.00	0.01	0.02	0.03	0.04	0.05	0.06	0.07	0.08	0.09	z
0.0	0.50000	0.50399	0.50798	0.51197	0.51595	0.51994	0.52392	0.52790	0.53188	0.53586	**0.0**
0.1	0.53983	0.54380	0.54776	0.55172	0.55567	0.55962	0.56356	0.56749	0.57142	0.57535	**0.1**
0.2	0.57926	0.58317	0.58706	0.59095	0.59483	0.59871	0.60257	0.60642	0.61026	0.61409	**0.2**
0.3	0.61791	0.62172	0.62552	0.62930	0.63307	0.63683	0.64058	0.64431	0.64803	0.65173	**0.3**
0.4	0.65542	0.65910	0.66276	0.66640	0.67003	0.67364	0.67724	0.68082	0.68439	0.68793	**0.4**
0.5	0.69146	0.69497	0.69847	0.70194	0.70540	0.70884	0.71226	0.71566	0.71904	0.72240	**0.5**
0.6	0.72575	0.72907	0.73237	0.73565	0.73891	0.74215	0.74537	0.74857	0.75175	0.75490	**0.6**
0.7	0.75804	0.76115	0.76424	0.76730	0.77035	0.77337	0.77637	0.77935	0.78230	0.78524	**0.7**
0.8	0.78814	0.79103	0.79389	0.79673	0.79955	0.80234	0.80511	0.80785	0.81057	0.81327	**0.8**
0.9	0.81594	0.81859	0.82121	0.82381	0.82639	0.82894	0.83147	0.83398	0.83646	0.83891	**0.9**
1.0	0.84134	0.84375	0.84614	0.84849	0.85083	0.85314	0.85543	0.85769	0.85993	0.86214	**1.0**
1.1	0.86433	0.86650	0.86864	0.87076	0.87286	0.87493	0.87698	0.87900	0.88100	0.88298	**1.1**
1.2	0.88493	0.88686	0.88877	0.89065	0.89251	0.89435	0.89617	0.89796	0.89973	0.90147	**1.2**
1.3	0.90320	0.90490	0.90658	0.90824	0.90988	0.91149	0.91309	0.91466	0.91621	0.91774	**1.3**
1.4	0.91924	0.92073	0.92220	0.92364	0.92507	0.92647	0.92785	0.92922	0.93056	0.93189	**1.4**
1.5	0.93319	0.93448	0.93574	0.93699	0.93822	0.93943	0.94062	0.94179	0.94295	0.94408	**1.5**
1.6	0.94520	0.94630	0.94738	0.94845	0.94950	0.95053	0.95154	0.95254	0.95352	0.95449	**1.6**
1.7	0.95543	0.95637	0.95728	0.95818	0.95907	0.95994	0.96080	0.96164	0.96246	0.96327	**1.7**
1.8	0.96407	0.96485	0.96562	0.96638	0.96712	0.96784	0.96856	0.96926	0.96995	0.97062	**1.8**
1.9	0.97128	0.97193	0.97257	0.97320	0.97381	0.97441	0.97500	0.97558	0.97615	0.97670	**1.9**
2.0	0.97725	0.97778	0.97831	0.97882	0.97932	0.97982	0.98030	0.98077	0.98124	0.98169	**2.0**
2.1	0.98214	0.98257	0.98300	0.98341	0.98382	0.98422	0.98461	0.98500	0.98537	0.98574	**2.1**
2.2	0.98610	0.98645	0.98679	0.98713	0.98745	0.98778	0.98809	0.98840	0.98870	0.98899	**2.2**
2.3	0.98928	0.98956	0.98983	0.99010	0.99036	0.99061	0.99086	0.99111	0.99134	0.99158	**2.3**
2.4	0.99180	0.99202	0.99224	0.99245	0.99266	0.99286	0.99305	0.99324	0.99343	0.99361	**2.4**
2.5	0.99379	0.99396	0.99413	0.99430	0.99446	0.99461	0.99477	0.99492	0.99506	0.99520	**2.5**
2.6	0.99534	0.99547	0.99560	0.99573	0.99585	0.99598	0.99609	0.99621	0.99632	0.99643	**2.6**
2.7	0.99653	0.99664	0.99674	0.99683	0.99693	0.99702	0.99711	0.99720	0.99728	0.99736	**2.7**
2.8	0.99744	0.99752	0.99760	0.99767	0.99774	0.99781	0.99788	0.99795	0.99801	0.99807	**2.8**
2.9	0.99813	0.99819	0.99825	0.99831	0.99836	0.99841	0.99846	0.99851	0.99856	0.99861	**2.9**
3.0	0.99865	0.99869	0.99874	0.99878	0.99882	0.99886	0.99889	0.99893	0.99896	0.99900	**3.0**
3.1	0.99903	0.99906	0.99910	0.99913	0.99916	0.99918	0.99921	0.99924	0.99926	0.99929	**3.1**
3.2	0.99931	0.99934	0.99936	0.99938	0.99940	0.99942	0.99944	0.99946	0.99948	0.99950	**3.2**
3.3	0.99952	0.99953	0.99955	0.99957	0.99958	0.99960	0.99961	0.99962	0.99964	0.99965	**3.3**
3.4	0.99966	0.99968	0.99969	0.99970	0.99971	0.99972	0.99973	0.99974	0.99975	0.99976	**3.4**
3.5	0.99977	0.99978	0.99978	0.99979	0.99980	0.99981	0.99981	0.99982	0.99983	0.99983	**3.5**
3.6	0.99984	0.99985	0.99985	0.99986	0.99986	0.99987	0.99987	0.99988	0.99988	0.99989	**3.6**
3.7	0.99989	0.99990	0.99990	0.99990	0.99991	0.99991	0.99992	0.99992	0.99992	0.99992	**3.7**
3.8	0.99993	0.99993	0.99993	0.99994	0.99994	0.99994	0.99994	0.99995	0.99995	0.99995	**3.8**
3.9	0.99995	0.99995	0.99996	0.99996	0.99996	0.99996	0.99996	0.99996	0.99997	0.99997	**3.9**

Percentage points of the normal distribution

The table gives the values of z satisfying $P(Z \leq z) = p$, where $Z \sim N(0, 1)$.

p	**0.00**	**0.01**	**0.02**	**0.03**	**0.04**	**0.05**	**0.06**	**0.07**	**0.08**	**0.09**	p
0.5	0.0000	0.0251	0.0502	0.0753	0.1004	0.1257	0.1510	0.1764	0.2019	0.2275	**0.5**
0.6	0.2533	0.2793	0.3055	0.3319	0.3585	0.3853	0.4125	0.4399	0.4677	0.4959	**0.6**
0.7	0.5244	0.5534	0.5828	0.6128	0.6433	0.6745	0.7063	0.7388	0.7722	0.8064	**0.7**
0.8	0.8416	0.8779	0.9154	0.9542	0.9945	1.0364	1.0803	1.1264	1.1750	1.2265	**0.8**
0.9	1.2816	1.3408	1.4051	1.4758	1.5548	1.6449	1.7507	1.8808	2.0537	2.3263	**0.9**
p	**0.000**	**0.001**	**0.002**	**0.003**	**0.004**	**0.005**	**0.006**	**0.007**	**0.008**	**0.009**	p
0.95	1.6449	1.6546	1.6646	1.6747	1.6849	1.6954	1.7060	1.7169	1.7279	1.7392	**0.95**
0.96	1.7507	1.7624	1.7744	1.7866	1.7991	1.8119	1.8250	1.8384	1.8522	1.8663	**0.96**
0.97	1.8808	1.8957	1.9110	1.9268	1.9431	1.9600	1.9774	1.9954	2.0141	2.0335	**0.97**
0.98	2.0537	2.0749	2.0969	2.1201	2.1444	2.1701	2.1973	2.2262	2.2571	2.2904	**0.98**
0.99	2.3263	2.3656	2.4089	2.4573	2.5121	2.5758	2.6521	2.7478	2.8782	3.0902	**0.99**

The cumulative binomial distribution function

This table gives the probability $P(X \leq x)$, where the random variable $X \sim B(n, p)$.

p	0.01	0.02	0.03	0.04	0.05	0.06	0.07	0.08	0.09	0.10	0.15	0.20	0.25	0.30	0.35	0.40	0.45	0.50	p
x	$n = 2$																		x
0	0.9801	0.9604	0.9409	0.9216	0.9025	0.8836	0.8649	0.8464	0.8281	0.8100	0.7225	0.6400	0.5625	0.4900	0.4225	0.3600	0.3025	0.2500	0
1	0.9999	0.9996	0.9991	0.9984	0.9975	0.9964	0.9951	0.9936	0.9919	0.9900	0.9775	0.9600	0.9375	0.9100	0.8775	0.8400	0.7975	0.7500	1
2	1.0000	1.0000	1.0000	1.0000	1.0000	1.0000	1.0000	1.0000	1.0000	1.0000	1.0000	1.0000	1.0000	1.0000	1.0000	1.0000	1.0000	1.0000	2
x	$n = 3$																		x
0	0.9703	0.9412	0.9127	0.8847	0.8574	0.8306	0.8044	0.7787	0.7536	0.7290	0.6141	0.5120	0.4219	0.3430	0.2746	0.2160	0.1664	0.1250	0
1	0.9997	0.9988	0.9974	0.9953	0.9928	0.9896	0.9860	0.9818	0.9772	0.9720	0.9393	0.8960	0.8438	0.7840	0.7183	0.6480	0.5748	0.5000	1
2	1.0000	1.0000	1.0000	0.9999	0.9999	0.9998	0.9997	0.9995	0.9993	0.9990	0.9966	0.9920	0.9844	0.9730	0.9571	0.9360	0.9089	0.8750	2
3				1.0000	1.0000	1.0000	1.0000	1.0000	1.0000	1.0000	1.0000	1.0000	1.0000	1.0000	1.0000	1.0000	1.0000	1.0000	3
x	$n = 4$																		x
0	0.9606	0.9224	0.8853	0.8493	0.8145	0.7807	0.7481	0.7164	0.6857	0.6561	0.5220	0.4096	0.3164	0.2401	0.1785	0.1296	0.0915	0.0625	0
1	0.9994	0.9977	0.9948	0.9909	0.9860	0.9801	0.9733	0.9656	0.9570	0.9477	0.8905	0.8192	0.7383	0.6517	0.5630	0.4752	0.3910	0.3125	1
2	1.0000	1.0000	0.9999	0.9998	0.9995	0.9992	0.9987	0.9981	0.9973	0.9963	0.9880	0.9728	0.9492	0.9163	0.8735	0.8208	0.7585	0.6875	2
3			1.0000	1.0000	1.0000	1.0000	1.0000	1.0000	0.9999	0.9999	0.9995	0.9984	0.9961	0.9919	0.9850	0.9744	0.9590	0.9375	3
4									1.0000	1.0000	1.0000	1.0000	1.0000	1.0000	1.0000	1.0000	1.0000	1.0000	4
x	$n = 5$																		x
0	0.9510	0.9039	0.8587	0.8154	0.7738	0.7339	0.6957	0.6591	0.6240	0.5905	0.4437	0.3277	0.2373	0.1681	0.1160	0.0778	0.0503	0.0313	0
1	0.9990	0.9962	0.9915	0.9852	0.9774	0.9681	0.9575	0.9456	0.9326	0.9185	0.8352	0.7373	0.6328	0.5282	0.4284	0.3370	0.2562	0.1875	1
2	1.0000	0.9999	0.9997	0.9994	0.9988	0.9980	0.9969	0.9955	0.9937	0.9914	0.9734	0.9421	0.8965	0.8369	0.7648	0.6826	0.5931	0.5000	2
3		1.0000	1.0000	1.0000	1.0000	0.9999	0.9999	0.9998	0.9997	0.9995	0.9978	0.9933	0.9844	0.9692	0.9460	0.9130	0.8688	0.8125	3
4						1.0000	1.0000	1.0000	1.0000	1.0000	0.9999	0.9997	0.9990	0.9976	0.9947	0.9898	0.9815	0.9688	4
5											1.0000	1.0000	1.0000	1.0000	1.0000	1.0000	1.0000	1.0000	5
x	$n = 6$																		x
0	0.9415	0.8858	0.8330	0.7828	0.7351	0.6899	0.6470	0.6064	0.5679	0.5314	0.3771	0.2621	0.1780	0.1176	0.0754	0.0467	0.0277	0.0156	0
1	0.9985	0.9943	0.9875	0.9784	0.9672	0.9541	0.9392	0.9227	0.9048	0.8857	0.7765	0.6554	0.5339	0.4202	0.3191	0.2333	0.1636	0.1094	1
2	1.0000	0.9998	0.9995	0.9988	0.9978	0.9962	0.9942	0.9915	0.9882	0.9842	0.9527	0.9011	0.8306	0.7443	0.6471	0.5443	0.4415	0.3438	2
3		1.0000	1.0000	1.0000	0.9999	0.9998	0.9997	0.9995	0.9992	0.9987	0.9941	0.9830	0.9624	0.9295	0.8826	0.8208	0.7447	0.6563	3
4					1.0000	1.0000	1.0000	1.0000	1.0000	0.9999	0.9996	0.9984	0.9954	0.9891	0.9777	0.9590	0.9308	0.8906	4
5										1.0000	1.0000	0.9999	0.9998	0.9993	0.9982	0.9959	0.9917	0.9844	5
6												1.0000	1.0000	1.0000	1.0000	1.0000	1.0000	1.0000	6
x	$n = 7$																		x
0	0.9321	0.8681	0.8080	0.7514	0.6983	0.6485	0.6017	0.5578	0.5168	0.4783	0.3206	0.2097	0.1335	0.0824	0.0490	0.0280	0.0152	0.0078	0
1	0.9980	0.9921	0.9829	0.9706	0.9556	0.9382	0.9187	0.8974	0.8745	0.8503	0.7166	0.5767	0.4449	0.3294	0.2338	0.1586	0.1024	0.0625	1
2	1.0000	0.9997	0.9991	0.9980	0.9962	0.9937	0.9903	0.9860	0.9807	0.9743	0.9262	0.8520	0.7564	0.6471	0.5323	0.4199	0.3164	0.2266	2
3		1.0000	1.0000	0.9999	0.9998	0.9996	0.9993	0.9988	0.9982	0.9973	0.9879	0.9667	0.9294	0.8740	0.8002	0.7102	0.6083	0.5000	3
4				1.0000	1.0000	1.0000	1.0000	0.9999	0.9999	0.9998	0.9988	0.9953	0.9871	0.9712	0.9444	0.9037	0.8471	0.7734	4
5								1.0000	1.0000	1.0000	0.9999	0.9996	0.9987	0.9962	0.9910	0.9812	0.9643	0.9375	5
6											1.0000	1.0000	0.9999	0.9998	0.9994	0.9984	0.9963	0.9922	6
7													1.0000	1.0000	1.0000	1.0000	1.0000	1.0000	7
x	$n = 8$																		x
0	0.9227	0.8508	0.7837	0.7214	0.6634	0.6096	0.5596	0.5132	0.4703	0.4305	0.2725	0.1678	0.1001	0.0576	0.0319	0.0168	0.0084	0.0039	0
1	0.9973	0.9897	0.9777	0.9619	0.9428	0.9208	0.8965	0.8702	0.8423	0.8131	0.6572	0.5033	0.3671	0.2553	0.1691	0.1064	0.0632	0.0352	1
2	0.9999	0.9996	0.9987	0.9969	0.9942	0.9904	0.9853	0.9789	0.9711	0.9619	0.8948	0.7969	0.6785	0.5518	0.4278	0.3154	0.2201	0.1445	2
3	1.0000	1.0000	0.9999	0.9998	0.9996	0.9993	0.9987	0.9978	0.9966	0.9950	0.9786	0.9437	0.8862	0.8059	0.7064	0.5941	0.4770	0.3633	3
4			1.0000	1.0000	1.0000	1.0000	0.9999	0.9999	0.9997	0.9996	0.9971	0.9896	0.9727	0.9420	0.8939	0.8263	0.7396	0.6367	4
5							1.0000	1.0000	1.0000	1.0000	0.9998	0.9988	0.9958	0.9887	0.9747	0.9502	0.9115	0.8555	5
6											1.0000	0.9999	0.9996	0.9987	0.9964	0.9915	0.9819	0.9648	6
7												1.0000	1.0000	0.9999	0.9998	0.9993	0.9983	0.9961	7
8														1.0000	1.0000	1.0000	1.0000	1.0000	8

The cumulative binomial distribution function (continued)

p	0.01	0.02	0.03	0.04	0.05	0.06	0.07	0.08	0.09	0.10	0.15	0.20	0.25	0.30	0.35	0.40	0.45	0.50	p
x	$n=9$																		x
0	0.9135	0.8337	0.7602	0.6925	0.6302	0.5730	0.5204	0.4722	0.4279	0.3874	0.2316	0.1342	0.0751	0.0404	0.0207	0.0101	0.0046	0.0020	0
1	0.9966	0.9869	0.9718	0.9522	0.9288	0.9022	0.8729	0.8417	0.8088	0.7748	0.5995	0.4362	0.3003	0.1960	0.1211	0.0705	0.0385	0.0195	1
2	0.9999	0.9994	0.9980	0.9955	0.9916	0.9862	0.9791	0.9702	0.9595	0.9470	0.8591	0.7382	0.6007	0.4628	0.3373	0.2318	0.1495	0.0898	2
3	1.0000	1.0000	0.9999	0.9997	0.9994	0.9987	0.9977	0.9963	0.9943	0.9917	0.9661	0.9144	0.8343	0.7297	0.6089	0.4826	0.3614	0.2539	3
4			1.0000	1.0000	1.0000	0.9999	0.9998	0.9997	0.9995	0.9991	0.9944	0.9804	0.9511	0.9012	0.8283	0.7334	0.6214	0.5000	4
5						1.0000	1.0000	1.0000	1.0000	0.9999	0.9994	0.9969	0.9900	0.9747	0.9464	0.9006	0.8342	0.7461	5
6										1.0000	1.0000	0.9997	0.9987	0.9957	0.9888	0.9750	0.9502	0.9102	6
7												1.0000	0.9999	0.9996	0.9986	0.9962	0.9909	0.9805	7
8													1.0000	1.0000	0.9999	0.9997	0.9992	0.9980	8
9															1.0000	1.0000	1.0000	1.0000	9
x	$n=10$																		x
0	0.9044	0.8171	0.7374	0.6648	0.5987	0.5386	0.4840	0.4344	0.3894	0.3487	0.1969	0.1074	0.0563	0.0282	0.0135	0.0060	0.0025	0.0010	0
1	0.9957	0.9838	0.9655	0.9418	0.9139	0.8824	0.8483	0.8121	0.7746	0.7361	0.5443	0.3758	0.2440	0.1493	0.0860	0.0464	0.0233	0.0107	1
2	0.9999	0.9991	0.9972	0.9938	0.9885	0.9812	0.9717	0.9599	0.9460	0.9298	0.8202	0.6778	0.5256	0.3828	0.2616	0.1673	0.0996	0.0547	2
3	1.0000	1.0000	0.9999	0.9996	0.9990	0.9980	0.9964	0.9942	0.9912	0.9872	0.9500	0.8791	0.7759	0.6496	0.5138	0.3823	0.2660	0.1719	3
4			1.0000	1.0000	0.9999	0.9998	0.9997	0.9994	0.9990	0.9984	0.9901	0.9672	0.9219	0.8497	0.7515	0.6331	0.5044	0.3770	4
5					1.0000	1.0000	1.0000	1.0000	0.9999	0.9999	0.9986	0.9936	0.9803	0.9527	0.9051	0.8338	0.7384	0.6230	5
6									1.0000	1.0000	0.9999	0.9991	0.9965	0.9894	0.9740	0.9452	0.8980	0.8281	6
7											1.0000	0.9999	0.9996	0.9984	0.9952	0.9877	0.9726	0.9453	7
8												1.0000	1.0000	0.9999	0.9995	0.9983	0.9955	0.9893	8
9														1.0000	1.0000	0.9999	0.9997	0.9990	9
10																1.0000	1.0000	1.0000	10
x	$n=11$																		x
0	0.8953	0.8007	0.7153	0.6382	0.5688	0.5063	0.4501	0.3996	0.3544	0.3138	0.1673	0.0859	0.0422	0.0198	0.0088	0.0036	0.0014	0.0005	0
1	0.9948	0.9805	0.9587	0.9308	0.8981	0.8618	0.8228	0.7819	0.7399	0.6974	0.4922	0.3221	0.1971	0.1130	0.0606	0.0302	0.0139	0.0059	1
2	0.9998	0.9988	0.9963	0.9917	0.9848	0.9752	0.9630	0.9481	0.9305	0.9104	0.7788	0.6174	0.4552	0.3127	0.2001	0.1189	0.0652	0.0327	2
3	1.0000	1.0000	0.9998	0.9993	0.9984	0.9970	0.9947	0.9915	0.9871	0.9815	0.9306	0.8389	0.7133	0.5696	0.4256	0.2963	0.1911	0.1133	3
4			1.0000	1.0000	0.9999	0.9997	0.9995	0.9990	0.9983	0.9972	0.9841	0.9496	0.8854	0.7897	0.6683	0.5328	0.3971	0.2744	4
5					1.0000	1.0000	1.0000	0.9999	0.9998	0.9997	0.9973	0.9883	0.9657	0.9218	0.8513	0.7535	0.6331	0.5000	5
6								1.0000	1.0000	1.0000	0.9997	0.9980	0.9924	0.9784	0.9499	0.9006	0.8262	0.7256	6
7											1.0000	0.9998	0.9988	0.9957	0.9878	0.9707	0.9390	0.8867	7
8												1.0000	0.9999	0.9994	0.9980	0.9941	0.9852	0.9673	8
9													1.0000	1.0000	0.9998	0.9993	0.9978	0.9941	9
10															1.0000	1.0000	0.9998	0.9995	10
11																	1.0000	1.0000	11
x	$n=12$																		x
0	0.8864	0.7847	0.6938	0.6127	0.5404	0.4759	0.4186	0.3677	0.3225	0.2824	0.1422	0.0687	0.0317	0.0138	0.0057	0.0022	0.0008	0.0002	0
1	0.9938	0.9769	0.9514	0.9191	0.8816	0.8405	0.7967	0.7513	0.7052	0.6590	0.4435	0.2749	0.1584	0.0850	0.0424	0.0196	0.0083	0.0032	1
2	0.9998	0.9985	0.9952	0.9893	0.9804	0.9684	0.9532	0.9348	0.9134	0.8891	0.7358	0.5583	0.3907	0.2528	0.1513	0.0834	0.0421	0.0193	2
3	1.0000	0.9999	0.9997	0.9990	0.9978	0.9957	0.9925	0.9880	0.9820	0.9744	0.9078	0.7946	0.6488	0.4925	0.3467	0.2253	0.1345	0.0730	3
4		1.0000	1.0000	0.9999	0.9998	0.9996	0.9991	0.9984	0.9973	0.9957	0.9761	0.9274	0.8424	0.7237	0.5833	0.4382	0.3044	0.1938	4
5				1.0000	1.0000	1.0000	0.9999	0.9998	0.9997	0.9995	0.9954	0.9806	0.9456	0.8822	0.7873	0.6652	0.5269	0.3872	5
6							1.0000	1.0000	1.0000	0.9999	0.9993	0.9961	0.9857	0.9614	0.9154	0.8418	0.7393	0.6128	6
7										1.0000	0.9999	0.9994	0.9972	0.9905	0.9745	0.9427	0.8883	0.8062	7
8											1.0000	0.9999	0.9996	0.9983	0.9944	0.9847	0.9644	0.9270	8
9												1.0000	1.0000	0.9998	0.9992	0.9972	0.9921	0.9807	9
10														1.0000	0.9999	0.9997	0.9989	0.9968	10
11															1.0000	1.0000	0.9999	0.9998	11
12																	1.0000	1.0000	12
x	$n=13$																		x
0	0.8775	0.7690	0.6730	0.5882	0.5133	0.4474	0.3893	0.3383	0.2935	0.2542	0.1209	0.0550	0.0238	0.0097	0.0037	0.0013	0.0004	0.0001	0
1	0.9928	0.9730	0.9436	0.9068	0.8646	0.8186	0.7702	0.7206	0.6707	0.6213	0.3983	0.2336	0.1267	0.0637	0.0296	0.0126	0.0049	0.0017	1
2	0.9997	0.9980	0.9938	0.9865	0.9755	0.9608	0.9422	0.9201	0.8946	0.8661	0.6920	0.5017	0.3326	0.2025	0.1132	0.0579	0.0269	0.0112	2
3	1.0000	0.9999	0.9995	0.9986	0.9969	0.9940	0.9897	0.9837	0.9758	0.9658	0.8820	0.7473	0.5843	0.4206	0.2783	0.1686	0.0929	0.0461	3
4		1.0000	1.0000	0.9999	0.9997	0.9993	0.9987	0.9976	0.9959	0.9935	0.9658	0.9009	0.7940	0.6543	0.5005	0.3530	0.2279	0.1334	4
5				1.0000	1.0000	0.9999	0.9999	0.9997	0.9995	0.9991	0.9925	0.9700	0.9198	0.8346	0.7159	0.5744	0.4268	0.2905	5
6						1.0000	1.0000	1.0000	0.9999	0.9999	0.9987	0.9930	0.9757	0.9376	0.8705	0.7712	0.6437	0.5000	6
7									1.0000	1.0000	0.9998	0.9988	0.9944	0.9818	0.9538	0.9023	0.8212	0.7095	7
8											1.0000	0.9998	0.9990	0.9960	0.9874	0.9679	0.9302	0.8666	8
9												1.0000	0.9999	0.9993	0.9975	0.9922	0.9797	0.9539	9
10													1.0000	0.9999	0.9997	0.9987	0.9959	0.9888	10
11														1.0000	1.0000	0.9999	0.9995	0.9983	11
12																1.0000	1.0000	0.9999	12
13																		1.0000	13

The cumulative binomial distribution function (continued)

p	0.01	0.02	0.03	0.04	0.05	0.06	0.07	0.08	0.09	0.10	0.15	0.20	0.25	0.30	0.35	0.40	0.45	0.50	p
x	$n =$ 14																		x
0	0.8687	0.7536	0.6528	0.5647	0.4877	0.4205	0.3620	0.3112	0.2670	0.2288	0.1028	0.0440	0.0178	0.0068	0.0024	0.0008	0.0002	0.0001	0
1	0.9916	0.9690	0.9355	0.8941	0.8470	0.7963	0.7436	0.6900	0.6368	0.5846	0.3567	0.1979	0.1010	0.0475	0.0205	0.0081	0.0029	0.0009	1
2	0.9997	0.9975	0.9923	0.9833	0.9699	0.9522	0.9302	0.9042	0.8745	0.8416	0.6479	0.4481	0.2811	0.1608	0.0839	0.0398	0.0170	0.0065	2
3	1.0000	0.9999	0.9994	0.9981	0.9958	0.9920	0.9864	0.9786	0.9685	0.9559	0.8535	0.6982	0.5213	0.3552	0.2205	0.1243	0.0632	0.0287	3
4		1.0000	1.0000	0.9998	0.9996	0.9990	0.9980	0.9965	0.9941	0.9908	0.9533	0.8702	0.7415	0.5842	0.4227	0.2793	0.1672	0.0898	4
5				1.0000	1.0000	0.9999	0.9998	0.9996	0.9992	0.9985	0.9885	0.9561	0.8883	0.7805	0.6405	0.4859	0.3373	0.2120	5
6						1.0000	1.0000	1.0000	0.9999	0.9998	0.9978	0.9884	0.9617	0.9067	0.8164	0.6925	0.5461	0.3953	6
7									1.0000	1.0000	0.9997	0.9976	0.9897	0.9685	0.9247	0.8499	0.7414	0.6047	7
8											1.0000	0.9996	0.9978	0.9917	0.9757	0.9417	0.8811	0.7880	8
9												1.0000	0.9997	0.9983	0.9940	0.9825	0.9574	0.9102	9
10													1.0000	0.9998	0.9989	0.9961	0.9886	0.9713	10
11														1.0000	0.9999	0.9994	0.9978	0.9935	11
12															1.0000	0.9999	0.9997	0.9991	12
13																1.0000	1.0000	0.9999	13
14																		1.0000	14
x	$n =$ 15																		x
0	0.8601	0.7386	0.6333	0.5421	0.4633	0.3953	0.3367	0.2863	0.2430	0.2059	0.0874	0.0352	0.0134	0.0047	0.0016	0.0005	0.0001	0.0000	0
1	0.9904	0.9647	0.9270	0.8809	0.8290	0.7738	0.7168	0.6597	0.6035	0.5490	0.3186	0.1671	0.0802	0.0353	0.0142	0.0052	0.0017	0.0005	1
2	0.9996	0.9970	0.9906	0.9797	0.9638	0.9429	0.9171	0.8870	0.8531	0.8159	0.6042	0.3980	0.2361	0.1268	0.0617	0.0271	0.0107	0.0037	2
3	1.0000	0.9998	0.9992	0.9976	0.9945	0.9896	0.9825	0.9727	0.9601	0.9444	0.8227	0.6482	0.4613	0.2969	0.1727	0.0905	0.0424	0.0176	3
4		1.0000	0.9999	0.9998	0.9994	0.9986	0.9972	0.9950	0.9918	0.9873	0.9383	0.8358	0.6865	0.5155	0.3519	0.2173	0.1204	0.0592	4
5			1.0000	1.0000	0.9999	0.9999	0.9997	0.9993	0.9987	0.9978	0.9832	0.9389	0.8516	0.7216	0.5643	0.4032	0.2608	0.1509	5
6					1.0000	1.0000	1.0000	0.9999	0.9998	0.9997	0.9964	0.9819	0.9434	0.8689	0.7548	0.6098	0.4522	0.3036	6
7								1.0000	1.0000	1.0000	0.9994	0.9958	0.9827	0.9500	0.8868	0.7869	0.6535	0.5000	7
8											0.9999	0.9992	0.9958	0.9848	0.9578	0.9050	0.8182	0.6964	8
9											1.0000	0.9999	0.9992	0.9963	0.9876	0.9662	0.9231	0.8491	9
10												1.0000	0.9999	0.9993	0.9972	0.9907	0.9745	0.9408	10
11													1.0000	0.9999	0.9995	0.9981	0.9937	0.9824	11
12														1.0000	0.9999	0.9997	0.9989	0.9963	12
13															1.0000	1.0000	0.9999	0.9995	13
14																	1.0000	1.0000	14
x	$n =$ 20																		x
0	0.8179	0.6676	0.5438	0.4420	0.3585	0.2901	0.2342	0.1887	0.1516	0.1216	0.0388	0.0115	0.0032	0.0008	0.0002	0.0000	0.0000	0.0000	0
1	0.9831	0.9401	0.8802	0.8103	0.7358	0.6605	0.5869	0.5169	0.4516	0.3917	0.1756	0.0692	0.0243	0.0076	0.0021	0.0005	0.0001	0.0000	1
2	0.9990	0.9929	0.9790	0.9561	0.9245	0.8850	0.8390	0.7879	0.7334	0.6769	0.4049	0.2061	0.0913	0.0355	0.0121	0.0036	0.0009	0.0002	2
3	1.0000	0.9994	0.9973	0.9926	0.9841	0.9710	0.9529	0.9294	0.9007	0.8670	0.6477	0.4114	0.2252	0.1071	0.0444	0.0160	0.0049	0.0013	3
4		1.0000	0.9997	0.9990	0.9974	0.9944	0.9893	0.9817	0.9710	0.9568	0.8298	0.6296	0.4148	0.2375	0.1182	0.0510	0.0189	0.0059	4
5			1.0000	0.9999	0.9997	0.9991	0.9981	0.9962	0.9932	0.9887	0.9327	0.8042	0.6172	0.4164	0.2454	0.1256	0.0553	0.0207	5
6				1.0000	1.0000	0.9999	0.9997	0.9994	0.9987	0.9976	0.9781	0.9133	0.7858	0.6080	0.4166	0.2500	0.1299	0.0577	6
7						1.0000	1.0000	0.9999	0.9998	0.9996	0.9941	0.9679	0.8982	0.7723	0.6010	0.4159	0.2520	0.1316	7
8								1.0000	1.0000	0.9999	0.9987	0.9900	0.9591	0.8867	0.7624	0.5956	0.4143	0.2517	8
9										1.0000	0.9998	0.9974	0.9861	0.9520	0.8782	0.7553	0.5914	0.4119	9
10											1.0000	0.9994	0.9961	0.9829	0.9468	0.8725	0.7507	0.5881	10
11												0.9999	0.9991	0.9949	0.9804	0.9435	0.8692	0.7483	11
12												1.0000	0.9998	0.9987	0.9940	0.9790	0.9420	0.8684	12
13													1.0000	0.9997	0.9985	0.9935	0.9786	0.9423	13
14														1.0000	0.9997	0.9984	0.9936	0.9793	14
15															1.0000	0.9997	0.9985	0.9941	15
16																1.0000	0.9997	0.9987	16
17																	1.0000	0.9998	17
18																		1.0000	18

The cumulative binomial distribution function (continued)

$n = 25$

p / x	0.01	0.02	0.03	0.04	0.05	0.06	0.07	0.08	0.09	0.10	0.15	0.20	0.25	0.30	0.35	0.40	0.45	0.50	p / x
0	0.7778	0.6035	0.4670	0.3604	0.2774	0.2129	0.1630	0.1244	0.0946	0.0718	0.0172	0.0038	0.0008	0.0001	0.0000	0.0000	0.0000	0.0000	**0**
1	0.9742	0.9114	0.8280	0.7358	0.6424	0.5527	0.4696	0.3947	0.3286	0.2712	0.0931	0.0274	0.0070	0.0016	0.0003	0.0001	0.0000	0.0000	**1**
2	0.9980	0.9868	0.9620	0.9235	0.8729	0.8129	0.7466	0.6768	0.6063	0.5371	0.2537	0.0982	0.0321	0.0090	0.0021	0.0004	0.0001	0.0000	**2**
3	0.9999	0.9986	0.9938	0.9835	0.9659	0.9402	0.9064	0.8649	0.8169	0.7636	0.4711	0.2340	0.0962	0.0332	0.0097	0.0024	0.0005	0.0001	**3**
4	1.0000	0.9999	0.9992	0.9972	0.9928	0.9850	0.9726	0.9549	0.9314	0.9020	0.6821	0.4207	0.2137	0.0905	0.0320	0.0095	0.0023	0.0005	**4**
5		1.0000	0.9999	0.9996	0.9988	0.9969	0.9935	0.9877	0.9790	0.9666	0.8385	0.6167	0.3783	0.1935	0.0826	0.0294	0.0086	0.0020	**5**
6			1.0000	1.0000	0.9998	0.9995	0.9987	0.9972	0.9946	0.9905	0.9305	0.7800	0.5611	0.3407	0.1734	0.0736	0.0258	0.0073	**6**
7					1.0000	0.9999	0.9998	0.9995	0.9989	0.9977	0.9745	0.8909	0.7265	0.5118	0.3061	0.1536	0.0639	0.0216	**7**
8						1.0000	1.0000	0.9999	0.9998	0.9995	0.9920	0.9532	0.8506	0.6769	0.4668	0.2735	0.1340	0.0539	**8**
9								1.0000	1.0000	0.9999	0.9979	0.9827	0.9287	0.8106	0.6303	0.4246	0.2424	0.1148	**9**
10										1.0000	0.9995	0.9944	0.9703	0.9022	0.7712	0.5858	0.3843	0.2122	**10**
11											0.9999	0.9985	0.9893	0.9558	0.8746	0.7323	0.5426	0.3450	**11**
12											1.0000	0.9996	0.9966	0.9825	0.9396	0.8462	0.6937	0.5000	**12**
13												0.9999	0.9991	0.9940	0.9745	0.9222	0.8173	0.6550	**13**
14												1.0000	0.9998	0.9982	0.9907	0.9656	0.9040	0.7878	**14**
15													1.0000	0.9995	0.9971	0.9868	0.9560	0.8852	**15**
16														0.9999	0.9992	0.9957	0.9826	0.9461	**16**
17														1.0000	0.9998	0.9988	0.9942	0.9784	**17**
18															1.0000	0.9997	0.9984	0.9927	**18**
19																0.9999	0.9996	0.9980	**19**
20																1.0000	0.9999	0.9995	**20**
21																	1.0000	0.9999	**21**
22																		1.0000	**22**

$n = 30$

x	0.01	0.02	0.03	0.04	0.05	0.06	0.07	0.08	0.09	0.10	0.15	0.20	0.25	0.30	0.35	0.40	0.45	0.50	x
0	0.7397	0.5455	0.4010	0.2939	0.2146	0.1563	0.1134	0.0820	0.0591	0.0424	0.0076	0.0012	0.0002	0.0000	0.0000	0.0000	0.0000	0.0000	**0**
1	0.9639	0.8795	0.7731	0.6612	0.5535	0.4555	0.3694	0.2958	0.2343	0.1837	0.0480	0.0105	0.0020	0.0003	0.0000	0.0000	0.0000	0.0000	**1**
2	0.9967	0.9783	0.9399	0.8831	0.8122	0.7324	0.6487	0.5654	0.4855	0.4114	0.1514	0.0442	0.0106	0.0021	0.0003	0.0000	0.0000	0.0000	**2**
3	0.9998	0.9971	0.9881	0.9694	0.9392	0.8974	0.8450	0.7842	0.7175	0.6474	0.3217	0.1227	0.0374	0.0093	0.0019	0.0003	0.0000	0.0000	**3**
4	1.0000	0.9997	0.9982	0.9937	0.9844	0.9685	0.9447	0.9126	0.8723	0.8245	0.5245	0.2552	0.0979	0.0302	0.0075	0.0015	0.0002	0.0000	**4**
5		1.0000	0.9998	0.9989	0.9967	0.9921	0.9838	0.9707	0.9519	0.9268	0.7106	0.4275	0.2026	0.0766	0.0233	0.0057	0.0011	0.0002	**5**
6			1.0000	0.9999	0.9994	0.9983	0.9960	0.9918	0.9848	0.9742	0.8474	0.6070	0.3481	0.1595	0.0586	0.0172	0.0040	0.0007	**6**
7				1.0000	0.9999	0.9997	0.9992	0.9980	0.9959	0.9922	0.9302	0.7608	0.5143	0.2814	0.1238	0.0435	0.0121	0.0026	**7**
8					1.0000	1.0000	0.9999	0.9996	0.9990	0.9980	0.9722	0.8713	0.6736	0.4315	0.2247	0.0940	0.0312	0.0081	**8**
9							1.0000	0.9999	0.9998	0.9995	0.9903	0.9389	0.8034	0.5888	0.3575	0.1763	0.0694	0.0214	**9**
10								1.0000	1.0000	0.9999	0.9971	0.9744	0.8943	0.7304	0.5078	0.2915	0.1350	0.0494	**10**
11										1.0000	0.9992	0.9905	0.9493	0.8407	0.6548	0.4311	0.2327	0.1002	**11**
12											0.9998	0.9969	0.9784	0.9155	0.7802	0.5785	0.3592	0.1808	**12**
13											1.0000	0.9991	0.9918	0.9599	0.8737	0.7145	0.5025	0.2923	**13**
14												0.9998	0.9973	0.9831	0.9348	0.8246	0.6448	0.4278	**14**
15												0.9999	0.9992	0.9936	0.9699	0.9029	0.7691	0.5722	**15**
16												1.0000	0.9998	0.9979	0.9876	0.9519	0.8644	0.7077	**16**
17													0.9999	0.9994	0.9955	0.9788	0.9286	0.8192	**17**
18													1.0000	0.9998	0.9986	0.9917	0.9666	0.8998	**18**
19														1.0000	0.9996	0.9971	0.9862	0.9506	**19**
20															0.9999	0.9991	0.9950	0.9786	**20**
21															1.0000	0.9998	0.9984	0.9919	**21**
22																1.0000	0.9996	0.9974	**22**
23																	0.9999	0.9993	**23**
24																	1.0000	0.9998	**24**
25																		1.0000	**25**

The cumulative binomial distribution function (continued)

p	0.01	0.02	0.03	0.04	0.05	0.06	0.07	0.08	0.09	0.10	0.15	0.20	0.25	0.30	0.35	0.40	0.45	0.50	p
x	$n = 40$																		x
0	0.6690	0.4457	0.2957	0.1954	0.1285	0.0842	0.0549	0.0356	0.0230	0.0148	0.0015	0.0001	0.0000	0.0000	0.0000	0.0000	0.0000	0.0000	**0**
1	0.9393	0.8095	0.6615	0.5210	0.3991	0.2990	0.2201	0.1594	0.1140	0.0805	0.0121	0.0015	0.0001	0.0000	0.0000	0.0000	0.0000	0.0000	**1**
2	0.9925	0.9543	0.8822	0.7855	0.6767	0.5665	0.4625	0.3694	0.2894	0.2228	0.0486	0.0079	0.0010	0.0001	0.0000	0.0000	0.0000	0.0000	**2**
3	0.9993	0.9918	0.9686	0.9252	0.8619	0.7827	0.6937	0.6007	0.5092	0.4231	0.1302	0.0285	0.0047	0.0006	0.0001	0.0000	0.0000	0.0000	**3**
4	1.0000	0.9988	0.9933	0.9790	0.9520	0.9104	0.8546	0.7868	0.7103	0.6290	0.2633	0.0759	0.0160	0.0026	0.0003	0.0000	0.0000	0.0000	**4**
5		0.9999	0.9988	0.9951	0.9861	0.9691	0.9419	0.9033	0.8535	0.7937	0.4325	0.1613	0.0433	0.0086	0.0013	0.0001	0.0000	0.0000	**5**
6		1.0000	0.9998	0.9990	0.9966	0.9909	0.9801	0.9624	0.9361	0.9005	0.6067	0.2859	0.0962	0.0238	0.0044	0.0006	0.0001	0.0000	**6**
7			1.0000	0.9998	0.9993	0.9977	0.9942	0.9873	0.9758	0.9581	0.7559	0.4371	0.1820	0.0553	0.0124	0.0021	0.0002	0.0000	**7**
8				1.0000	0.9999	0.9995	0.9985	0.9963	0.9919	0.9845	0.8646	0.5931	0.2998	0.1110	0.0303	0.0061	0.0009	0.0001	**8**
9					1.0000	0.9999	0.9997	0.9990	0.9976	0.9949	0.9328	0.7318	0.4395	0.1959	0.0644	0.0156	0.0027	0.0003	**9**
10						1.0000	0.9999	0.9998	0.9994	0.9985	0.9701	0.8392	0.5839	0.3087	0.1215	0.0352	0.0074	0.0011	**10**
11							1.0000	1.0000	0.9999	0.9996	0.9880	0.9125	0.7151	0.4406	0.2053	0.0709	0.0179	0.0032	**11**
12									1.0000	0.9999	0.9957	0.9568	0.8209	0.5772	0.3143	0.1285	0.0386	0.0083	**12**
13										1.0000	0.9986	0.9806	0.8968	0.7032	0.4408	0.2112	0.0751	0.0192	**13**
14											0.9996	0.9921	0.9456	0.8074	0.5721	0.3174	0.1326	0.0403	**14**
15											0.9999	0.9971	0.9738	0.8849	0.6946	0.4402	0.2142	0.0769	**15**
16											1.0000	0.9990	0.9884	0.9367	0.7978	0.5681	0.3185	0.1341	**16**
17												0.9997	0.9953	0.9680	0.8761	0.6885	0.4391	0.2148	**17**
18												0.9999	0.9983	0.9852	0.9301	0.7911	0.5651	0.3179	**18**
19												1.0000	0.9994	0.9937	0.9637	0.8702	0.6844	0.4373	**19**
20													0.9998	0.9976	0.9827	0.9256	0.7870	0.5627	**20**
21													1.0000	0.9991	0.9925	0.9608	0.8669	0.6821	**21**
22														0.9997	0.9970	0.9811	0.9233	0.7852	**22**
23														0.9999	0.9989	0.9917	0.9595	0.8659	**23**
24														1.0000	0.9996	0.9966	0.9804	0.9231	**24**
25															0.9999	0.9988	0.9914	0.9597	**25**
26															1.0000	0.9996	0.9966	0.9808	**26**
27																0.9999	0.9988	0.9917	**27**
28																1.0000	0.9996	0.9968	**28**
29																	0.9999	0.9989	**29**
30																	1.0000	0.9997	**30**
31																		0.9999	**31**
32																		1.0000	**32**

The cumulative binomial distribution function (continued)

p	0.01	0.02	0.03	0.04	0.05	0.06	0.07	0.08	0.09	0.10	0.15	0.20	0.25	0.30	0.35	0.40	0.45	0.50	p
x	$n = 50$																		x
0	0.6050	0.3642	0.2181	0.1299	0.0769	0.0453	0.0266	0.0155	0.0090	0.0052	0.0003	0.0000	0.0000	0.0000	0.0000	0.0000	0.0000	0.0000	**0**
1	0.9106	0.7358	0.5553	0.4005	0.2794	0.1900	0.1265	0.0827	0.0532	0.0338	0.0029	0.0002	0.0000	0.0000	0.0000	0.0000	0.0000	0.0000	**1**
2	0.9862	0.9216	0.8108	0.6767	0.5405	0.4162	0.3108	0.2260	0.1605	0.1117	0.0142	0.0013	0.0001	0.0000	0.0000	0.0000	0.0000	0.0000	**2**
3	0.9984	0.9822	0.9372	0.8609	0.7604	0.6473	0.5327	0.4253	0.3303	0.2503	0.0460	0.0057	0.0005	0.0000	0.0000	0.0000	0.0000	0.0000	**3**
4	0.9999	0.9968	0.9832	0.9510	0.8964	0.8206	0.7290	0.6290	0.5277	0.4312	0.1121	0.0185	0.0021	0.0002	0.0000	0.0000	0.0000	0.0000	**4**
5	1.0000	0.9995	0.9963	0.9856	0.9622	0.9224	0.8650	0.7919	0.7072	0.6161	0.2194	0.0480	0.0070	0.0007	0.0001	0.0000	0.0000	0.0000	**5**
6		0.9999	0.9993	0.9964	0.9882	0.9711	0.9417	0.8981	0.8404	0.7702	0.3613	0.1034	0.0194	0.0025	0.0002	0.0000	0.0000	0.0000	**6**
7		1.0000	0.9999	0.9992	0.9968	0.9906	0.9780	0.9562	0.9232	0.8779	0.5188	0.1904	0.0453	0.0073	0.0008	0.0001	0.0000	0.0000	**7**
8			1.0000	0.9999	0.9992	0.9973	0.9927	0.9833	0.9672	0.9421	0.6681	0.3073	0.0916	0.0183	0.0025	0.0002	0.0000	0.0000	**8**
9				1.0000	0.9998	0.9993	0.9978	0.9944	0.9875	0.9755	0.7911	0.4437	0.1637	0.0402	0.0067	0.0008	0.0001	0.0000	**9**
10					1.0000	0.9998	0.9994	0.9983	0.9957	0.9906	0.8801	0.5836	0.2622	0.0789	0.0160	0.0022	0.0002	0.0000	**10**
11						1.0000	0.9999	0.9995	0.9987	0.9968	0.9372	0.7107	0.3816	0.1390	0.0342	0.0057	0.0006	0.0000	**11**
12							1.0000	0.9999	0.9996	0.9990	0.9699	0.8139	0.5110	0.2229	0.0661	0.0133	0.0018	0.0002	**12**
13								1.0000	0.9999	0.9997	0.9868	0.8894	0.6370	0.3279	0.1163	0.0280	0.0045	0.0005	**13**
14									1.0000	0.9999	0.9947	0.9393	0.7481	0.4468	0.1878	0.0540	0.0104	0.0013	**14**
15										1.0000	0.9981	0.9692	0.8369	0.5692	0.2801	0.0955	0.0220	0.0033	**15**
16											0.9993	0.9856	0.9017	0.6839	0.3889	0.1561	0.0427	0.0077	**16**
17											0.9998	0.9937	0.9449	0.7822	0.5060	0.2369	0.0765	0.0164	**17**
18											0.9999	0.9975	0.9713	0.8594	0.6216	0.3356	0.1273	0.0325	**18**
19											1.0000	0.9991	0.9861	0.9152	0.7264	0.4465	0.1974	0.0595	**19**
20												0.9997	0.9937	0.9522	0.8139	0.5610	0.2862	0.1013	**20**
21												0.9999	0.9974	0.9749	0.8813	0.6701	0.3900	0.1611	**21**
22												1.0000	0.9990	0.9877	0.9290	0.7660	0.5019	0.2399	**22**
23													0.9996	0.9944	0.9604	0.8438	0.6134	0.3359	**23**
24													0.9999	0.9976	0.9793	0.9022	0.7160	0.4439	**24**
25													1.0000	0.9991	0.9900	0.9427	0.8034	0.5561	**25**
26														0.9997	0.9955	0.9686	0.8721	0.6641	**26**
27														0.9999	0.9981	0.9840	0.9220	0.7601	**27**
28														1.0000	0.9993	0.9924	0.9556	0.8389	**28**
29															0.9997	0.9966	0.9765	0.8987	**29**
30															0.9999	0.9986	0.9884	0.9405	**30**
31															1.0000	0.9995	0.9947	0.9675	**31**
32																0.9998	0.9978	0.9836	**32**
33																0.9999	0.9991	0.9923	**33**
34																1.0000	0.9997	0.9967	**34**
35																	0.9999	0.9987	**35**
36																	1.0000	0.9995	**36**
37																		0.9998	**37**
38																		1.0000	**38**

Answers

Chapter 1: Numerical Measures

1. Representing Data

Exercise 1.1 — Data basics

Q1 a) Make, Colour

b) Mileage, Number of doors, Cost of service

Q2 a) Number of medals won last season, Shoe size

b) Height, Mass

Q3 a) There are no 'gaps' between possible heights.

b)

Height, h (cm)	No. of members	lower class b'dary (cm)	upper class b'dary (cm)	class width (cm)	class mid-point (cm)
$140 \le h < 150$	3	140	150	10	145
$150 \le h < 160$	9	150	160	10	155
$160 \le h < 170$	17	160	170	10	165
$170 \le h < 180$	12	170	180	10	175
$180 \le h < 190$	5	180	190	10	185
$190 \le h < 200$	1	190	200	10	195

2. Location: Mean, Median and Mode

Exercise 2.1 — The mean

Q1 The sum of all 12 prices is £13.92.
So the mean price is £13.92 ÷ 12 = £1.16

Q2 1672 ÷ 20 = 83.6

Q3

Number of goals, x	0	1	2	3	4	*Total*
Frequency, f	5	7	4	3	1	***20***
fx	0	7	8	9	4	***28***

So the mean is 28 ÷ 20 = 1.4 goals

Q4 a) 15 × 47.4 = 711 years

b) New total of ages = 711 + 17 = 728
So new mean = 728 ÷ 16 = 45.5 years
Or you could have used the formula with $n_1 = 15$, $\overline{x_1} = 47.4$, $n_2 = 1$ and $\overline{x_2} = 17$ to get the same answer.

Exercise 2.2 — The mode and the median

Q1 a) First put the amounts in order:
£19, £45, £67, £77, £84, £98, £101, £108, £110, £123, £140, £185, £187, £194, £216, £250, £500

There are 17 amounts in total. Since 17 ÷ 2 = 8.5 is not a whole number, round this up to 9 to find the position of the median.
So the median = £110.

b) All the values occur just once.

Q2 a) 6.9%

b) First put the rates in order:
6.2%, 6.2%, 6.3%, 6.4%, 6.4%, 6.5%, 6.9%, 6.9%, 6.9%, 7.4%, 8.8%, 9.9%

There are 12 rates in total. Since 12 ÷ 2 = 6 is a whole number, the median is halfway between the 6th and 7th values in the ordered list.
So the median = (6.5% + 6.9%) ÷ 2 = 6.7%.

Q3 a) 5

b) There are 176 ratings in total.
176 ÷ 2 = 88, so the median is midway between the 88th and 89th values.

Add a column to the table to show cumulative frequencies:

Rating	Number of customers	Cumulative frequency
1	7	7
2	5	12
3	25	37
4	67	104
5	72	176

From the cumulative frequencies, the 88th and 89th values are both 4, so the median = 4.

Q4 a) 0 rows

b) Add a row to the table for cumulative frequency:

Rows empty	0	1	2	3	4	5
Number of performances	10	7	6	7	4	1
Cumulative frequency	10	17	23	30	34	35

There are 35 values altogether.
Since 35 ÷ 2 = 17.5 is not a whole number, round this up to 18 to find the position of the median. Data values 18 to 23 are all 2, so the median = 2 rows.

Q5 a) (i) 6 seconds

(ii) 4 seconds and 6 seconds

b) Add two rows to the table for the cumulative frequency for Kwasi and Ben.

Time to start program (s)	3	4	5	6	7
Frequency for Kwasi's computer	3	5	4	7	3
Cumulative frequency (Kwasi)	3	8	12	19	22
Frequency for Ben's computer	0	6	5	6	2
Cumulative frequency (Ben)	0	6	11	17	19

(i) There are 22 values altogether.
Since 22 ÷ 2 = 11 is a whole number, the median is halfway between the 11th and 12th values in the ordered list.
So the median = 5 seconds.

(ii) There are 19 values altogether. Since $19 \div 2 = 9.5$ is not a whole number, round this up to 10 to find the position of the median. So the median = 5 seconds.

Exercise 2.3 — Averages of grouped data

Q1 a)

Time (t, mins)	Frequency, f	Mid-point, x	fx
$3 \le t < 4$	7	3.5	24.5
$4 \le t < 5$	14	4.5	63
$5 \le t < 6$	24	5.5	132
$6 \le t < 8$	10	7	70
$8 \le t < 10$	5	9	45

b) $\sum f = 60$, $\sum fx = 334.5$
So estimate of mean = $334.5 \div 60$
= 5.6 mins (to 1 d.p.).
You could add an extra row to the table to show the column totals.

Q2 a) 0-2 letters

b) Add some extra columns to the table:

Number of letters	Number of houses, f	Mid-point, x	fx
0-2	20	1	20
3-5	16	4	64
6-8	7	7	49
9-11	5	10	50
12-14	2	13	26

$\sum f = 50$, $\sum fx = 209$
So estimate of mean = $209 \div 50 = 4.18$ letters

c) Since $\sum f \div 2 = 50 \div 2 = 25$, the median is halfway between the values in this position (25) and the next position (26) in the ordered list. So the median must be in the class 3-5.

Q3 a) Add some extra columns to the table:

Rainfall (r, mm)	Frequency	Mid-point, x	fx
$20 \le r < 40$	5	30	150
$40 \le r < 50$	7	45	315
$50 \le r < 60$	9	55	495
$60 \le r < 80$	15	70	1050
$80 \le r < 100$	8	90	720
$100 \le r < 120$	2	110	220

$\sum f = 46$, $\sum fx = 2950$
So estimate of mean = $2950 \div 46$
= 64 mm (to the nearest mm).

b) Since $\sum f \div 2 = 46 \div 2 = 23$, the median is halfway between the values in this position (23) and the next position (24) in the ordered list. So the median must be in the class $60 \le r < 80$.

Q4 $\sum f = 60$.
Estimated mean = $16740 \div 60 = 279$ minutes

Exercise 2.4 — Comparing measures of location

Q1 a) Median — most employees will earn relatively low salaries but a few may earn much higher salaries, so the mean could be heavily affected by a few high salaries.

b) Mean — the data should be reasonably symmetrical so the mean would be a good measure of location. The median would be good as well (for a symmetric data set, it should be roughly equal to the mean).

c) Mode — make of car is qualitative data so the mode is the only average that can be found.

d) Mean — the data should be reasonably symmetrical so the mean would be a good measure of location. The median would be good as well (for a symmetric data set, it should be roughly equal to the mean).

e) Median — most employees will perhaps travel fairly short distances to work but a few employees may live much further away. The median would not be affected by these few high values.
The mode is unlikely to be suitable in b), d) and e) (and possibly a) as well) because all the values may well be different.

Q2 There is a very extreme value of 8 that would affect the mean quite heavily.

3. Dispersion

Exercise 3.1 — Range and interquartile range

Q1 a) Highest value = 88 846 miles
Lowest value = 3032 miles
So range = 88 846 – 3032 = 85 814 miles

b) (i) There are 8 values, and the ordered list is 3032, 4222, 7521, 7926, 30778, 31 763, 74 898, 88 846

Since $\frac{n}{4} = 2$, the lower quartile (Q_1) is halfway between the values in this position (2) and the next position (3) in the ordered list.
So $Q_1 = (4222 + 7521) \div 2 = 5871.5$ miles.

(ii) Since $\frac{3n}{4} = 6$, the upper quartile (Q_3) is halfway between the values in this position (6) and the next position (7) in the ordered list. So $Q_3 = (31\,763 + 74\,898) \div 2$
= 53 330.5 miles.

(iii) IQR = $Q_3 - Q_1$ = 53 330.5 – 5871.5
= 47 459 miles

Q2 a) and b)

In town at 8:45 am:
The ordered list of 18 values is:
13, 14, 14, 15, 15, 15, 15, 15, 16, 16, 16, 16, 16, 17, 17, 18, 18, 18

So the range = 18 – 13 = 5 mph

Since $\frac{n}{4} = 4.5$, the lower quartile (Q_1) is in position 5 in the ordered list. So $Q_1 = 15$ mph.

Since $\frac{3n}{4} = 13.5$, the upper quartile (Q_3) is in position 14 in the ordered list. So $Q_3 = 17$ mph.

This means IQR = $Q_3 - Q_1 = 17 - 15 = 2$ mph.

In town at 10:45 am:
The ordered list of 18 values is:
25, 29, 29, 29, 30, 30, 31, 31, 31, 32, 33, 34, 34, 35, 36, 36, 38, 39

So the range = 39 – 25 = 14 mph

The lower quartile (Q_1) is in position 5 in the ordered list. So $Q_1 = 30$ mph.

The upper quartile (Q_3) is in position 14 in the ordered list. So $Q_3 = 35$ mph.

This means IQR = $Q_3 - Q_1 = 35 - 30 = 5$ mph.

On the motorway at 1 pm:
The ordered list of 18 values is:
67, 69, 69, 71, 71, 73, 73, 74, 74, 75, 75, 76, 76, 76, 78, 78, 88, 95

So the range = 95 – 67 = 28 mph

The lower quartile (Q_1) is in position 5 in the ordered list. So $Q_1 = 71$ mph.

The upper quartile (Q_3) is in position 14 in the ordered list. So $Q_3 = 76$ mph.

This means IQR = $Q_3 - Q_1 = 76 - 71 = 5$ mph.

Q3 a) Add a column showing cumulative frequency to the table:

Empty seats	Frequency	Cumulative frequency
1	2	2
2	5	7
3	7	14
4	1	15
5	4	19
6-8	3	22
9-15	3	25

So $\frac{n}{4} = 25 \div 4 = 6.25$, so round up to 7.
The lower quartile (Q_1) is the 7th data value, so looking at the cumulative frequency column, $Q_1 = 2$.

b) $\frac{3n}{4} = 3 \times 25 \div 4 = 18.75$, meaning the upper quartile (Q_3) is the 19th data value (rounding up). So using the cumulative frequency table, $Q_3 = 5$.

c) So IQR = $Q_3 - Q_1 = 5 - 2 = 3$.

Exercise 3.2 — Variance and standard deviation

Q1 a) $\bar{x} = \frac{756 + 755 + 764 + 778 + 754 + 759}{6}$

$= \frac{4566}{6} = 761$

b) $\sum x^2 = 756^2 + 755^2 + 764^2 + 778^2 + 754^2 + 759^2$

$= 3\,475\,138$

c) variance $= \frac{\sum x^2}{n} - \bar{x}^2 = \frac{3\,475\,138}{6} - 761^2$

$= 68.666... = 68.7$ (to 3 sig. fig.).

d) standard deviation = $\sqrt{\text{variance}} = \sqrt{68.666...}$
$= 8.29$ (to 3 sig. fig.).

e) There are no extreme values to affect the standard deviation in a way that would make it unrepresentative of the rest of the data set.

Q2 a) $\bar{x} = \frac{\sum x}{n} = \frac{480}{8} = 60$

$\sum x^2 = 35\,292$

variance $= \frac{\sum x^2}{n} - \bar{x}^2 = \frac{35\,292}{8} - 60^2 = 811.5$

b) standard deviation = $\sqrt{\text{variance}} = \sqrt{811.5}$
$= 28.5$ (to 3 sig. fig.).

Q3 a) Start by adding an extra row to the table for fx.

x	1	2	3	4
frequency, f	7	8	4	1
fx	7	16	12	4

Then $\bar{x} = \frac{\sum fx}{\sum f} = \frac{39}{20} = 1.95$

b) Now add two more rows to the table.

x	1	2	3	4
frequency, f	7	8	4	1
fx	7	16	12	4
x^2	1	4	9	16
fx^2	7	32	36	16

So $\sum fx^2 = 7 + 32 + 36 + 16 = 91$

c) variance $= \frac{\sum fx^2}{\sum f} - \bar{x}^2 = \frac{91}{20} - 1.95^2 = 0.7475$

d) standard deviation = $\sqrt{\text{variance}} = \sqrt{0.7475}$
$= 0.865$ (to 3 sig. fig.).

Q4 Extend the table to include fx, x^2 and fx^2.

x	7	8	9	10	11	12
frequency, f	2	3	5	7	4	2
fx	14	24	45	70	44	24
x^2	49	64	81	100	121	144
fx^2	98	192	405	700	484	288

So $\sum f = 2 + 3 + 5 + 7 + 4 + 2 = 23$

$\sum fx = 14 + 24 + 45 + 70 + 44 + 24 = 221$

$\sum fx^2 = 98 + 192 + 405 + 700 + 484 + 288 = 2167$

This means $\bar{x} = \frac{\sum fx}{f} = \frac{221}{23}$.

And so variance $= \frac{\sum fx^2}{\sum f} - \bar{x}^2 = \frac{2167}{23} - \left(\frac{221}{23}\right)^2$

$= 1.8903... = 1.89$ (to 3 sig. fig.)

Q5 a)

Pulse rate	56-60	61-65	66-70	71-75	76-80
frequency, f	1	2	4	8	5
(i) mid-point, x	58	63	68	73	78
(ii) fx	58	126	272	584	390
(iii) x^2	3364	3969	4624	5329	6084
(iv) fx^2	3364	7938	18496	42632	30420

b) **(i)** $\sum f = 20$

(ii) $\sum fx = 1430$

(iii) $\sum fx^2 = 102\,850$

c) Variance $= \frac{\sum fx^2}{\sum f} - \left(\frac{\sum fx}{\sum f}\right)^2$

$= \frac{102850}{20} - \left(\frac{1430}{20}\right)^2$

$= 30.25$

Q6 a) Add some more columns to the table showing the class mid-points (x), as well as fx, x^2 and fx^2.

Yield, w (kg)	f	Mid-point, x	fx	x^2	fx^2
$50 \leq w < 60$	23	55	1265	3025	69575
$60 \leq w < 70$	12	65	780	4225	50700
$70 \leq w < 80$	15	75	1125	5625	84375
$80 \leq w < 90$	6	85	510	7225	43350
$90 \leq w < 100$	2	95	190	9025	18050

So $\sum f = 58$, $\sum fx = 3870$, $\sum fx^2 = 266\,050$.

Then:

Variance $= \frac{\sum fx^2}{\sum f} - \left(\frac{\sum fx}{\sum f}\right)^2$

$= \frac{266\,050}{58} - \left(\frac{3870}{58}\right)^2$

$= 134.95838... = 135\text{ kg}^2$ (to 3 sig. fig.)

b) Standard deviation $= \sqrt{134.95838...}$

$= 11.6$ kg (to 3 sig. fig.)

Q7 a) Work out the total duration of all the 23 eruptions that Su has timed.

This is $\sum x = n\bar{x} = 23 \times 3.42 = 78.66$ minutes.

Work out the total duration of all the 37 eruptions that Ellen has timed.

This is $\sum y = n\bar{y} = 37 \times 3.92 = 145.04$ minutes

So the total duration of the last 60 eruptions is:

$\sum x + \sum y = 78.66 + 145.04 = 223.7$ minutes

This gives a mean duration of:

$\frac{223.7}{60} = 3.72833...$

$= 3.73$ minutes (to 3 sig. fig.).

b) Work out the sum of squares of the durations of all the 23 eruptions that Su has timed — use the formula for variance.

variance $= \frac{\sum x^2}{n} - \bar{x}^2 \Rightarrow 1.07^2 = \frac{\sum x^2}{23} - 3.42^2$

So $\sum x^2 = 23 \times (1.07^2 + 3.42^2) = 295.3499$

Do the same for the 37 eruptions that Ellen has timed — use the formula for variance.

variance $= \frac{\sum y^2}{n} - \bar{y}^2 \Rightarrow 0.97^2 = \frac{\sum y^2}{37} - 3.92^2$

So $\sum y^2 = 37 \times (0.97^2 + 3.92^2) = 603.3701$

Now you can work out the total sum of squares (for all 60 eruptions):

$\sum x^2 + \sum y^2 = 295.3499 + 603.3701 = 898.72$

So the variance for all 60 eruptions is:

variance $= \frac{898.72}{60} - \left(\frac{223.7}{60}\right)^2$

$= 1.0781... = 1.08\text{ min}^2$ (to 3 sig. fig.)

c) This means the standard deviation of the durations is $\sqrt{1.0781...} = 1.0383...$

$= 1.04$ min (to 3 sig. fig.)

Exercise 3.3 — Linear scaling

Q1 a) Since $y = x - 500$, $\bar{x} = \bar{y} + 500$.

So $\bar{x} = 12 + 500 = 512$.

standard deviation of x = standard deviation of y
$= 4.22$

b) Since $y = 4x$, $\bar{x} = \frac{\bar{y}}{4} = \frac{6}{4} = 1.5$

stan. dev. of $x = \frac{\text{stan. dev. of } y}{4} = \frac{2.14}{4} = 0.535$

c) $y = \frac{x - 20\,000}{15}$, so $\bar{y} = \frac{\bar{x} - 20\,000}{15}$.

This means $\bar{x} = 15 \times 12.4 + 20000 = 20186$.

stan. dev. of x $= 15 \times$ stan. dev. of y
$= 15 \times 1.34 = 20.1$

Q2 a) The scaled data values are 3, 7 and 8.
The mean of these is $\bar{y} = (3 + 7 + 8) \div 3 = 6$.
The standard deviation of the scaled values is

$$\sqrt{\frac{3^2 + 7^2 + 8^2}{3} - 6^2} = 2.16 \text{ (to 3 sig. fig.)}.$$

So the mean of the original data values is
$\bar{x} = \bar{y} + 2000 = 6 + 2000 = 2006$.

The standard deviation of the original values is the same as the standard deviation of the scaled values — this is 2.16 (to 3 sig. fig.).

b) The scaled data values are 2, 17, 3, 11 and 7.
The mean of these is:
$\bar{y} = (2 + 17 + 3 + 11 + 7) \div 5 = 8$.
The standard deviation of the scaled values is

$$\sqrt{\frac{2^2 + 17^2 + 3^2 + 11^2 + 7^2}{5} - 8^2}$$

$= 5.51$ (to 3 sig. fig.).

So the mean of the original data values is
$\bar{x} = \bar{y} \div 100 = 8 \div 100 = 0.08$.

The standard deviation of x
= standard deviation of $y \div 100$,
so standard deviation of $x = 5.51 \div 100$
= 0.0551 (to 3 sig. fig.).

c) The scaled data values are 7, 2, 20 and 15.
The mean of these is:
$\bar{y} = (7 + 2 + 20 + 15) \div 4 = 11$.
The standard deviation of the scaled values is

$$\sqrt{\frac{7^2 + 2^2 + 20^2 + 15^2}{4} - 11^2}$$

$= 6.96$ (to 3 sig. fig.).

So the mean of the original data values is
$\bar{x} = \frac{\bar{y}}{2} + 350 = \frac{11}{2} + 350 = 355.5$.
The standard deviation of x
= standard deviation of $y \div 2$,
so standard deviation of x
$= 6.96 \div 2 = 3.48$ (to 3 sig. fig.).

d) The scaled data values are 10, 7, 4, 0 and 6.
The mean of these is:
$\bar{y} = (10 + 7 + 4 + 0 + 6) \div 5 = 5.4$.
The standard deviation of the scaled values is

$$\sqrt{\frac{10^2 + 7^2 + 4^2 + 0^2 + 6^2}{5} - 5.4^2}$$

$= 3.32$ (to 3 sig. fig.).

So the mean of the original data values is
$\bar{x} = 10\bar{y} - 8000 = 10 \times 5.4 - 8000 = -7946$.

The standard deviation of x
= standard deviation of $y \times 10$,
so standard deviation of x
$= 3.32 \times 10 = 33.2$ (to 3 sig. fig.).

Q3 a) All the values are of the form '0.6_', and so if you subtract 0.6 from all the values, and then multiply what's left by 100, you'll end up with scaled data values between 1 and 10.
So scale the data values using $y = 100(x - 0.6)$, where x is an original data value and y is the corresponding scaled value.
This gives y-values of: 1, 7, 3, 3, 6, 5, 4, 8, 4, 2

b) $\bar{y} = \frac{1 + 7 + 3 + 3 + 6 + 5 + 4 + 8 + 4 + 2}{10}$

$= \frac{43}{10} = 4.3$

Find the sum of squares of the scaled values, $\sum y^2$. This is $\sum y^2 = 229$.

So variance $= \frac{\sum y^2}{n} - \bar{y}^2 = \frac{229}{10} - 4.3^2$

$= 4.41$

This gives a standard deviation of $\sqrt{4.41} = 2.1$

c) Since $y = 100(x - 0.6)$, $\bar{y} = 100(\bar{x} - 0.6)$.
This means:

$\bar{x} = \frac{\bar{y}}{100} + 0.6 = \frac{4.3}{100} + 0.6 = 0.643$ cm
Since $y = 100(x - 0.6)$,
stan. dev. of $y = 100 \times$ stan. dev. of x
So stan. dev. of x = stan. dev. of $y \div 100$
$= 2.1 \div 100 = 0.021$ cm

Q4 Make a new table showing the class mid-points (x) and their corresponding scaled values (y), as well as fy, y^2 and fy^2.

Weight (to nearest g)	100-104	105-109	110-114	115-119
Frequency, f	2	6	3	1
Class mid-point, x	102	107	112	117
Scaled value, y	0	5	10	15
fy	0	30	30	15
y^2	0	25	100	225
fy^2	0	150	300	225

Then $\bar{y} = \frac{\sum fy}{\sum f} = \frac{75}{12} = 6.25$

variance of $y = \frac{\sum fy^2}{\sum f} - \bar{y}^2 = \frac{675}{12} - 6.25^2$

$= 17.1875$

This means standard deviation of $y = \sqrt{17.1875}$
= 4.15 (to 3 sig. fig.).

Now you can convert these back to values for x.

Since $y = x - 102$:

$\bar{x} = \bar{y} + 102 = 108.25$ g

stan. dev. of x = stan. dev. of y = 4.15 g (to 3 sig. fig.).

Q5 Use the scaling $y = x + 2$.
Then $\sum y = 7$ and $\sum y^2 = 80$.

So $\bar{y} = \frac{\sum y}{n} = \frac{7}{20} = 0.35$
And the variance of y is:
$\frac{\sum y^2}{n} - \bar{y}^2 = \frac{80}{20} - 0.35^2 = 3.8775$
This gives a standard deviation for y of $\sqrt{3.8775} = 1.97$ (to 3 sig. fig.)

So $\bar{x} = \bar{y} - 2 = 0.35 - 2 = -1.65$.
And standard deviation of x
= standard deviation of y = 1.97 (to 3 sig. fig.)

Exercise 3.4 — Comparing distributions

Q1 a) (i) For the men:

$$\text{mean} = \frac{\sum x}{n} = \frac{73}{10} = 7.3 \text{ hours}$$

There are 10 values, so the median is halfway between the 5th and 6th values in the ordered list. So the median is 7 hours.

Don't forget to sort the list before trying to find the median — it's an easy mistake to make.

For the women:

$$\text{mean} = \frac{\sum x}{n} = \frac{85}{10} = 8.5 \text{ hours}$$

Again, there are 10 values, so the median is halfway between the 5th and 6th values. So the median is 8.5 hours.

(ii) The mean and median are both higher for the women, so they get between 1 and 1.5 hours more sleep per night, on average, than the men.

b) (i) For the men:

$$\text{stan. dev.} = \sqrt{\frac{\sum x^2}{n} - \bar{x}^2} = \sqrt{\frac{553}{10} - 7.3^2}$$

$= 1.42$ hours (to 3 sig. fig.)

For the women:

$$\text{stan. dev.} = \sqrt{\frac{\sum x^2}{n} - \bar{x}^2} = \sqrt{\frac{749}{10} - 8.5^2}$$

$= 1.63$ hours (to 3 sig. fig.)

(ii) The standard deviation is slightly higher for the women, so the number of hours of sleep for the women varies slightly more from the average than it does for the men.

Q2 a) The mean and median are both higher at Whiteley's Fine Leather — the mean is approximately £19 higher and the median is £19 higher.
This means that shoes are generally more expensive at Whiteley's Fine Leather than at Simson's Sporting Supplies.

b) The interquartile range at Whiteley's Fine Leather is 65 – 49 = 16 and at Simson's Sporting Supplies it is 41 – 29 = 12. So the IQR and the range are higher at Whiteley's Fine Leather. So the shoe prices are more spread out at Whiteley's Fine Leather.

Review Exercise — Chapter 1

Q1 Add a row to the table showing fx.

x	0	1	2	3	4
f	5	4	4	2	1
fx	0	4	8	6	4

$\sum f = 16$, $\sum fx = 22$, so mean = 22 ÷ 16 = 1.375
Since there are 16 values, the median will be halfway between the 8th and the 9th values (which are both 1), so median = 1
Mode = 0.

Q2 Extend the table to show the cumulative frequency, class mid-points (x) and the values of fx.

Speed (mph)	30-34	35-39	40-44	45-50
Frequency	12	37	9	2
Cumulative frequency	12	49	58	60
Class mid-point (x)	32	37	42	47.5
fx	384	1369	378	95

a) $\sum f = 60$, $\sum fx = 2226$, so estimated mean = 2226 ÷ 60 = 37.1 mph.

b) The modal class is 35 - 39 mph.

c) $\sum f \div 2 = 60 \div 2 = 30$, so the median will be halfway between the 30th and 31st values. The cumulative frequency row shows that the median is in the class 35 - 39 mph.
Always work out the class mid-points very carefully.

Q3
$$\text{Mean} = \frac{11 + 12 + 14 + 17 + 21 + 23 + 27}{7}$$
$$= \frac{125}{7} = 17.9 \text{ (to 3 sig. fig.)}.$$

$$\text{Stan. dev.} = \sqrt{\frac{\sum x^2}{n} - \bar{x}^2} = \sqrt{\frac{2449}{7} - \left(\frac{125}{7}\right)^2}$$
$= 5.57$ (to 3 sig. fig.).

Q4 You need to extend the table here:

Score	100-106	107-113	114-120	121-127	128-134
Frequency, f	6	11	22	9	2
Class mid-point, x	103	110	117	124	131
fx	618	1210	2574	1116	262
x^2	10609	12100	13689	15376	17161
fx^2	63654	133100	301158	138384	34322

$\sum f = 50$, $\sum fx = 5780$, and $\sum fx^2 = 670618$

so mean $= \frac{5780}{50} = 115.6$

and variance $= \frac{670\,618}{50} - 115.6^2 = 49$

Q5 Let $y = x - 20$.
Then:
$\bar{y} = \bar{x} - 20$ or $\bar{x} = \bar{y} + 20$
$\sum y = 125$ and $\sum y^2 = 221$
So $\bar{y} = \frac{125}{100} = 1.25$ and $\bar{x} = 1.25 + 20 = 21.25$

And:
variance for $y = \frac{221}{100} - 1.25^2 = 0.6475$ and so standard deviation for $y = 0.805$ to 3 sig. fig.
But since $y = x - 20$, this must also equal the standard deviation for x.
So standard deviation for $x = 0.805$ (to 3 sig. fig.).

Q6

Time to nearest minute	30-33	34-37	38-41	42-45
Frequency, f	3	6	7	4
Class mid-point, x	31.5	35.5	39.5	43.5
Scaled value, y	–4	0	4	8
fy	–12	0	28	32
y^2	16	0	16	64
fy^2	48	0	112	256

Then $\sum f = 20$, $\sum fy = 48$, and $\sum fy^2 = 416$

This gives:

$\bar{y} = \frac{48}{20} = 2.4$

So $\bar{x} = \bar{y} + 35.5 = 2.4 + 35.5 = 37.9$ minutes

And:

variance for $y = \frac{416}{20} - 2.4^2 = 15.04$ and so

standard deviation for $y = 3.88$ to 3 sig. fig.

But since $y = x - 35.5$, this must also equal the standard deviation for x. So standard deviation for $x = 3.88$ minutes (to 3 sig. fig.).

Q7 Put the 20 items of data in order:

1, 4, 5, 5, 5, 5, 5, 6, 6, 7, 7, 8, 10, 10, 12, 15, 20, 20, 30, 50

Since $n \div 2 = 20 \div 2 = 10$, the median is halfway between the values in positions 10 and 11, and since the 10th and the 11th items are both 7, the median = £7.

Since $n \div 4 = 20 \div 4 = 5$, the lower quartile is halfway between the values in positions 5 and 6, and since the 5th and 6th values are both 5, the lower quartile is £5.

Since $3n \div 4 = 15$, the upper quartile is halfway between the values in positions 15 and 16.
So upper quartile = (12 + 15) ÷ 2 = £13.50.

Q8 **a)** **(i)** Put the times in order first:
Times = 2, 3, 4, 4, 5, 5, 5, 7, 10, 12
Since $n \div 2 = 10 \div 2 = 5$, the median will be halfway between the 5th and 6th values.
So the median is 5 minutes.

(ii) Since $n \div 4 = 10 \div 4 = 2.5$, the lower quartile will be the 3rd value.
So the lower quartile is 4 minutes.
The upper quartile is the 8th value, which is 7 minutes.
So the IQR = 7 – 4 = 3 minutes.

b) **(i)** For Worker B, the ordered list is:
4, 4, 6, 7, 8, 8, 9, 9, 10, 11
Since $n \div 2 = 10 \div 2 = 5$, the median will be halfway between the 5th and 6th values.
So the median is 8 minutes.

(ii) Since $n \div 4 = 10 \div 4 = 2.5$, the lower quartile will be the 3rd value.
So the lower quartile is 6 minutes.
The upper quartile is the 8th value, which is 9 minutes.
So the IQR = 9 – 6 = 3 minutes.

c) You could say various things — here, you can choose whether to say something about the location or dispersion.
E.g. the times for Worker B are 3 minutes longer than those for Worker A, on average (comparing medians).

The IQR for both workers is the same — generally they both work with the same consistency.
The range for Worker A is larger than that for Worker B. Worker A had a few items he/she could iron very quickly and a few which took a long time.

d) Worker A would be better to employ. The median time is less than for Worker B, and the upper quartile is less than the median of Worker B. Worker A would generally iron more items in a given time than worker B.

Exam-Style Questions — Chapter 1

1 **a)** The mode is 1 goal.

There are 26 data values in total, so the median is halfway between the 13th and 14th data values. The 13th data value is 1 and the 14th is 2, so the median = 1.5 goals ***[1 mark]***.

26 ÷ 4 = 6.5, so the lower quartile is the 7th data value so Q_1 = 1 goal ***[1 mark]***.

(3 × 26) ÷ 4 = 19.5, so the upper quartile is the 20th data value, so Q_3 = 3 goals ***[1 mark]***.

b) Again, there are 26 data values, so Q_1 is the 7th data value and Q_3 is the 20th.

So Q_1 = 1 goal ***[1 mark]*** and
Q_3 = 3 goals ***[1 mark]***.

This means the interquartile range is
$Q_3 - Q_1 = 3 - 1 = 2$ goals ***[1 mark]***.

c) **(i)** Add a column to the table for Player A showing fx, and a row showing the totals. (Here, the number of goals in a game is x, and f (the frequency) is the number of appearances in which the player scores that many goals.)

Number of goals, x	f for Player A	fx
0	6	0
1	7	7
2	6	12
3	3	9
4	2	8
5	1	5
6	0	0
7	1	7
	$\sum f = 26$	$\sum fx = 48$

[1 mark for $\sum fx = 48$]

The mean $\bar{x} = \frac{\sum fx}{\sum f}$

$= \frac{48}{26} = 1.85$ (3 sig. fig.) ***[1 mark]***

(ii) Now add two more columns to the table, showing x^2 and fx^2.

Number of goals, x	f for Player A	x^2	fx^2
0	6	0	0
1	7	1	7
2	6	4	24
3	3	9	27
4	2	16	32
5	1	25	25
6	0	36	0
7	1	49	49
	$\sum f = 26$		$\sum fx^2 = 164$

[1 mark for $\sum fx^2 = 164$]

Then the variance $= \dfrac{\sum fx^2}{\sum f} - \bar{x}^2$

$= \dfrac{164}{26} - \left(\dfrac{48}{26}\right)^2 = \dfrac{1960}{676}$

$= \dfrac{490}{169} = 2.90$ (3 sig. fig.) ***[1 mark]***

d) The mean number of goals per match is higher for Player B than it is for Player A ***[1 mark]***.

The variance for Player A is higher than the variance for Player B, so Player B seems more consistent ***[1 mark]***.

2 a) Add a row to the table showing fx:

No. of hits, x	12	13	14	15	16	17	18
Frequency, f	7	4	6	6	6	4	4
fx	84	52	84	90	96	68	72

No. of hits, x	19	20	21	22	23	24	25
Frequency, f	2	1	7	0	0	0	1
fx	38	20	147	0	0	0	25

$\sum fx = 776$ and $\sum f = 48$ ***[1 mark]***

So the mean is $\dfrac{\sum fx}{\sum f} = \dfrac{776}{48}$

$= 16.2$ (to 3 sig. fig.) ***[1 mark]***

There are 48 data values so the median is halfway between the 24th and 25th values in the ordered list ***[1 mark]***.
24th value = 25th value = 16,
so median = 16 hits ***[1 mark]***.
There are two modes: 12 hits and 21 hits ***[1 mark]***

b) The mode is the least appropriate measure of location ***[1 mark]*** because there are two of them ***[1 mark]***.

The two modes are also both fairly 'extreme', so neither is particularly representative of where most of the data lies.

3 a) Let $y = x - 30$. Then

$\bar{y} = \dfrac{228}{19} = 12$, so $\bar{x} = \bar{y} + 30 = 42$ ***[1 mark]***

variance of $y = \dfrac{3040}{19} - 12^2 = 16$ ***[1 mark]***,

and so standard deviation of $y = 4$. But standard deviation of x = standard deviation of y and so standard deviation of $x = 4$ ***[1 mark]***

b) $\bar{x} = \dfrac{\sum x}{19} = 42$

And so $\sum x = 42 \times 19 = 798$ ***[1 mark]***

Variance of $x = \dfrac{\sum x^2}{19} - \bar{x}^2$

$= \dfrac{\sum x^2}{19} - 42^2 = 16$ ***[1 mark]***

And so $\sum x^2 = (16 + 42^2) \times 19$

$= 33820$ ***[1 mark]***

c) New $\sum x = 798 + 32 = 830$ ***[1 mark]***

So new $\bar{x} = \dfrac{830}{20} = 41.5$ ***[1 mark]***

New $\sum x^2 = 33820 + 32^2 = 34844$ ***[1 mark]***

So new variance $= \dfrac{34844}{20} - 41.5^2 = 19.95$

and new stan. dev. = 4.47 to 3 sig. fig. ***[1 mark]***

4 a) $\bar{a} = \dfrac{60.3}{20} = 3.015$ g ***[1 mark]***

b) Variance $= \dfrac{219}{20} - 3.015^2$ ***[1 mark]***

$= 1.8597...$ g^2 ***[1 mark]***

So standard deviation = 1.36 g (to 3 sig. fig.) ***[1 mark]***

c) Brand A chocolate drops are heavier on average than Brand B. Brand B chocolate drops vary in mass much less than brand A.
[1 mark for each of 2 sensible statements]

d) Combined mean $= \dfrac{\sum a + \sum b}{50}$

$= \dfrac{60.3 + (30 \times 2.95)}{50}$

$= 2.976$ g ***[1 mark]***

Standard deviation for B = 1, so $\dfrac{\sum b^2}{30} - 2.95^2 = 1$,

and so $\sum b^2 = 291.075$ ***[1 mark]***

Combined variance $= \dfrac{\sum a^2 + \sum b^2}{50} - 2.976^2$

$= \dfrac{219 + 291.075}{50} - 2.976^2$

$= 1.3449...$ ***[1 mark]***

So combined standard deviation for all 50 chocolate drops is $\sqrt{1.3449...} = 1.16$ g
[1 mark]

Work through each step carefully so you don't make silly mistakes and lose marks.

5 a) Mean $= \frac{\sum x}{n} = \frac{1051}{16} = 65.6875$ ***[1 mark]***

To find the standard deviation you need the variance. Find the sum of the squares first:

$\sum x^2 = 2025 + 3136 + 3249 + 3721 + 3844 + 3969 + 3969 + 4096 + 4225 + 4356 + 4489 + 4761 + 5184 + 5476 + 6084 + 7921 = 70505$

So variance $= \frac{\sum x^2}{n} - \bar{x}^2 = \frac{70505}{16} - 65.6875^2$

$= 91.714... = 91.71$ (2 d.p.) ***[1 mark]***

So standard deviation $= \sqrt{91.714...} = 9.5767...$
$= 9.58$ (2 d.p.). ***[1 mark]***

b) There are 20 students in total, so the median is halfway between the 10th and 11th data values.

Don't forget that four students got 0, so you'll need to count these four data values at the start of your ordered list.

So median = 63. ***[1 mark]***

20 ÷ 4 = 5 so the lower quartile is halfway between the 5th and 6th values.

$Q_1 = \frac{45 + 56}{2} = 50.5$. ***[1 mark]***

(3 × 20) ÷ 4 = 15 so the upper quartile is halfway between the 15th and 16th values.

$Q_3 = \frac{67 + 69}{2} = 68$ ***[1 mark]***.

So the interquartile range $= Q_3 - Q_1$
$= 68 - 50.5 = 17.5$ ***[1 mark]***

c) mode = 0 ***[1 mark]***

d) The mode is the least appropriate measure of location for this data set because the scores of the four students who automatically got 0 make the mode unrepresentative of the data set as a whole. ***[1 mark]***

Chapter 2: Probability

1. Elementary Probability

Exercise 1.1 — Finding probabilities using equally likely outcomes or relative frequency

Q1 a) There is 1 outcome corresponding to the 7 of diamonds, and 52 outcomes in total.

So, P(7 of diamonds) = $\frac{1}{52}$

b) There is 1 outcome corresponding to the queen of spades, and 52 outcomes in total.

So, P(queen of spades) = $\frac{1}{52}$

c) There are 4 outcomes corresponding to a '9', and 52 outcomes in total.

So, P(9 of any suit) = $\frac{4}{52} = \frac{1}{13}$

d) There are 26 outcomes corresponding to a heart or a diamond, and 52 outcomes in total.

So, P(heart or diamond) = $\frac{26}{52} = \frac{1}{2}$

Q2 a) 6 of the 36 outcomes are prime numbers.

So, P(product is a prime number) = $\frac{6}{36} = \frac{1}{6}$

b) 14 of the 36 outcomes are less than 7.

So, P(product is less than 7) = $\frac{14}{36} = \frac{7}{18}$

c) 6 of the 36 outcomes are multiples of 10.

So, P(product is a multiple of 10) = $\frac{6}{36} = \frac{1}{6}$

Q3 a) E.g.

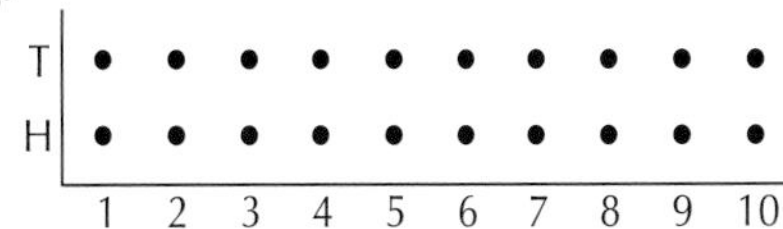

b) There are 5 ways of getting an even number and 'tails', and 20 outcomes altogether.

So, P(even number and tails) = $\frac{5}{20} = \frac{1}{4}$

Q4 a) It's easiest if you draw a sample-space diagram to show all the possible outcomes. E.g.

–	1	2	3	4	5	6
1	0	1	2	3	4	5
2	1	0	1	2	3	4
3	2	1	0	1	2	3
4	3	2	1	0	1	2
5	4	3	2	1	0	1
6	5	4	3	2	1	0

6 of the 36 outcomes are zero.

So, P(score is zero) = $\frac{6}{36} = \frac{1}{6}$

b) None of the outcomes are greater than 5.

So, P(score is greater than 5) = 0

c) The most likely score is the one corresponding to the most outcomes — so it's 1.

10 of the 36 outcomes give a score of 1, so:

P(1) = $\frac{10}{36} = \frac{5}{18}$

Q5 a) There are 35 red ladybirds and 3 orange ladybirds in the study, and there are 50 ladybirds in total.

So P(red or orange) = $\frac{38}{50} = \frac{19}{25}$ or 0.76.

b) Add the frequencies for 'yellow' and 'fewer than 10 spots', but then subtract 9 so you don't count 'yellow <u>and</u> fewer than 10' twice:

12 + 30 – 9 = 33

So P(yellow or fewer than 10) = $\frac{33}{50}$ or 0.66.

Q6 The frequency of odd numbers in the 60 rolls = 8 + 4 + 12 = 24, so the relative frequency = $\frac{24}{60} = \frac{2}{5}$.

So an estimate of P(odd number) = $\frac{2}{5}$.

2. Solving Probability Problems

Exercise 2.1 — Using Venn diagrams and tables

Q1 a) Label the diagram by starting in the middle with the probability for $A \cap B$. Then subtract this probability from P(A) and P(B). And remember to find $P(A' \cap B')$ by subtracting the other probabilities from 1. So:

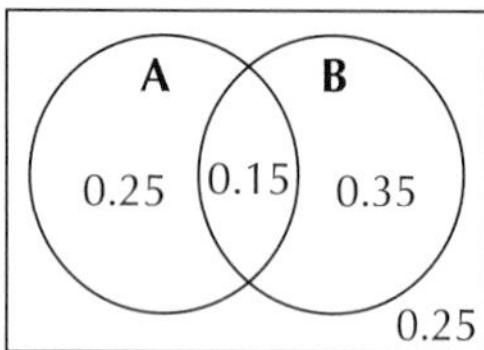

b) $P(A \cap B') = 0.25$

c) $P(B \cap A') = 0.35$

d) $P(A \cup B) = 0.75$

e) $P(A' \cap B') = 0.25$

Q2 a) Let M be 'studies maths' and P be 'studies physics'. Start by filling in the total number of students in M, the total in P, the number in $M \cap P$ and the overall total. Then you can use the totals to fill in the gaps.

	M	M'	Total
P	19	19	38
P'	27	79	106
Total	46	98	144

b) $M \cup P$ has 19 + 27 + 19 = 65 outcomes.
So $P(M \cup P) = \frac{65}{144}$

c) So you're only interested in the 46 students who study maths. 19 students study maths and physics, so P(P, given M) = $\frac{19}{46}$.

Q3 a) $P(L \cap M) = 0.1$

b) $P(L \cap N) = 0$

c) $P(L' \cap N) = 0.25$
Since N doesn't overlap with L, $L' \cap N$ is just N.

d) $P(L' \cap M' \cap N') = 1 - (0.25 + 0.1 + 0.15 + 0.25)$
$= 0.25$

e) $P(L \cup M) = 0.25 + 0.1 + 0.15 = 0.5$

f) $P(M') = 0.25 + 0.25 + 0.25 = 0.75$
Don't forget to include $P(L' \cap M' \cap N')$. You could also find P(M') by doing $1 - P(M) = 1 - (0.1 + 0.15)$.

Q4 a)

	F	F'	Total
S	0.3	0.05	0.35
S'	0.35	0.3	0.65
Total	0.65	0.35	1.00

b) (i) P(France, but not Spain) = $P(F \cap S') = 0.35$
(ii) P(Spain, but not France) = $P(S \cap F') = 0.05$
(iii) P(neither France nor Spain) = $P(F' \cap S') = 0.3$

3. Laws of Probability

Exercise 3.1 — The addition law

Q1 a) $P(A') = 1 - P(A) = 1 - 0.3 = 0.7$

b) $P(A \cup B) = P(A) + P(B) - P(A \cap B)$
$= 0.3 + 0.5 - 0.15 = 0.65$

c) $P(A' \cap B') = 1 - P(A \cup B) = 1 - 0.65 = 0.35$
Remember, $A' \cap B'$ is the complement of $A \cup B$.

Q2 a) $P(B') = 1 - P(B) = 1 - 0.44 = 0.56$

b) $P(A \cup B) = P(A) + P(B) - P(A \cap B)$
$= (1 - 0.36) + 0.44 - 0.27 = 0.81$

c) $P(A \cap B') = P(A) - P(A \cap B) = 0.64 - 0.27 = 0.37$

d) $P(A \cup B') = P(A) + P(B') - P(A \cap B')$
$= 0.64 + 0.56 - 0.37 = 0.83$

Q3 Let B = 'car is blue' and E = 'car is an estate'.

a) $P(B') = 1 - P(B) = 1 - 0.25 = 0.75$

b) $P(B \cup E) = P(B) + P(E) - P(B \cap E)$
$= 0.25 + 0.15 - 0.08 = 0.32$

c) $P(B' \cap E') = 1 - P(B \cup E) = 1 - 0.32 = 0.68$

Q4 a) $P(Y') = 1 - P(Y) = 1 - 0.56 = 0.44$

b) $P(X \cap Y) = P(X) + P(Y) - P(X \cup Y)$
$= 0.43 + 0.56 - 0.77 = 0.22$

c) $P(X' \cap Y') = 1 - P(X \cup Y) = 1 - 0.77 = 0.23$

d) $P(X' \cup Y') = 1 - P(X \cap Y) = 1 - 0.22 = 0.78$

Q5 a) $P(C' \cap D) = P(C') + P(D) - P(C' \cup D)$
$= (1 - 0.53) + 0.44 - 0.65 = 0.26$

b) $P(C' \cap D') = P(C') - P(C' \cap D)$
$= 0.47 - 0.26 = 0.21$
Just as $C = C \cap D + C \cap D'$,
$C' = C' \cap D + C' \cap D'$.

c) $P(C' \cup D') = P(C') + P(D') - P(C' \cap D')$
$= 0.47 + 0.56 - 0.21 = 0.82$

d) $P(C \cap D) = P(C) + P(D) - P(C \cup D)$
$= P(C) + P(D) - [1 - P(C' \cap D')]$
$= 0.53 + 0.44 - (1 - 0.21) = 0.18$

Q6 Let M = 'has read To Kill a Mockingbird' and A = 'has read Animal Farm'. Then, P(M) = 0.62, P(A') = 0.66, and $P(M \cup A) = 0.79$.

a) $P(M \cap A) = P(M) + P(A) - P(M \cup A)$
$= 0.62 + (1 - 0.66) - 0.79 = 0.17$

b) $P(M' \cap A) = P(A) - P(M \cap A) = 0.34 - 0.17 = 0.17$

c) $P(M' \cap A') = 1 - P(M \cup A) = 1 - 0.79 = 0.21$

Exercise 3.2 — Mutually exclusive events

Q1 **a)** $P(X \cap Y) = 0$

b) $P(X \cup Y) = P(X) + P(Y) = 0.48 + 0.37 = 0.85$

c) $P(X' \cap Y') = 1 - P(X \cup Y) = 1 - 0.85 = 0.15$

Q2 Let R = wears red tie and O = wears orange tie. These two events are mutually exclusive, so: P(orange or red) = $P(O \cup R) = P(O) + P(R)$ $= 0.03 + 0.02 = 0.05$.

Q3 **a)** Let B = 'goes bowling', C = 'goes to the cinema', and D = 'goes out for dinner'. All 3 events are mutually exclusive, so:
$P(B \cup C) = P(B) + P(C) = 0.17 + 0.43 = 0.6$

b) P(doesn't do B, C or D) = $P(B' \cap C' \cap D')$
Since either none of B, C and D happen, or at least one of B, C and D happen, $B' \cap C' \cap D'$ and $B \cup C \cup D$ are complementary events. So:
$P(B' \cap C' \cap D') = 1 - P(B \cup C \cup D)$
$= 1 - [P(B) + P(C) + P(D)]$
$= 1 - (0.17 + 0.43 + 0.22)$
$= 1 - 0.82$
$= 0.18$

Q4 **a)** $P(A \cap B) = P(A) + P(B) - P(A \cup B)$
$= 0.28 + 0.66 - 0.86 = 0.08$
$P(A \cap B) \neq 0$, so A and B are not mutually exclusive.

b) $P(A \cap C) = P(A) + P(C) - P(A \cup C)$
$= 0.28 + 0.49 - 0.77 = 0$
$P(A \cap C) = 0$, so A and C are mutually exclusive.

c) $P(B \cap C) = P(B) + P(C) - P(B \cup C)$
$= 0.66 + 0.49 - 0.92 = 0.23$
$P(B \cap C) \neq 0$, so B and C are not mutually exclusive.

Q5 **a)** You need to show that $P(C \cap D) = 0$.
$P(C) = 1 - 0.6 = 0.4$.
$P(C \cap D) = P(C) - P(C \cap D') = 0.4 - 0.4 = 0$, so C and D are mutually exclusive.

b) $P(C \cup D) = P(C) + P(D) = 0.4 + 0.25 = 0.65$

Q6 Out of the total of 50 biscuits, 30 are plain, and 20 are chocolate-coated. Half of the biscuits are in wrappers, so 25 biscuits are in wrappers. Since there are more biscuits in wrappers than there are chocolate-coated ones, there must be some biscuits (at least 5) which are plain and in wrappers. So events P and W can happen at the same time (i.e. $P(P \cap W) \neq 0$), which means they are not mutually exclusive.

Exercise 3.3 — The multiplication law — conditional probability

Q1 **a)** $P(G \mid H) = \frac{P(G \cap H)}{P(H)} = \frac{0.24}{0.63} = \frac{24}{63} = \frac{8}{21}$

You could give the answer as a decimal instead, but using a fraction means you can give an exact answer.

b) $P(H \mid G) = \frac{P(G \cap H)}{P(G)} = \frac{0.24}{0.7} = \frac{24}{70} = \frac{12}{35}$

Q2 **a)** $P(B \mid A) = \frac{P(A \cap B)}{P(A)} = \frac{0.34}{0.68} = 0.5$

b) $P(A \mid C) = \frac{P(A \cap C)}{P(C)} = \frac{0.16}{0.44} = \frac{16}{44} = \frac{4}{11}$

c) $P(C' \mid B) = \frac{P(B \cap C')}{P(B)} = \frac{0.49}{1 - 0.44} = 0.875$

Q3 Let F = 'over 6 feet tall' and G = 'can play in goal'.

a) $P(G \mid F) = \frac{P(F \cap G)}{P(F)}$

$P(F \cap G) = \frac{2}{11}$ and $P(F) = \frac{5}{11}$

So, $P(G \mid F) = \frac{P(F \cap G)}{P(F)} = \frac{\frac{2}{11}}{\frac{5}{11}} = \frac{2}{5}$

b) $P(F \mid G) = \frac{P(F \cap G)}{P(G)}$ and $P(G) = \frac{3}{11}$. So:

$P(F \mid G) = \frac{P(F \cap G)}{P(G)} = \frac{\frac{2}{11}}{\frac{3}{11}} = \frac{2}{3}$

Q4 Let N_S = 'Nida buys shoes' and S_S = 'Sally buys shoes'.
Then $P(N_S) = 0.6$, $P(S_S \mid N_S) = 0.7$ and $P(S_S \mid N'_S) = 0.3$.

a) $P(N_S \cap S_S) = P(N_S) \times P(S_S \mid N_S) = 0.6 \times 0.7 = 0.42$.

b) $P(N'_S \cap S'_S) = P(N'_S) \times P(S'_S \mid N'_S)$
$= (1 - 0.6) \times (1 - 0.3)$
$= 0.4 \times 0.7 = 0.28$.

Q5 **a)** $P(Y) = 1 - P(Y') = 1 - 0.72 = 0.28$

b) $P(X \cap Y) = P(X|Y)P(Y) = 0.75 \times 0.28 = 0.21$

c) $P(X \cap Z) = P(Z|X)P(X) = 0.25 \times 0.44 = 0.11$

d) $P(Y \mid Z') = \frac{P(Y \cap Z')}{P(Z')} = \frac{0.2}{1 - 0.61} = \frac{20}{39}$

e) $P(X \cap Y \cap Z) = P(X \cap Y \mid Z)P(Z)$
$= \frac{7}{61} \times \frac{61}{100}$
$= \frac{7}{100} = 0.07$

There are lots of ways to write an expression for $P(X \cap Y \cap Z)$ — e.g. $P(Z \mid X \cap Y)P(X \cap Y)$ or $P(X \mid Y \cap Z)P(Y \cap Z)$. You have to choose the way that makes best use of the information in the question.

Exercise 3.4 — Independent events

Q1 $P(X \cap Y) = P(X)P(Y) = 0.62 \times 0.32 = 0.1984$

Q2 $P(A)P(B) = P(A \cap B)$, so:

$P(A) = \frac{P(A \cap B)}{P(B)} = \frac{0.45}{1 - 0.25} = 0.6$

Q3 **a)** $P(M \cap N) = P(M)P(N) = 0.4 \times 0.7 = 0.28$

b) $P(M \cup N) = P(M) + P(N) - P(M \cap N)$
$= 0.4 + 0.7 - 0.28 = 0.82$

c) $P(M \cap N') = P(M)P(N') = 0.4 \times 0.3 = 0.12$

Q4 **a)** Let A = '1st card is hearts' and B = '2nd card is hearts'. Then, since the first card is replaced before the second is picked, A and B are independent events.
So, $P(A \cap B) = P(A) \times P(B)$
There are 13 hearts out of the 52 cards, so P(A) and P(B) both equal $\frac{13}{52} = \frac{1}{4}$.
So, $P(A \cap B) = \frac{1}{4} \times \frac{1}{4} = \frac{1}{16}$.

b) Let A = '1st card is ace of hearts' and B = '2nd card is ace of hearts'. Then, since the first card is replaced before the second is picked, A and B are independent events.
So, $P(A \cap B) = P(A) \times P(B)$
There is 1 'ace of hearts' out of the 52 cards, so P(A) and P(B) both equal $\frac{1}{52}$.
So, $P(A \cap B) = \frac{1}{52} \times \frac{1}{52} = \frac{1}{2704}$.

Q5 A and B:
$P(A) \times P(B) = \frac{3}{11} \times \frac{1}{3} = \frac{3}{33} = \frac{1}{11}$
$P(A) \times P(B) = \frac{1}{11} = P(A \cap B)$,
so A and B are independent.

A and C:
$P(A) \times P(C) = \frac{3}{11} \times \frac{15}{28} = \frac{45}{308}$
$P(A) \times P(C) = \frac{45}{308} \neq P(A \cap C) = \frac{2}{15}$,
so A and C are not independent.

B and C:
$P(B) \times P(C) = \frac{1}{3} \times \frac{15}{28} = \frac{15}{84} = \frac{5}{28}$
$P(B) \times P(C) = \frac{5}{28} = P(B \cap C)$,
so B and C are independent.

Q6 **a)** $P(X \cap Y) = P(X)P(Y) = 0.84 \times 0.68 = 0.5712$
b) $P(Y' \cap Z') = P(Y')P(Z') = 0.32 \times 0.52 = 0.1664$
c) Since Y and Z are independent,
$P(Y \mid Z) = P(Y) = 0.68$
d) Since Z' and Y' are independent,
$P(Z' \mid Y') = P(Z') = 1 - 0.48 = 0.52$
e) Since Y and X' are independent,
$P(Y \mid X') = P(Y) = 0.68$

Q7 Let J = 'Jess buys a DVD', K = 'Keisha buys a DVD' and L = 'Lucy buys a DVD'.
a) The probability that all 3 buy a DVD is $P(J \cap K \cap L)$. Since the 3 events are independent, you can multiply their probabilities together to get: $P(J) \times P(K) \times P(L) = 0.66 \times 0.5 \times 0.3 = 0.099$
b) The probability that at least 2 of them buy a DVD will be the probability that one of the following happens: $J \cap K \cap L$ or $J \cap K \cap L'$ or $J \cap K' \cap L$ or $J' \cap K \cap L$.
Since these events are mutually exclusive, you can add their probabilities together to give:
$0.099 + (0.66 \times 0.5 \times 0.7) + (0.66 \times 0.5 \times 0.3) + (0.34 \times 0.5 \times 0.3)$
$= 0.099 + 0.231 + 0.099 + 0.051$
$= 0.48$

Exercise 3.5 — Tree diagrams

Q1 **a)** The events are not independent because the probability that Jake wins his 2nd match depends on whether or not he won his 1st match.
b) **(i)** P(Win then Win) = $0.6 \times 0.75 = 0.45$
(ii) P(Wins at least 1) = P(Win then Win) + P(Win then Lose) + P(Lose then Win)
$= 0.45 + (0.6 \times 0.25) + (0.4 \times 0.35)$
$= 0.74$
Or you could find 1 – P(Lose then Lose).

Q2 **a)**
$\frac{1}{6}$ **6** — $\frac{1}{2}$ **Heads**, $\frac{1}{2}$ **Tails**
$\frac{5}{6}$ **Not 6** — $\frac{1}{2}$ **Heads**, $\frac{1}{2}$ **Tails**

b) $P(\text{wins}) = P(6 \cap \text{Tails}) = \frac{1}{6} \times \frac{1}{2} = \frac{1}{12}$

Q3 **a)** Let D = 'passed driving test' and U = 'intend to go to university'. Since D and U are independent, $P(U \mid D') = P(U \mid D)$, and so:

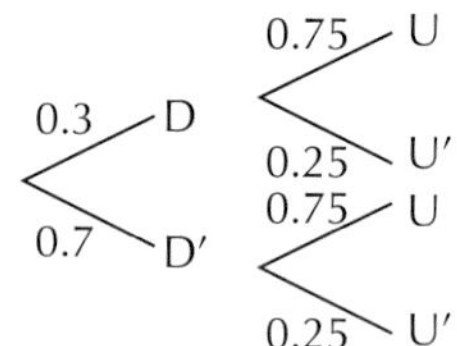

b) $P(D' \cap U') = 0.7 \times 0.25 = 0.175$
c) $P(U') = P(D \cap U') + P(D' \cap U')$
$= (0.3 \times 0.25) + 0.175$
$= 0.25$
Or, since the events are independent, $P(U') = P(U' \mid D) = P(U' \mid D') = 0.25$ (reading from the tree diagram above).

Q4 Let R = 'orders roast dinner' and let A = 'orders apple pie for pudding'. Then you can draw the following tree diagram:

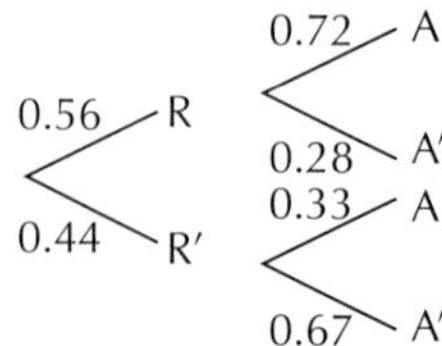

So $P(A) = P(R \cap A) + P(R' \cap A)$
$= (0.56 \times 0.72) + (0.44 \times 0.33)$
$= 0.5484$

Q5 Let S = 'owns smartphone' and let C = 'has contract costing more than £25 a month'. Then you know the following probabilities: P(S) = 0.62, P(C) = 0.539 and P(C' | S) = 0.29, and you want to find P(S | C).
Using the conditional probability formula:

$P(S \mid C) = \frac{P(S \cap C)}{P(C)}$.

Use a tree diagram to help you find P(S ∩ C). You don't need to label all the branches, just the ones that help you answer the question:

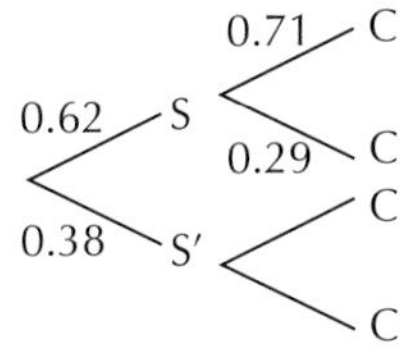

So P(S ∩ C) = 0.62 × 0.71 = 0.4402, and so:

$P(S \mid C) = \frac{P(S \cap C)}{P(C)} = \frac{0.4402}{0.539} = 0.817\ (3\text{ s.f.})$.

Q6 a) Let D = 'Dave falls off', J = 'Juan falls off' and C = 'Callum falls off'. Then P(D) = 0.3, P(J) = 0.4 and P(C) = 0.6.
Using a tree diagram:

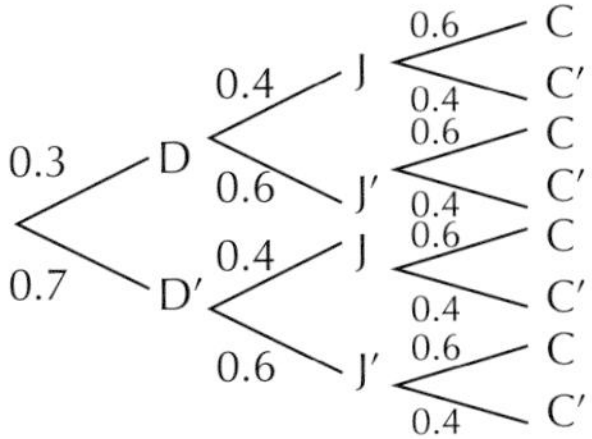

P(at least 2 fall off) = P(2 fall off) + P(3 fall off)
P(2 fall off)
= P(D ∩ J ∩ C') + P(D ∩ J' ∩ C) + P(D' ∩ J ∩ C)
= (0.3 × 0.4 × 0.4) + (0.3 × 0.6 × 0.6) + (0.7 × 0.4 × 0.6)
= 0.048 + 0.108 + 0.168
= 0.324
P(3 fall off)
= P(D ∩ J ∩ C) = 0.3 × 0.4 × 0.6 = 0.072
So P(at least 2 fall off) = 0.324 + 0.072 = 0.396.

b) On each of the 4 rides, P(Dave doesn't fall off) = P(D') = 0.7.
So P(doesn't fall off for 4 rides) = 0.7^4 = 0.2401.

Review Exercise — Chapter 2

Q1 a) The sample space looks like this:

		Dice					
		1	2	3	4	5	6
Coin	H	2	4	6	8	10	12
	T	5	6	7	8	9	10

b) There are 12 outcomes in total, and 9 are more than 5, so P(score more than 5) = $\frac{9}{12} = \frac{3}{4}$.

c) There are 6 outcomes which have a tail showing, and 3 of these are even, so P(even score given that a tail is thrown) = $\frac{3}{6} = \frac{1}{2}$.

Q2 a) There are 30 workers in total and 12 drink coffee, so: P(drinks coffee) = $\frac{12}{30} = \frac{2}{5}$

b) 7 workers drink milky tea without sugar, so: P(drinks milky tea without sugar) = $\frac{7}{30}$

c) There are 7 + 4 + 6 + 1 + 3 = 21 workers who either drink tea or take only sugar, so:
P(drinks tea or takes only sugar) = $\frac{21}{30} = \frac{7}{10}$

Q3 a) Let S = 'eats sausages' and C = 'eats chips'. Then P(S) = 0.5, P(C) = 0.2 and P(S ∩ C) = 0.02. To work out the probabilities, it might help to draw a Venn diagram or two-way table. E.g.:

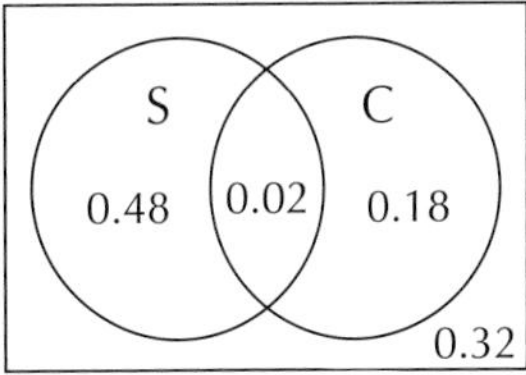

So P(C ∩ S') = 0.2 – 0.02 = 0.18.

b) P(chips or sausages but not both)
= P(C ∩ S') + P(S ∩ C')
= 0.18 + (0.5 – 0.02)
= 0.66

Q4 It's best to start by drawing a sample-space diagram:

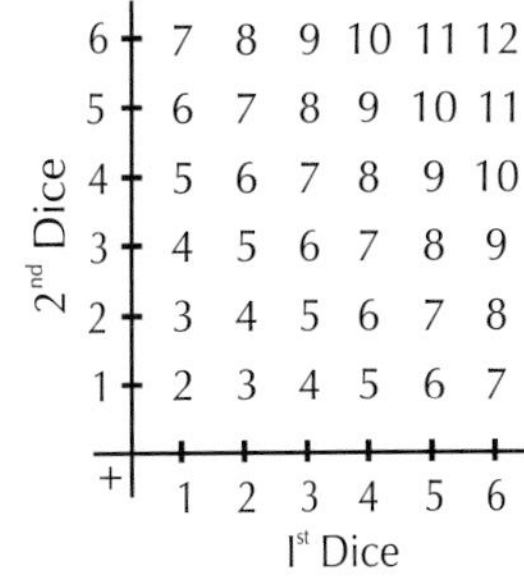

a) 15 of the 36 outcomes are prime (since 2, 3, 5, 7 and 11 are prime), so P(prime) = $\frac{15}{36} = \frac{5}{12}$.

b) 7 of the 36 outcomes are square numbers (since 4 and 9 are square), so P(square) = $\frac{7}{36}$

c) It isn't possible for her score to be both a prime number and a square number, so the events P and S are mutually exclusive.

d) Since P and S are mutually exclusive,
P(P ∪ S) = P(P) + P(S) = $\frac{5}{12} + \frac{7}{36} = \frac{22}{36} = \frac{11}{18}$

e) The score from the second experiment is unaffected by the score from the first experiment, so the events S_1 and S_2 are independent.

f) $P(S_1 \cap S_2) = P(S_1)P(S_2) = \frac{7}{36} \times \frac{7}{36} = \frac{49}{1296}$

Q5 Let B = boy, G = girl, U = 'in upper school' and L = 'in lower school', then:

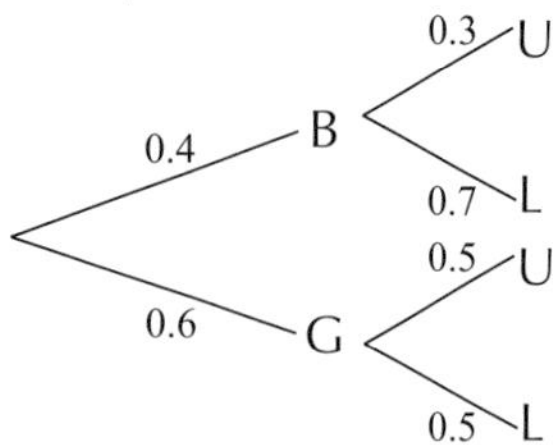

a) Reading from the tree diagram, P(L | B) = 0.7.

b) P(G ∩ L) = 0.6 × 0.5 = 0.3

c) Choosing an upper school pupil means either 'boy and upper' or 'girl and upper'.
P(B ∩ U) = 0.4 × 0.3 = 0.12
P(G ∩ U) = 0.6 × 0.5 = 0.30
So P(U) = 0.12 + 0.30 = 0.42

Exam-Style Questions — Chapter 2

1 **a)** Use the totals to fill in the gaps:

	A	A'	Total
B	0.05	**0.05**	0.10
B'	**0.35**	**0.55**	**0.90**
Total	0.40	**0.60**	1.00

[3 marks available — 1 mark for each of 3 correct rows]

b) P(doesn't buy soap) = P(A' ∩ B') = 0.55 ***[1 mark]***

2 Let R_1 = '1st counter is red', W_1 = '1st counter is white', G_1 = '1st counter is green', R_2 = '2nd counter is red', W_2 = '2nd counter is white' and G_2 = '2nd counter is green'. Then you can draw the following tree diagram to help you:

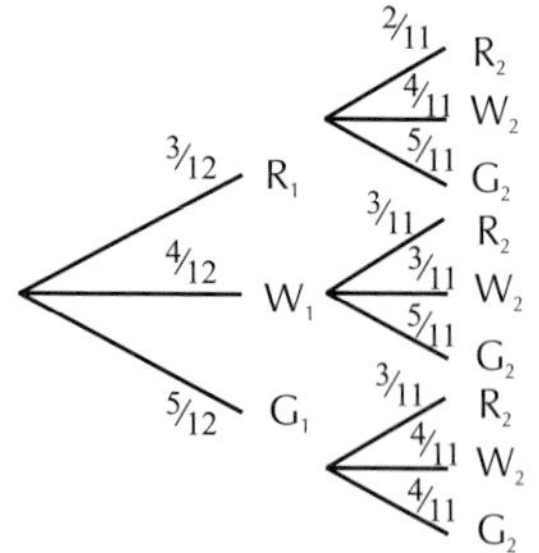

a) The second counter is green means one of three results: 'red then green' or 'white then green' or 'green then green'. So P(2nd is green) =
$\left(\frac{3}{12} \times \frac{5}{11}\right) + \left(\frac{4}{12} \times \frac{5}{11}\right) + \left(\frac{5}{12} \times \frac{4}{11}\right)$ ***[1 mark]***
$= \frac{15}{132} + \frac{20}{132} + \frac{20}{132} = \frac{55}{132} = \frac{5}{12}$ ***[1 mark]***

b) For both to be red there's only one possibility: 'red then red' ***[1 mark]***.
P(both red) $= \frac{3}{12} \times \frac{2}{11} = \frac{6}{132} = \frac{1}{22}$ ***[1 mark]***

c) 'Both same colour' is the complementary event of 'not both same colour'. So P(not same colour) = 1 – P(both same colour) ***[1 mark]***. Both same colour is either R_1 and R_2, or W_1 and W_2, or G_1 and G_2. So P(not same colour)
$= 1 - \left[\left(\frac{3}{12} \times \frac{2}{11}\right) + \left(\frac{4}{12} \times \frac{3}{11}\right) + \left(\frac{5}{12} \times \frac{4}{11}\right)\right]$
[1 mark]
$= 1 - \frac{38}{132} = \frac{94}{132} = \frac{47}{66}$ ***[1 mark]***

(Alternatively, 1 mark for showing P(R_1W_2 or R_1G_2 or W_1R_2 or W_1G_2 or G_1R_2 or G_1W_2), 1 mark for adding the 6 correct probabilities and 1 mark for the correct answer.)

3 **a)** **(i)** J and K are independent, so
P(J ∩ K) = P(J) × P(K) = 0.7 × 0.1 = 0.07
[1 mark]

(ii) P(J ∪ K) = P(J) + P(K) – P(J ∩ K) ***[1 mark]***
= 0.7 + 0.1 – 0.07 = 0.73 ***[1 mark]***

b) Drawing a quick Venn Diagram often helps:

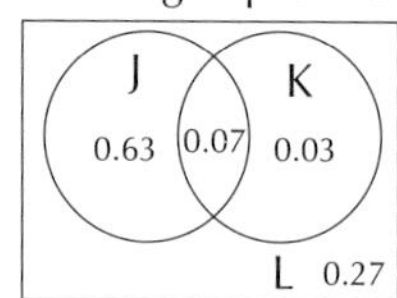

P(L|K') = P(L ∩ K') ÷ P(K')
Now L ∩ K' = L — think about it — all of L is contained in K', so L ∩ K' (the bits in both L and K') are just the bits in L.
Therefore P(L ∩ K') = P(L)
= 1 – P(K ∪ J) = 1 – 0.73 = 0.27 ***[1 mark]***
P(K') = 1 – P(K) = 1 – 0.1 = 0.9 ***[1 mark]***
And so P(L|K') = 0.27 ÷ 0.9 = 0.3 ***[1 mark]***

4 It's a good idea to start by drawing a tree diagram. Let C = 'eats chicken', B = 'eats beef', I = 'eats ice cream' and S = 'eats sponge pudding'.

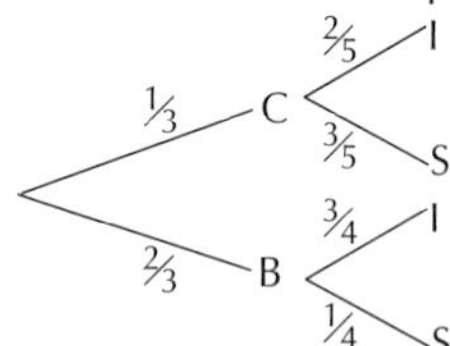

a) P(chicken or ice cream but not both)
= P(C ∩ S) + P(B ∩ I) ***[1 mark]***
$= \left(\frac{1}{3} \times \frac{3}{5}\right) + \left(\frac{2}{3} \times \frac{3}{4}\right)$ ***[1 mark]***
$= \frac{3}{15} + \frac{6}{12} = \frac{7}{10}$ ***[1 mark]***

b) P(ice cream) = P(C ∩ I) + P(B ∩ I) ***[1 mark]***
$= \left(\frac{1}{3} \times \frac{2}{5}\right) + \left(\frac{2}{3} \times \frac{3}{4}\right)$ ***[1 mark]***
$= \frac{2}{15} + \frac{6}{12} = \frac{19}{30}$ ***[1 mark]***

c) P(chicken | ice cream)

$= P(C \mid I) = \frac{P(C \cap I)}{P(I)}$ ***[1 mark]***

$P(C \cap I) = \frac{2}{15}$ and $P(I) = \frac{19}{30}$ (both from b) above)

So $\frac{P(C \cap I)}{P(I)} = \frac{2}{15} \div \frac{19}{30}$ ***[1 mark]***

$= \frac{4}{19}$ ***[1 mark]***

5 a) Let E = 'goes every week' and R = 'plans to renew membership'. Then $P(E) = \frac{14}{20}$, $P(R) = \frac{13}{20}$ and $P(E \mid R) = \frac{10}{13}$.

$P(R \cap E) = P(E \mid R)P(R)$ ***[1 mark]***

$= \frac{10}{13} \times \frac{13}{20}$ ***[1 mark]***

$= \frac{10}{20} = \frac{1}{2}$ ***[1 mark]***

b) $P(E \cap R') = P(E) - P(E \cap R)$ ***[1 mark]***

$= \frac{14}{20} - \frac{1}{2} = \frac{1}{5}$ ***[1 mark]***

c) $P(E) \times P(R) = \frac{14}{20} \times \frac{13}{20} = \frac{91}{200} \neq P(E \cap R) = \frac{1}{2}$

[1 mark]

So going to the club every week and renewing membership are not independent ***[1 mark]***.

Or you could say that P(E) ≠ P(E | R).

6 a) $P(B') = 1 - 0.2 = 0.8$ ***[1 mark]***

b) It'll help if you draw a tree diagram before going any further. If F = 'roll a 6 on the fair dice':

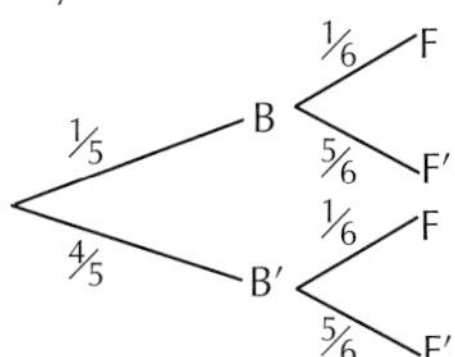

You want to find $P(B \cup F)$. Now, either at least one of the dice shows a 6 or neither of them do, so these are complementary events.

So $P(B \cup F) = 1 - P(B' \cap F')$ ***[1 mark]***

$= 1 - \left(\frac{4}{5} \times \frac{5}{6}\right) = 1 - \frac{20}{30} = \frac{1}{3}$ ***[1 mark]***

Or you can use the addition rule:
$P(B \cup F) = P(B) + P(F) - P(B \cap F)$

c) P(exactly one 6 | at least one 6)

$= \frac{P(\text{exactly one 6} \cap \text{at least one 6})}{P(\text{at least one 6})}$ ***[1 mark]***

The next step might be a bit easier to figure out if you draw a Venn diagram:

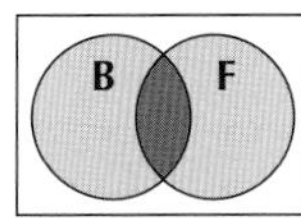

'exactly one 6' ∩ 'at least one 6' = 'exactly one 6' (Look at the diagram — 'exactly one 6' is the light grey area, and 'at least one 6' is the light grey area plus the dark grey bit. So the bit in common to both is just the light grey area.)

Now, that means P(exactly one 6 ∩ at least one 6) $= P(B \cap F') + P(B' \cap F)$ — this is the light grey area in the Venn diagram,

i.e. P(exactly one 6 ∩ at least one 6)

$= \left(\frac{1}{5} \times \frac{5}{6}\right) + \left(\frac{4}{5} \times \frac{1}{6}\right) = \frac{9}{30} = \frac{3}{10}$

[1 mark]

P(at least one 6) $= \frac{1}{3}$ (from b) above).

And all of this means...

P(exactly one 6 | at least one 6)

$= \frac{3}{10} \div \frac{1}{3}$ ***[1 mark]*** $= \frac{9}{10}$ ***[1 mark]***

Chapter 3: The Binomial Distribution

2. Binomial Distributions

Exercise 2.1 — Binomial coefficients

Q1 a) All 8 letters are different, so there are 8! = 40 320 different arrangements.

b) If all 9 letters were different, there would be 9! = 362 880 different arrangements. But since two of the letters are the same, you need to divide this by 2! = 2. So there are 9! ÷ 2! = 181 440 different arrangements.

c) If all 7 letters were different, there would be 7! = 5040 different arrangements. But there are 2 Ts and 2 Rs, so you need to divide this by 2! twice. So there are 7! ÷ 2! ÷ 2! = 1260 different arrangements.

Q2 $\binom{20}{11} = \frac{20!}{11!9!} = 167\,960$ different ways

Q3 a) $\binom{10}{3} = \binom{10}{7} = \frac{10!}{3!7!} = 120$ ways

b) $\binom{10}{5} = \frac{10!}{5!5!} = 252$ ways

Q4 a) $\binom{11}{4} = \binom{11}{7} = \frac{11!}{4!7!} = 330$ ways

b) $\binom{11}{6} = \binom{11}{5} = \frac{11!}{6!5!} = 462$ ways

c) $\binom{11}{8} = \binom{11}{3} = \frac{11!}{8!3!} = 165$ ways

Exercise 2.2 — The binomial distribution

Q1 a) Not a binomial distribution — the number of trials is not fixed.

b) Here, X will follow a binomial distribution. $X \sim B(2000, 0.005)$.

c) Here, Y will follow a binomial distribution. $Y \sim B(10, 0.5)$.

Q2 The number of trials is fixed (i.e. the 15 acts), each trial can either succeed or fail, X is the total number of successes, and the probability of success is the same each time if the trials are independent. So to model this situation with a binomial distribution, you would need to assume that all the trials are independent.

Q3 The number of trials is fixed, each trial can either succeed or fail, and X is the total number of successes. To make the probability of success the same each time, the cards would need to be replaced, and to make each pick independent you could shuffle the pack after replacing the picked cards. If this is done, then $X \sim B(10, \frac{3}{13})$.

Q4 The number of trials is fixed (650), each trial can either succeed or fail, X is the total number of successes, and the probability of each button falling off is the same if the trials are independent. So to model this situation with a binomial distribution, you would need to assume that all the trials are independent (i.e. the probability of each separate button falling off should not depend on whether any other button has fallen off). If this assumption is satisfied, then $X \sim B(650, 0.001)$.

Exercise 2.3 — Using the binomial probability function

Q1 a) Use the binomial probability function with $n = 10$ and $p = 0.14$.

(i) $P(X = 2) = \binom{10}{2} \times 0.14^2 \times (1 - 0.14)^{10-2}$
$= \frac{10!}{2!8!} \times 0.14^2 \times 0.86^8$
$= 0.264$ (to 3 sig. fig.)

(ii) $P(X = 4) = \binom{10}{4} \times 0.14^4 \times (1 - 0.14)^{10-4}$
$= \frac{10!}{4!6!} \times 0.14^4 \times 0.86^6$
$= 0.0326$ (to 3 sig. fig.)

(iii) $P(X = 5) = \binom{10}{5} \times 0.14^5 \times (1 - 0.14)^{10-5}$
$= \frac{10!}{5!5!} \times 0.14^5 \times 0.86^5$
$= 0.00638$ (to 3 sig. fig.)

b) Use the binomial probability function with $n = 8$ and $p = 0.27$.

(i) $P(X = 3) = \binom{8}{3} \times 0.27^3 \times (1 - 0.27)^{8-3}$
$= \frac{8!}{3!5!} \times 0.27^3 \times 0.73^5$
$= 0.229$ (to 3 sig. fig.)

(ii) $P(X = 5) = \binom{8}{5} \times 0.27^5 \times (1 - 0.27)^{8-5}$
$= \frac{8!}{5!3!} \times 0.27^5 \times 0.73^3$
$= 0.0313$ (to 3 sig. fig.)

(iii) $P(X = 7) = \binom{8}{7} \times 0.27^7 \times (1 - 0.27)^{8-7}$
$= \frac{8!}{7!1!} \times 0.27^7 \times 0.73^1$
$= 0.000611$ (to 3 sig. fig.)

Q2 a) Use the binomial probability function with $n = 20$ and $p = 0.16$.

(i) $P(X < 2) = P(X = 0) + P(X = 1)$
$= \frac{20!}{0!20!} \times 0.16^0 \times (1 - 0.16)^{20-0}$
$+ \frac{20!}{1!19!} \times 0.16^1 \times (1 - 0.16)^{20-1}$
$= 0.03059... + 0.11653...$
$= 0.147$ (to 3 sig. fig.)

(ii) $P(X \leq 3) = P(X = 0) + P(X = 1)$
$+ P(X = 2) + P(X = 3)$
$= 0.03059... + 0.11653...$
$+ \frac{20!}{2!18!} \times 0.16^2 \times (1 - 0.16)^{20-2}$
$+ \frac{20!}{3!17!} \times 0.16^3 \times (1 - 0.16)^{20-3}$
$= 0.03059... + 0.11653...$
$+ 0.21087... + 0.24099...$
$= 0.599$ (to 3 sig. fig.)

(iii) $P(1 < X \leq 4) = P(X = 2) + P(X = 3)$
$+ P(X = 4)$
$= 0.21087... + 0.24099...$
$+ \frac{20!}{4!16!} \times 0.16^4 \times 0.84^{16}$
$= 0.21087... + 0.24099...$
$+ 0.19509...$
$= 0.647$ (to 3 sig. fig.)

b) Use the binomial probability function with $n = 30$ and $p = 0.88$.

(i) $P(X > 28) = P(X = 29) + P(X = 30)$

$= \frac{30!}{29!1!} \times 0.88^{29} \times 0.12^{1}$

$+ \frac{30!}{30!0!} \times 0.88^{30} \times 0.12^{0}$

$= 0.088369... + 0.021601...$

$= 0.110$ (to 3 sig. fig.)

(ii) $P(25 < X < 28) = P(X = 26) + P(X = 27)$

$= \frac{30!}{26!4!} \times 0.88^{26} \times 0.12^{4}$

$+ \frac{30!}{27!3!} \times 0.88^{27} \times 0.12^{3}$

$= 0.204693... + 0.222383...$

$= 0.427$ (to 3 sig. fig.)

(iii) $P(X \geq 27) = P(X = 27) + P(X = 28)$

$+ P(X = 29) + P(X = 30)$

$= 0.222383...$

$+ \frac{30!}{28!2!} \times 0.88^{28} \times 0.12^{2}$

$+ 0.088369... + 0.021601...$

$= 0.222383... + 0.174729...$

$+ 0.088369... + 0.021601...$

$= 0.507$ (to 3 sig. fig.)

Q3 a) Use the binomial probability function with $n = 5$ and $p = \frac{1}{2}$.

(i) $P(X \leq 4) = 1 - P(X > 4) = 1 - P(X = 5)$

$= 1 - \frac{5!}{5!0!} \times \left(\frac{1}{2}\right)^5 \times \left(\frac{1}{2}\right)^0$

$= 1 - 0.03125$

$= 0.969$ (to 3 sig. fig.)

(ii) $P(X > 1) = 1 - P(X \leq 1)$

$= 1 - P(X = 0) - P(X = 1)$

$= 1 - \frac{5!}{0!5!} \times \left(\frac{1}{2}\right)^0 \times \left(\frac{1}{2}\right)^5$

$- \frac{5!}{1!4!} \times \left(\frac{1}{2}\right)^1 \times \left(\frac{1}{2}\right)^4$

$= 1 - 0.03125 - 0.15625$

$= 0.813$ (to 3 sig. fig.)

(iii) $P(1 \leq X \leq 4) = 1 - P(X = 0) - P(X = 5)$

$= 1 - \frac{5!}{0!5!} \times \left(\frac{1}{2}\right)^0 \times \left(\frac{1}{2}\right)^5$

$- \frac{5!}{5!0!} \times \left(\frac{1}{2}\right)^5 \times \left(\frac{1}{2}\right)^0$

$= 1 - 0.03125 - 0.03125$

$= 0.938$ (to 3 sig. fig.)

b) Use the binomial probability function with $n = 8$ and $p = \frac{2}{3}$.

(i) $P(X < 7) = 1 - P(X \geq 7)$

$= 1 - P(X = 7) - P(X = 8)$

$= 1 - \frac{8!}{7!1!} \times \left(\frac{2}{3}\right)^7 \times \left(\frac{1}{3}\right)^1$

$- \frac{8!}{8!0!} \times \left(\frac{2}{3}\right)^8 \times \left(\frac{1}{3}\right)^0$

$= 1 - 0.156073... - 0.039018...$

$= 0.805$ (to 3 sig. fig.)

(ii) $P(X \geq 2) = 1 - P(X < 2)$

$= 1 - P(X = 0) - P(X = 1)$

$= 1 - \frac{8!}{0!8!} \times \left(\frac{2}{3}\right)^0 \times \left(\frac{1}{3}\right)^8$

$- \frac{8!}{1!7!} \times \left(\frac{2}{3}\right)^1 \times \left(\frac{1}{3}\right)^7$

$= 1 - 0.00015241...$

$- 0.00243865...$

$= 0.997$ (to 3 sig. fig.)

(iii) $P(0 \leq X \leq 8) = 1$

This must be 1, since X can only take values from 0 to 8.

Q4 $n = 5$ and $p = P(\text{roll a six}) = \frac{1}{6}$, so

$P(2 \text{ sixes}) = \binom{5}{2} \times \left(\frac{1}{6}\right)^2 \times \left(\frac{5}{6}\right)^3 = 0.161$ (to 3 sig. fig.)

Q5 a) $X \sim B(12, \frac{1}{3})$

b) $P(X < 3) = P(X = 0) + P(X = 1)$

$+ P(X = 2)$

$= \frac{12!}{0!12!} \times \left(\frac{1}{3}\right)^0 \times \left(\frac{2}{3}\right)^{12-0}$

$+ \frac{12!}{1!11!} \times \left(\frac{1}{3}\right)^1 \times \left(\frac{2}{3}\right)^{12-1}$

$+ \frac{12!}{2!10!} \times \left(\frac{1}{3}\right)^2 \times \left(\frac{2}{3}\right)^{12-2}$

$= 0.00770... + 0.04624...$

$+ 0.12717...$

$= 0.181$ (to 3 sig. fig.)

Q6 a) $X \sim B(10, 0.65)$

b) $P(4 < X \leq 7) = P(X = 5) + P(X = 6)$

$+ P(X = 7)$

$= \frac{10!}{5!5!} \times 0.65^5 \times 0.35^5$

$+ \frac{10!}{6!4!} \times 0.65^6 \times 0.35^4$

$+ \frac{10!}{7!3!} \times 0.65^7 \times 0.35^3$

$= 0.15357... + 0.23766...$

$+ 0.25221...$

$= 0.643$ (to 3 sig. fig.)

Q7 Let X represent the number of defective items. Then $X \sim B(15, 0.05)$, and you need to find $P(1 \leq X \leq 3)$.

$$P(1 \leq X \leq 3) = P(X = 1) + P(X = 2) + P(X = 3)$$
$$= \frac{15!}{1!14!} \times 0.05^1 \times 0.95^{14} + \frac{15!}{2!13!} \times 0.05^2 \times 0.95^{13} + \frac{15!}{3!12!} \times 0.05^3 \times 0.95^{12}$$
$$= 0.36575... + 0.13475... + 0.03073...$$
$$= 0.531 \text{ (to 3 sig. fig.)}$$

3. Using Binomial Tables

Exercise 3.1 — Using tables to find probabilities

Q1 **a)** $P(X \leq 2) = 0.5256$

b) $P(X \leq 7) = 0.9996$

c) $P(X \leq 9) = 1.0000$

d) $P(X < 5) = P(X \leq 4) = 0.9219$

e) $P(X < 4) = P(X \leq 3) = 0.7759$

f) $P(X < 6) = P(X \leq 5) = 0.9803$

Q2 **a)** $P(X > 3) = 1 - P(X \leq 3) = 1 - 0.0905 = 0.9095$

b) $P(X > 6) = 1 - P(X \leq 6) = 1 - 0.6098 = 0.3902$

c) $P(X > 10) = 1 - P(X \leq 10) = 1 - 0.9907 = 0.0093$

d) $P(X \geq 5) = 1 - P(X < 5) = 1 - P(X \leq 4)$
$= 1 - 0.2173 = 0.7827$

e) $P(X \geq 3) = 1 - P(X < 3) = 1 - P(X \leq 2)$
$= 1 - 0.0271 = 0.9729$

f) $P(X \geq 13) = 1 - P(X < 13) = 1 - P(X \leq 12)$
$= 1 - 0.9997 = 0.0003$

Q3 **a)** $P(X = 7) = P(X \leq 7) - P(X \leq 6)$
$= 0.6010 - 0.4166 = 0.1844$

b) $P(X = 12) = P(X \leq 12) - P(X \leq 11)$
$= 0.9940 - 0.9804 = 0.0136$

c) $P(2 < X \leq 4) = P(X \leq 4) - P(X \leq 2)$
$= 0.1182 - 0.0121 = 0.1061$

d) $P(10 < X \leq 15) = P(X \leq 15) - P(X \leq 10)$
$= 1.0000 - 0.9468 = 0.0532$

e) $P(7 \leq X \leq 10) = P(X \leq 10) - P(X \leq 6)$
$= 0.9468 - 0.4166 = 0.5302$

f) $P(3 \leq X < 11) = P(X \leq 10) - P(X \leq 2)$
$= 0.9468 - 0.0121 = 0.9347$

Q4 Define a new random variable $Y \sim B(25, 0.2)$.

a) $P(X \geq 17) = P(Y \leq 8) = 0.9532$

b) $P(X \geq 20) = P(Y \leq 5) = 0.6167$

c) $P(X > 14) = P(Y < 11) = P(Y \leq 10) = 0.9944$

d) $P(X = 21) = P(Y = 4) = P(Y \leq 4) - P(Y \leq 3)$
$= 0.4207 - 0.2340 = 0.1867$

e) $P(3 \leq X < 14) = P(11 < Y \leq 22)$
$= P(Y \leq 22) - P(Y \leq 11)$
$= 1.0000 - 0.9985 = 0.0015$

f) $P(12 \leq X < 18) = P(7 < Y \leq 13)$
$= P(Y \leq 13) - P(Y \leq 7)$
$= 0.9999 - 0.8909 = 0.1090$

Q5 Let X represent the number of heads. Then $X \sim B(7, 0.5)$, so use the table for $n = 7$.
$P(X > 4) = 1 - P(X \leq 4) = 1 - 0.7734 = 0.2266$

Q6 Let X represent the number of faulty items. Then $X \sim B(25, 0.05)$, so use the table for $n = 25$.
$P(X < 6) = P(X \leq 5) = 0.9988$

Exercise 3.2 — Using binomial tables 'backwards'

Q1 **a)** Use the table for $n = 8$ and the column for $p = 0.35$. Reading down the column tells you that $P(X \leq 2) = 0.4278$, so $a = 2$.

b) $P(X < b) = 0.9747$, so $P(X \leq b - 1) = 0.9747$.
From the table, $P(X \leq 5) = 0.9747$.
So $b - 1 = 5$, which means that $b = 6$.

c) $P(X > c) = 0.8309$, so $P(X \leq c) = 1 - P(X > c)$
$= 1 - 0.8309 = 0.1691$.
From the table, $P(X \leq 1) = 0.1691$, which means that $c = 1$.

d) $P(X \geq d) = 0.1061$, so $P(X < d) = 1 - P(X \geq d)$
$= 1 - 0.1061 = 0.8939$.
This means that $P(X \leq d - 1) = 0.8939$.
From the table, $P(X \leq 4) = 0.8939$, which means that $d - 1 = 4$, so $d = 5$.

Q2 **a)** Let X be the score of someone who guesses the answer to each question. Then $X \sim B(30, 0.25)$. Use the table for $n = 30$ and the column for $p = 0.25$.

You need to find the minimum value m for which $P(X \geq m) \leq 0.1$. This is the minimum value m for which $P(X < m) \geq 0.9$, or $P(X \leq m - 1) \geq 0.9$.

$P(X \leq 10) = 0.8943$, but $P(X \leq 11) = 0.9493$. This means that $m - 1 = 11$, so the pass mark should be at least 12.

b) This time you need to find the minimum value m for which $P(X \geq m) < 0.01$. This is the minimum value m for which $P(X < m) > 0.99$, or $P(X \leq m - 1) > 0.99$.

$P(X \leq 12) = 0.9784$, but $P(X \leq 13) = 0.9918$. This means that $m - 1 = 13$, so the pass mark should be at least 14.

Q3 Here, $X \sim B(20, 0.5)$. You need $P(X \geq x) < 0.05$. This means $P(X < x) > 0.95$, or $P(X \leq x - 1) > 0.95$.

Use the table for $n = 20$, and the column for $p = 0.5$. $P(X \leq 13) = 0.9423$, but $P(X \leq 14) = 0.9793$.

This means that $x - 1 = 14$, so x should be at least 15.

4. Mean and Variance

Exercise 4.1 — Mean and variance of the binomial distribution

Q1 a) (i) $\mu = 10 \times 0.9 = 9$

(ii) $\sigma^2 = 10 \times 0.9 \times (1 - 0.9) = 0.9$

(iii) $\sigma = \sqrt{0.9} = 0.949$ (to 3 sig. fig.)

b) (i) $\mu = 25 \times 0.7 = 17.5$

(ii) $\sigma^2 = 25 \times 0.7 \times (1 - 0.7) = 5.25$

(iii) $\sigma = \sqrt{5.25} = 2.29$ (to 3 sig. fig.)

c) (i) $\mu = 50 \times 0.05 = 2.5$

(ii) $\sigma^2 = 50 \times 0.05 \times (1 - 0.05) = 2.375$

(iii) $\sigma = \sqrt{2.375} = 1.54$ (to 3 sig. fig.)

d) (i) $\mu = 70 \times 0.85 = 59.5$

(ii) $\sigma^2 = 70 \times 0.85 \times (1 - 0.85) = 8.925$

(iii) $\sigma = \sqrt{8.925} = 2.99$ (to 3 sig. fig.)

e) (i) $\mu = 15 \times 0.1 = 1.5$

(ii) $\sigma^2 = 15 \times 0.1 \times (1 - 0.1) = 1.35$

(iii) $\sigma = \sqrt{1.35} = 1.16$ (to 3 sig. fig.)

f) (i) $\mu = 100 \times 0.35 = 35$

(ii) $\sigma^2 = 100 \times 0.35 \times (1 - 0.35) = 22.75$

(iii) $\sigma = \sqrt{22.75} = 4.77$ (to 3 sig. fig.)

Q2 a) $X \sim B(60, 0.6)$

b) Mean of X: $\mu = 60 \times 0.6 = 36$
Variance of X: $\sigma^2 = 60 \times 0.6 \times (1 - 0.6) = 14.4$

Q3 a) $Y \sim B(150, p)$
$E(Y) = 150p = 30$, so $p = 30 \div 150 = 0.2$

b) $\text{Var}(Y) = np(1 - p) = 150 \times 0.2 \times (1 - 0.2) = 24$

Q4 a) $X \sim B(1600, 0.1)$
$E(X) = 1600 \times 0.1 = 160$

b) $\sigma^2 = 1600 \times 0.1 \times (1 - 0.1) = 144$

5. Modelling Real Problems

Exercise 5.1 — Modelling real problems with B(*n*, *p*)

Q1 a) Each person who passes can be considered a separate trial, where 'success' means they take a leaflet, and 'failure' means they don't.
Since there is a fixed number of independent trials (50), a constant probability of success (0.25), and X is the total number of successes, $X \sim B(50, 0.25)$.

b) $P(X > 4) = 1 - P(X \leq 4) = 1 - 0.0021 = 0.9979$

c) $P(X = 10) = P(X \leq 10) - P(X \leq 9)$
$= 0.2622 - 0.1637 = 0.0985$

d) $E(X) = np = 50 \times 0.25 = 12.5$ people

e) $\text{Var}(X) = \sigma^2 = 50 \times 0.25 \times (1 - 0.25) = 9.375$
So $\sigma = \sqrt{9.375} = 3.06$ people (to 3 sig. fig.)

Q2 a) Let X represent the number of plants with yellow flowers in a tray. Then $X \sim B(15, 0.35)$.
Using binomial tables for $n = 15$ and $p = 0.35$:
$P(X = 5) = P(X \leq 5) - P(X \leq 4)$
$= 0.5643 - 0.3519 = 0.2124$

b) P(more yellow flowers than white flowers)
$= P(X \geq 8) = 1 - P(X < 8) = 1 - P(X \leq 7)$
$= 1 - 0.8868 = 0.1132$

Q3 a) $X \sim B(n, 0.15)$.
$E(X) = 0.15n = 6$, so $n = 6 \div 0.15 = 40$.

b) Using the binomial table for $n = 40$:
$P(X < 6) = P(X \leq 5) = 0.4325$

c) $Y \sim B(m, 0.15)$.
$E(Y) = mp = 0.15m = 24$, so $m = 24 \div 0.15 = 160$.
$\text{Var}(Y) = mp(1 - p) = 160 \times 0.15 \times 0.85$
$= 20.4$

Review Exercise — Chapter 3

Q1 The probabilities of all the possible values that a discrete random variable can take add up to 1.

$$\sum_{x=0,1,2} P(X = x) = P(X = 0) + P(X = 1) + P(X = 2)$$
$$= \frac{2}{3} + \frac{2}{3} + \frac{2}{3} = \frac{6}{3} = 2$$

These probabilities don't add up to 1, so this is not a probability function.

Q2 a) There are 21 objects altogether, so if all the balls were different colours, there would be 21! ways to arrange them. But since 15 of the objects are identical, you need to divide this figure by 15!. So there are 21! ÷ 15! = 39 070 080 possible arrangements.

b) There are $\frac{16!}{4!4!4!4!} = 63\,063\,000$ possible arrangements.

c) There are $\binom{12}{7} = \binom{12}{5} = \frac{12!}{7!5!} = 792$ possible arrangements.

Q3 a)
$$P(5\text{ heads}) = \binom{10}{5} \times 0.5^5 \times 0.5^5$$
$$= \frac{10!}{5!5!} \times 0.5^{10}$$
$$= 0.246 \text{ (to 3 sig. fig.)}.$$

b)
$$P(9\text{ heads}) = \binom{10}{9} \times 0.5^9 \times 0.5$$
$$= \frac{10!}{9!1!} \times 0.5^{10}$$
$$= 0.00977 \text{ (to 3 sig. fig.)}.$$

Q4 a) Binomial — there are a fixed number of independent trials (30) with two possible results ('prime' / 'not prime'), a constant probability of success, and the random variable is the total number of successes.

b) Binomial — there are a fixed number of independent trials (however many students are in the class) with two possible results ('heads' / 'tails'), a constant probability of success, and the random variable is the total number of successes.

c) Not binomial — the probability of being dealt an ace changes with each card dealt, since the total number of cards decreases as each card is dealt.

d) Not binomial — the number of trials is not fixed.

Q5 a) Use tables with $n = 10$ and $p = 0.5$.
If X represents the number of heads, then:
$P(X \geq 5) = 1 - P(X < 5) = 1 - P(X \leq 4)$
$= 1 - 0.3770 = 0.6230$

b) $P(X \geq 9) = 1 - P(X < 9) = 1 - P(X \leq 8)$
$= 1 - 0.9893 = 0.0107$

Q6 a) You can't use tables here (because they don't include $p = 0.27$), so you have to use the probability function.

$$P(X = 4) = \binom{14}{4} \times 0.27^4 \times (1 - 0.27)^{10}$$
$$= 0.229 \text{ (to 3 sig. fig.)}$$

b) $$P(X < 2) = P(X = 0) + P(X = 1)$$
$$= \binom{14}{0} \times 0.27^0 \times (1 - 0.27)^{14} + \binom{14}{1} \times 0.27^1 \times (1 - 0.27)^{13}$$
$$= 0.012204... + 0.063195...$$
$$= 0.0754 \text{ (to 3 sig. fig.)}$$

c) $$P(5 < X \leq 8) = P(X = 6) + P(X = 7) + P(X = 8)$$
$$= \binom{14}{6} \times 0.27^6 \times (1 - 0.27)^8 + \binom{14}{7} \times 0.27^7 \times (1 - 0.27)^7 + \binom{14}{8} \times 0.27^8 \times (1 - 0.27)^6$$
$$= 0.093825... + 0.039660... + 0.012835...$$
$$= 0.146 \text{ (to 3 sig. fig.)}$$

Q7 For parts a)-c), use tables with $n = 25$ and $p = 0.15$.

a) $P(X \leq 3) = 0.4711$

b) $P(X \leq 7) = 0.9745$

c) $P(X \leq 15) = 1.0000$

For parts d)-f), define a new random variable $T = 15 - Y$, with $T \sim B(15, 0.35)$. Then if Y represents the number of successes in 15 trials, T represents the number of failures.
Now you can use tables with $n = 15$ and $p = 0.35$.

d) $P(Y \leq 3) = P(T \geq 12) = 1 - P(T < 12)$
$= 1 - P(T \leq 11) = 1 - 0.9995 = 0.0005$

e) $P(Y \leq 7) = P(T \geq 8) = 1 - P(T < 8)$
$= 1 - P(T \leq 7) = 1 - 0.8868 = 0.1132$

f) $P(Y \leq 15) = 1$ (since 15 is the maximum possible value).
These last few parts (where you can't use the tables directly) are quite awkward, so make sure you get lots of practice.

Q8 From tables:

a) $P(X \leq 15) = 0.9997$

b) $P(X < 4) = P(X \leq 3) = 0.1302$

c) $P(X > 7) = 1 - P(X \leq 7) = 1 - 0.0639 = 0.9361$

For parts d)-f) where $X \sim B(n, p)$ with $p > 0.5$, define a new random variable $Y \sim B(n, q)$, where $q = 1 - p$ and $Y = n - X$. Then use tables.

d) Define $Y \sim B(50, 0.2)$.
Then $P(X \geq 40) = P(Y \leq 10) = 0.5836$

e) Define $Y \sim B(30, 0.3)$.
Then $P(X = 20) = P(Y = 10) = P(Y \leq 10) - P(Y \leq 9)$
$= 0.7304 - 0.5888 = 0.1416$

f) Define $Y \sim B(10, 0.25)$.
Then $P(X = 7) = P(Y = 3) = P(Y \leq 3) - P(Y \leq 2)$
$= 0.7759 - 0.5256 = 0.2503$

Q9 Using the table for $n = 30$ and $p = 0.35$:

a) $a = 13$

b) Since $P(X \geq b) = 0.8762$, you know that $P(X < b) = 1 - 0.8762 = 0.1238$.
This means that $P(X \leq b - 1) = 0.1238$.
So from tables, $b - 1 = 7$, which gives $b = 8$.

c) $P(X \leq 5) = 0.0233$, but $P(X \leq 6) = 0.0586$.
So the maximum value for c with $P(X \leq c) < 0.05$ must be $c = 5$.

Q10 a) mean $= 20 \times 0.4 = 8$
variance $= 20 \times 0.4 \times 0.6 = 4.8$

b) mean $= 40 \times 0.15 = 6$
variance $= 40 \times 0.15 \times 0.85 = 5.1$

c) mean $= 25 \times 0.45 = 11.25$
variance $= 25 \times 0.45 \times 0.55 = 6.1875$

d) mean $= 50 \times 0.8 = 40$
variance $= 50 \times 0.8 \times 0.2 = 8$

e) mean $= 30 \times 0.7 = 21$
variance $= 30 \times 0.7 \times 0.3 = 6.3$

f) mean $= 45 \times 0.012 = 0.54$
variance $= 45 \times 0.012 \times 0.988 = 0.53352$

Exam-Style Questions — Chapter 3

1 **a)** **(i)** Let X represent the number of apples that contain a maggot.
Then $X \sim B(40, 0.15)$ ***[1 mark]***.
$P(X < 6) = P(X \leq 5) = 0.4325$ ***[1 mark]***

(ii) $P(X > 2) = 1 - P(X \leq 2)$ ***[1 mark]***
$= 1 - 0.0486 = 0.9514$ ***[1 mark]***

(iii) $P(X = 12) = P(X \leq 12) - P(X \leq 11)$ ***[1 mark]***
$= 0.9957 - 0.9880 = 0.0077$ ***[1 mark]***

Or you could use the probability function for (iii):

$$P(X = 12) = \binom{40}{12} \times 0.15^{12} \times 0.85^{28}$$
$$= 0.0077 \text{ (to 4 d.p.)}.$$

b) The probability that a crate contains more than 2 apples with maggots is 0.9514 (from part **a) (ii)**).
So define a random variable Y, where Y is the number of crates that contain more than 2 apples with maggots.
Then $Y \sim B(3, 0.9514)$ ***[1 mark]***.
You need to find $P(Y = 2) + P(Y = 3)$. This is:

$$\binom{3}{2} \times 0.9514^2 \times (1 - 0.9514)$$
$$+ \binom{3}{3} \times 0.9514^3 \times (1 - 0.9514)^0 \textbf{ [1 mark]}$$
$$= 0.1319... + 0.8611...$$
$$= 0.993 \text{ (to 3 d.p.)} \textbf{ [1 mark]}$$

c) **(i)** Mean $= E(M) = np = 5 \times 0.1 = 0.5$ ***[1 mark]***
Variance $= Var(M) = np(1 - p)$
$= 5 \times 0.1 \times 0.9 = 0.45$ ***[1 mark]***

(ii) The mean is the same as Jim's claim and the variance is similar ***[1 mark]***.
Jim's claim seems to be accurate ***[1 mark]***.

2 **a)** **(i)** The probability of Simon being able to solve each crossword needs to remain the same ***[1 mark]***, and all the outcomes need to be independent (i.e. Simon solving or not solving a puzzle one day should not affect whether he will be able to solve it on another day) ***[1 mark]***.

(ii) The total number of puzzles he solves (or the number he fails to solve) ***[1 mark]***.

b) $P(X = 4) = \frac{14!}{4!10!} \times p^4 \times (1 - p)^{10}$ ***[1 mark]***

$P(X = 5) = \frac{14!}{5!9!} \times p^5 \times (1 - p)^9$ ***[1 mark]***

So $\frac{14!}{4!10!} \times p^4 \times (1 - p)^{10}$
$= \frac{14!}{5!9!} \times p^5 \times (1 - p)^9$ ***[1 mark]***

Dividing by things that occur on both sides gives:

$\frac{1 - p}{10} = \frac{p}{5}$ ***[1 mark]***, or $5 = 15p$.

This means $p = \frac{5}{15} = 0.333$ (to 3 sig. fig.) ***[1 mark]***.

c) $E(X) = np = 14 \times \frac{1}{3} = 4.667$ (3 d.p.) ***[1 mark]***
$E(Y) = np = 7 \times 0.2 = 1.4$ ***[1 mark]***

So the total expected number of puzzles solved is $4.667 + 1.4 = 6.067$ (to 3 d.p.). So you would expect Simon to solve approximately 6 puzzles in these two weeks. ***[1 mark]***

3 **a)** Let the random variable X represent the number of 'treble-20's the player gets in a set of 3 darts.
Then $X \sim B(3, 0.75)$ ***[1 mark]***.
$P(X \geq 2) = P(X = 2) + P(X = 3)$

$P(X = 2) = \binom{3}{2} \times 0.75^2 \times (1 - 0.75)$
$= 0.421875$

$P(X = 3) = \binom{3}{3} \times 0.75^3 \times (1 - 0.75)^0$
$= 0.421875$

So $P(X \geq 2) = 0.421875 + 0.421875$
$= 0.84375 = 0.844$ (to 3 sig. fig.) ***[1 mark]***

b) Let the random variable Y represent the number of sets of darts in which the player gets a 'treble-20' with at least 2 darts.
Then $Y \sim B(5, 0.84375)$ ***[1 mark]***.
$E(Y) = np = 5 \times 0.84375$
$= 4.21875$
$= 4.22$ (to 3 sig. fig.) ***[1 mark]***

c) **(i)** Now let X represent the number of 'treble-20's the player scores with 30 darts.
Then $X \sim B(30, 0.75)$.
You need to find $P(X \geq 26)$.
Define a new random variable $Y = 30 - X$, with $Y \sim B(30, 0.25)$.
Then $P(X \geq 26) = P(Y \leq 4)$ ***[1 mark]***.
From tables, $P(Y \leq 4) = 0.0979$ ***[1 mark]***.

(ii) $P(22 \leq X \leq 25) = P(5 \leq Y \leq 8)$ ***[1 mark]***
$= P(Y \leq 8) - P(Y \leq 4)$ ***[1 mark]***
$= 0.6736 - 0.0979 = 0.5757$ ***[1 mark]***

4 **a)** Let the random variable X represent the number of bronze coins Jessica picks out in n picks.
Then $X \sim B(n, 0.3)$.
$E(X) = np = 0.3n = 7.5$ ***[1 mark]***.
So $n = 7.5 \div 0.3 = 25$ ***[1 mark]***.

b) If the ratio of bronze coins : silver coins is 1 : 4, then Jessica will have picked out 5 bronze coins.
Using tables:
$P(X = 5) = P(X \leq 5) - P(X \leq 4)$ ***[1 mark]***
$= 0.1935 - 0.0905 = 0.1030$ ***[1 mark]***
You could use the probability function here if you prefer.

5 **a)** **(i)** Here, $X \sim B(12, 0.06)$.

$P(X = 0) = \binom{12}{0} \times 0.06^0 \times (1 - 0.06)^{12}$

[1 mark]

$= 0.475920... = 0.476$ (to 3 sig. fig.) ***[1 mark]***

(ii) $P(X > 2) = 1 - P(X \leq 2)$

$= 1 - P(X = 0) - P(X = 1) - P(X = 2)$ ***[1 mark]***

$P(X = 1) = \binom{12}{1} \times 0.06^1 \times (1 - 0.06)^{11}$

$= 0.364534...$

$P(X = 2) = \binom{12}{2} \times 0.06^2 \times (1 - 0.06)^{10}$

$= 0.127974...$

So $P(X > 2) = 1 - 0.475920... - 0.364534... - 0.127974...$ ***[1 mark]***

$= 0.031570...$

$= 0.0316$ (to 3 sig. fig.) ***[1 mark]***

b) **(i)** $Y \sim B(50, 0.0316)$ ***[1 mark]***

(ii) $P(Y \geq 1) = 1 - P(Y < 1) = 1 - P(Y = 0)$ ***[1 mark]***

$= 1 - \binom{50}{0} \times 0.0316^0 \times (1 - 0.0316)^{50}$

$= 1 - 0.20078...$

$= 0.799$ (to 3 sig. fig.) ***[1 mark]***

Chapter 4: The Normal Distribution

2. The Standard Normal Distribution, Z

Exercise 2.1 — The standard normal distribution

Q1 **a)** Using the $\Phi(z)$ table, $\Phi(1.87) = 0.96926$

b) Using the $\Phi(z)$ table, $\Phi(0.39) = 0.65173$

c) Using the $\Phi(z)$ table, $\Phi(0.99) = 0.83891$

d) Using the $\Phi(z)$ table, $\Phi(3.15) = 0.99918$

Q2 **a)** $P(Z > 2.48) = 1 - P(Z \leq 2.48)$
$= 1 - 0.99343 = 0.00657$

b) $P(Z > 0.85) = 1 - P(Z \leq 0.85)$
$= 1 - 0.80234 = 0.19766$

c) $P(Z \geq 1.23) = 1 - P(Z < 1.23)$
$= 1 - 0.89065 = 0.10935$

d) $P(Z \geq 0.14) = 1 - P(Z < 0.14)$
$= 1 - 0.55567 = 0.44433$

Q3 **a)** Use a sketch to find an area you can look up in the table:

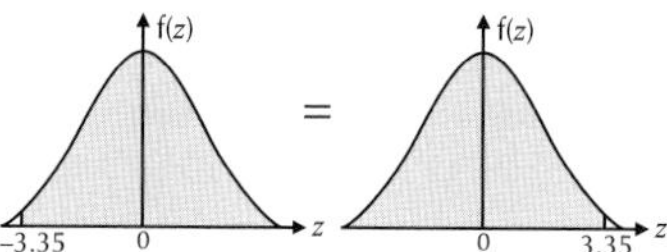

So, $P(Z > -3.35) = P(Z < 3.35) = 0.99960$

b) Use a sketch to find an area you can look up in the table:

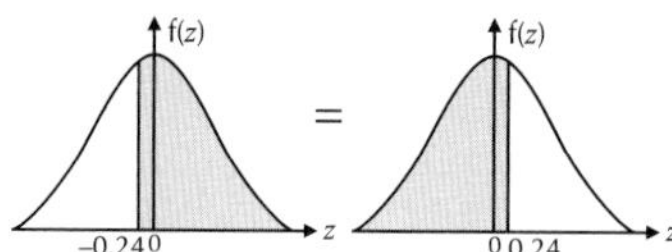

So, $P(Z > -0.24) = P(Z < 0.24) = 0.59483$

c) Use a sketch to find an area you can look up in the table:

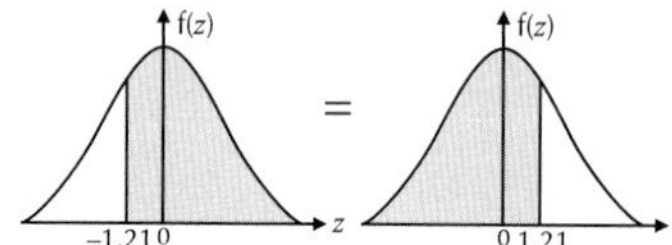

So, $P(Z > -1.21) = P(Z < 1.21) = 0.88686$

d) The $\Phi(z)$ table doesn't contain negative values of z, so use a sketch to show an equivalent area:

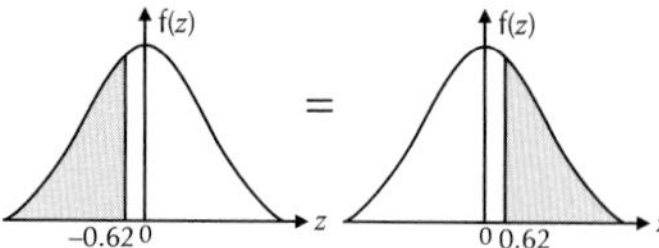

So, $P(Z < -0.62) = P(Z > 0.62)$
$= 1 - P(Z \leq 0.62) = 1 - 0.73237 = 0.26763$

e) The $\Phi(z)$ table doesn't contain negative values of z, so use a sketch to show an equivalent area:

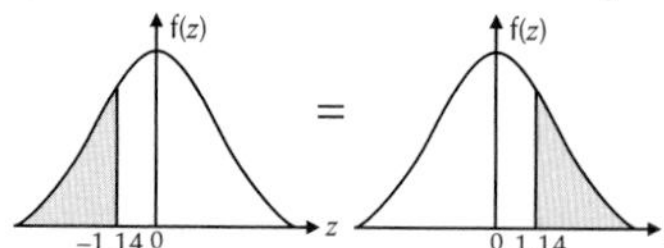

So, $P(Z < -1.14) = P(Z > 1.14)$
$= 1 - P(Z \leq 1.14) = 1 - 0.87286 = 0.12714$

f) The $\Phi(z)$ table doesn't contain negative values of z, so use a sketch to show an equivalent area:

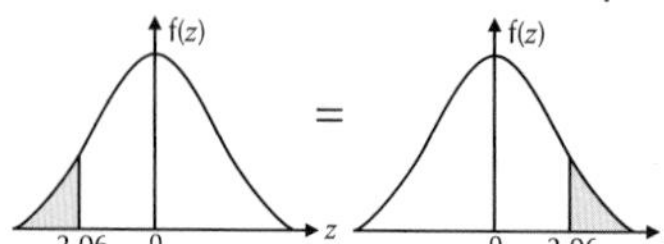

So, $P(Z \leq -2.06) = P(Z \geq 2.06)$
$= 1 - P(Z < 2.06) = 1 - 0.98030 = 0.01970$

We haven't drawn diagrams for the answers to Q4 below, but it often makes it easier to see how to tackle a question if you do a quick sketch.

Q4 a) $P(1.34 < Z < 2.18) = P(Z < 2.18) - P(Z \leq 1.34)$
$= 0.98537 - 0.90988 = 0.07549$

b) $P(0.76 < Z < 1.92) = P(Z < 1.92) - P(Z \leq 0.76)$
$= 0.97257 - 0.77637 = 0.1962$

c) $P(-1.45 < Z < 0.17) = P(Z < 0.17) - P(Z \leq -1.45)$
$= P(Z < 0.17) - P(Z \geq 1.45)$
Remember, $P(Z \leq -z) = P(Z \geq z)$.
$= P(Z < 0.17) - [1 - P(Z < 1.45)]$
$= 0.56749 - (1 - 0.92647) = 0.49396$

d) $P(-2.14 < Z < 1.65) = P(Z < 1.65) - P(Z \leq -2.14)$
$= P(Z < 1.65) - P(Z \geq 2.14)$
$= P(Z < 1.65) - [1 - P(Z < 2.14)]$
$= 0.95053 - (1 - 0.98382) = 0.93435$

e) $P(-1.66 < Z < 1.66) = P(Z < 1.66) - P(Z \leq -1.66)$
$= P(Z < 1.66) - P(Z \geq 1.66)$
$= P(Z < 1.66) - [1 - P(Z < 1.66)]$
$= 0.95154 - (1 - 0.95154) = 0.90308$

f) $P(-0.34 < Z < 0.34) = P(Z < 0.34) - P(Z \leq -0.34)$
$= P(Z < 0.34) - P(Z \geq 0.34)$
$= P(Z < 0.34) - [1 - P(Z < 0.34)]$
$= 0.63307 - (1 - 0.63307) = 0.26614$

g) $P(-3.25 < Z < -2.48) = P(2.48 < Z < 3.25)$
$= P(Z < 3.25) - P(Z \leq 2.48)$
$= 0.99942 - 0.99343 = 0.00599$

h) $P(-1.11 < Z < -0.17) = P(0.17 < Z < 1.11)$
$= P(Z < 1.11) - P(Z \leq 0.17)$
$= 0.86650 - 0.56749 = 0.29901$

There are different ways of answering some of these, so don't worry if you used a different method to get the same answer.

Exercise 2.2 — Finding a z-value

Q1 a) Using the $\Phi(z)$ table, $\Phi(z) = 0.85769$ for $z = 1.07$

b) Using the $\Phi(z)$ table, $\Phi(z) = 0.82639$ for $z = 0.94$

c) $P(Z < z) = 0.37828 \Rightarrow P(Z > -z) = 0.37828$
$\Rightarrow P(Z \leq -z) = 0.62172 \Rightarrow -z = 0.31 \Rightarrow z = -0.31$

d) $P(Z < z) = 0.00402 \Rightarrow P(Z > -z) = 0.00402$
$\Rightarrow P(Z \leq -z) = 0.99598 \Rightarrow -z = 2.65 \Rightarrow z = -2.65$

e) $P(Z > z) = 0.75804 \Rightarrow P(Z < -z) = 0.75804$
$\Rightarrow -z = 0.70 \Rightarrow z = -0.70$

f) $P(Z > z) = 0.94408 \Rightarrow P(Z < -z) = 0.94408$
$\Rightarrow -z = 1.59 \Rightarrow z = -1.59$

g) $P(Z > z) = 0.48006 \Rightarrow P(Z \leq z) = 0.51994$
$\Rightarrow z = 0.05$

h) $P(Z > z) = 0.0951 \Rightarrow P(Z \leq z) = 0.9049$
$\Rightarrow z = 1.31$

Q2 a) Using the percentage-points table, $p = 0.995$ for $z = 2.5758$

b) Using the percentage-points table, $p = 0.8$ for $z = 0.8416$

c) $P(Z > z) = 0.3 \Rightarrow P(Z \leq z) = 0.7 \Rightarrow z = 0.5244$

d) $P(Z > z) = 0.15 \Rightarrow P(Z \leq z) = 0.85 \Rightarrow z = 1.0364$

e) $P(Z > z) = 0.9 \Rightarrow P(Z \leq -z) = 0.9$
$\Rightarrow -z = 1.2816 \Rightarrow z = -1.2816$

f) $P(Z > z) = 0.85 \Rightarrow P(Z \leq -z) = 0.85$
$\Rightarrow -z = 1.0364 \Rightarrow z = -1.0364$

g) $P(Z < z) = 0.4 \Rightarrow P(Z > -z) = 0.4 \Rightarrow P(Z \leq -z) = 0.6$
$\Rightarrow -z = 0.2533 \Rightarrow z = -0.2533$

h) $P(Z < z) = 0.01 \Rightarrow P(Z > -z) = 0.01$
$\Rightarrow P(Z \leq -z) = 0.99 \Rightarrow -z = 2.3263 \Rightarrow z = -2.3263$

Q3 a) $P(-z < Z < z) = 0.5991$, so the remaining area is $1 - 0.5991 = 0.4009$. Using symmetry,
$P(Z \geq z) = 0.4009 \div 2 = 0.20045$
$\Rightarrow P(Z < z) = 0.79955 \Rightarrow z = 0.84$
An alternative way of doing this is to divide 0.5991 by 2 to get $P(0 < Z < z) = 0.29955$. Then add 0.5 to get $P(Z < z) = 0.79955$.

b) $P(-z < Z < z) = 0.94256$, so the remaining area is $1 - 0.94256 = 0.05744$. Using symmetry,
$P(Z \geq z) = 0.05744 \div 2 = 0.02872$
$\Rightarrow P(Z < z) = 0.97128 \Rightarrow z = 1.90$

c) $P(-z < Z < z) = 0.4$, so the remaining area is $1 - 0.4 = 0.6$. Using symmetry,
$P(Z \geq z) = 0.6 \div 2 = 0.3 \Rightarrow P(Z < z) = 0.7$.
Using the percentage-points table,
$p = 0.7$ for $z = 0.5244$

d) $P(-z < Z < z) = 0.98$, so the remaining area is $1 - 0.98 = 0.02$. Using symmetry,
$P(Z \geq z) = 0.02 \div 2 = 0.01 \Rightarrow P(Z < z) = 0.99$.
Using the percentage-points table,
$p = 0.99$ for $z = 2.3263$

Q4 a) $P(0 < Z < z) = 0.38686$
$\Rightarrow P(Z < z) = 0.38686 + P(Z \leq 0)$
$= 0.38686 + 0.5 = 0.88686$
$\Phi(z) = 0.88686$ for $z = 1.21$

b) $P(0 < Z < z) = 0.48537$
$\Rightarrow P(Z < z) = 0.48537 + P(Z \leq 0)$
$= 0.48537 + 0.5 = 0.98537$
$\Phi(z) = 0.98537$ for $z = 2.18$

Q5 a) $P(z < Z < 0) = 0.24215$
$\Rightarrow P(0 < Z < -z) = 0.24215$
$\Rightarrow P(Z < -z) = 0.24215 + 0.5 = 0.74215$
$\Phi(z) = 0.74215$ tells you that $-z = 0.65$
$\Rightarrow z = -0.65$

b) $P(z < Z < 0) = 0.14431$
$\Rightarrow P(0 < Z < -z) = 0.14431$
$\Rightarrow P(Z < -z) = 0.14431 + 0.5 = 0.64431$
$\Phi(z) = 0.64431$ tells you that $-z = 0.37 \Rightarrow z = -0.37$

Q6 a) $P(1.5 < Z < z) = 0.04062$
$\Rightarrow P(Z < z) - P(Z \leq 1.5) = 0.04062$
$\Rightarrow P(Z < z) = 0.04062 + P(Z \leq 1.5)$
$\Rightarrow P(Z < z) = 0.04062 + 0.93319 = 0.97381$
$\Phi(z) = 0.97381$ for $z = 1.94$

b) $P(0.58 < Z < z) = 0.0691$
$\Rightarrow P(Z < z) - P(Z \leq 0.58) = 0.0691$
$\Rightarrow P(Z < z) = 0.0691 + P(Z \leq 0.58)$
$\Rightarrow P(Z < z) = 0.0691 + 0.71904 = 0.78814$
$\Phi(z) = 0.78814$ for $z = 0.80$

c) $P(-1.3 < Z < z) = 0.87104$
$\Rightarrow P(Z < z) - P(Z \leq -1.3) = 0.87104$
$\Rightarrow P(Z < z) = 0.87104 + P(Z \leq -1.3)$
$\Rightarrow P(Z < z) = 0.87104 + [1 - P(Z < 1.3)]$
$\Rightarrow P(Z < z) = 0.87104 + (1 - 0.9032) = 0.96784$
$\Phi(z) = 0.96784$ for $z = 1.85$

d) $P(-0.54 < Z < z) = 0.66704$
$\Rightarrow P(Z < z) - P(Z \leq -0.54) = 0.66704$
$\Rightarrow P(Z < z) = 0.66704 + P(Z \leq -0.54)$
$\Rightarrow P(Z < z) = 0.66704 + [1 - P(Z < 0.54)]$
$\Rightarrow P(Z < z) = 0.66704 + (1 - 0.7054) = 0.96164$
$\Phi(z) = 0.96164$ for $z = 1.77$

e) $P(z < Z < 0.27) = 0.54585$
$\Rightarrow P(Z < 0.27) - P(Z \leq z) = 0.54585$
$\Rightarrow P(Z \leq z) = P(Z < 0.27) - 0.54585$
$\Rightarrow P(Z \leq z) = 0.60642 - 0.54585 = 0.06057$
But you can't look up 0.06057 in the table, so there's still some work to do...
$\Rightarrow P(Z \geq -z) = 0.06057 \Rightarrow P(Z < -z) = 0.93943$
$\Phi(z) = 0.93943$ tells you that $-z = 1.55$
$\Rightarrow z = -1.55$

f) $P(z < Z < -1.25) = 0.09493$
$\Rightarrow P(Z < -1.25) - P(Z \leq z) = 0.09493$
$\Rightarrow P(Z \leq z) = P(Z < -1.25) - 0.09493$
$\Rightarrow P(Z \leq z) = P(Z > 1.25) - 0.09493$
$\Rightarrow P(Z \leq z) = [1 - P(Z \leq 1.25)] - 0.09493$
$\Rightarrow P(Z \leq z) = (1 - 0.89435) - 0.09493 = 0.01072$
$\Rightarrow P(Z \geq -z) = 0.01072 \Rightarrow P(Z < -z) = 0.98928$
$\Phi(z) = 0.98928$ tells you that $-z = 2.30$
$\Rightarrow z = -2.30$

3. Normal Distributions and *Z*-Tables

Exercise 3.1 — Converting to the *Z* distribution

Q1 a) $P(X < 50) = P\left(Z < \frac{50 - 40}{5}\right) = P(Z < 2) = 0.97725$

b) $P(X < 43) = P\left(Z < \frac{43 - 40}{5}\right)$
$= P(Z < 0.6) = 0.72575$

Q2 a) $P(X > 28) = P\left(Z > \frac{28 - 24}{\sqrt{6}}\right) = P(Z > 1.63)$
$= 1 - P(Z \leq 1.63) = 1 - 0.94845 = 0.05155$

b) $P(X > 25) = P\left(Z > \frac{25 - 24}{\sqrt{6}}\right) = P(Z > 0.41)$
$= 1 - P(Z \leq 0.41) = 1 - 0.6591 = 0.3409$

Q3 a) $P(X > 107) = P\left(Z > \frac{107 - 120}{\sqrt{40}}\right) = P(Z > -2.06)$
$= P(Z < 2.06) = 0.98030$

b) $P(X > 115) = P\left(Z > \frac{115 - 120}{\sqrt{40}}\right) = P(Z > -0.79)$
$= P(Z < 0.79) = 0.78524$

Q4 a) $P(X < 15) = P\left(Z < \frac{15 - 17}{3}\right) = P(Z < -0.67)$
$= P(Z > 0.67) = 1 - (Z \leq 0.67)$
$= 1 - 0.74857 = 0.25143$

b) $P(X < 12) = P\left(Z < \frac{12 - 17}{3}\right) = P(Z < -1.67)$
$= P(Z > 1.67) = 1 - (Z \leq 1.67)$
$= 1 - 0.95254 = 0.04746$

Q5 a) $P(52 < X < 63) = P\left(\frac{52 - 50}{5} < Z < \frac{63 - 50}{5}\right)$
$= P(0.4 < Z < 2.6)$
$= P(Z < 2.6) - P(Z \leq 0.4)$
$= 0.99534 - 0.65542 = 0.33992$

b) $P(57 < X < 66) = P\left(\frac{57 - 50}{5} < Z < \frac{66 - 50}{5}\right)$
$= P(1.4 < Z < 3.2)$
$= P(Z < 3.2) - P(Z \leq 1.4)$
$= 0.99931 - 0.91924 = 0.08007$

Q6 a) $P(0.45 < X < 0.55)$
$= P\left(\frac{0.45 - 0.6}{0.2} < Z < \frac{0.55 - 0.6}{0.2}\right)$
$= P(-0.75 < Z < -0.25)$
$= P(0.25 < Z < 0.75)$
$= P(Z < 0.75) - P(Z \leq 0.25)$
$= 0.77337 - 0.59871 = 0.17466$

b) $P(0.53 < X < 0.58)$
$= P\left(\frac{0.53 - 0.6}{0.2} < Z < \frac{0.58 - 0.6}{0.2}\right)$
$= P(-0.35 < Z < -0.1)$
$= P(0.1 < Z < 0.35)$
$= P(Z < 0.35) - P(Z \leq 0.1)$
$= 0.63683 - 0.53983 = 0.097$

Q7 a) $P(240 < X < 280)$
$= P\left(\frac{240 - 260}{15} < Z < \frac{280 - 260}{15}\right)$
$= P(-1.33 < Z < 1.33)$
$= P(Z < 1.33) - P(Z \leq -1.33)$
$= P(Z < 1.33) - P(Z \geq 1.33)$
$= P(Z < 1.33) - [1 - P(Z < 1.33)]$
$= 2 \times P(Z < 1.33) - 1$
$= 2 \times 0.90824 - 1 = 0.81648$

b) $P(232 < X < 288)$
$= P\left(\frac{232 - 260}{15} < Z < \frac{288 - 260}{15}\right)$
$= P(-1.87 < Z < 1.87)$
$= P(Z < 1.87) - P(Z \leq -1.87)$
$= P(Z < 1.87) - P(Z \geq 1.87)$
$= P(Z < 1.87) - [1 - P(Z < 1.87)]$
$= 2 \times P(Z < 1.87) - 1$
$= 2 \times 0.96926 - 1 = 0.93852$

Q8 a) $P(X < a) = 0.99379 \Rightarrow P\left(Z < \frac{a - 70}{4}\right) = 0.99379$
Using the $\Phi(z)$ table, $\Phi(z) = 0.99379$ for $z = 2.50$.
So, $\frac{a - 70}{4} = 2.5 \Rightarrow a = 2.5 \times 4 + 70 = 80$

b) $P(X < b) = 0.77337 \Rightarrow P\left(Z < \frac{b - 70}{4}\right) = 0.77337$
Using the $\Phi(z)$ table, $\Phi(z) = 0.77337$ for $z = 0.75$.
So, $\frac{b - 70}{4} = 0.75 \Rightarrow b = 0.75 \times 4 + 70 = 73$

Q9 a) $P(X > m) = 0.01017 \Rightarrow P\left(Z > \frac{m - 95}{5}\right) = 0.01017$
$\Rightarrow P\left(Z \leq \frac{m - 95}{5}\right) = 0.98983$
Using the $\Phi(z)$ table, $\Phi(z) = 0.98983$ for $z = 2.32$.
So, $\frac{m - 95}{5} = 2.32 \Rightarrow m = 2.32 \times 5 + 95 = 106.6$

b) $P(X > t) = 0.22965 \Rightarrow P\left(Z > \frac{t-95}{5}\right) = 0.22965$
$\Rightarrow P\left(Z \leq \frac{t-95}{5}\right) = 0.77035$
Using the $\Phi(z)$ table, $\Phi(z) = 0.77035$ for $z = 0.74$.
So, $\frac{t-95}{5} = 0.74 \Rightarrow t = 0.74 \times 5 + 95 = 98.7$

Q10 a) $P(X < c) = 0.12507 \Rightarrow P\left(Z < \frac{c-48}{10}\right) = 0.12507$
$\Rightarrow P\left(Z > \frac{48-c}{10}\right) = 0.12507$
Switch c and 48 around to get −z.
$\Rightarrow P\left(Z \leq \frac{48-c}{10}\right) = 0.87493$
Using the $\Phi(z)$ table, $\Phi(z) = 0.87493$ for $z = 1.15$.
So, $\frac{48-c}{10} = 1.15 \Rightarrow c = 48 - 1.15 \times 10 = 36.5$

b) $P(X < d) = 0.00964 \Rightarrow P\left(Z < \frac{d-48}{10}\right) = 0.00964$
$\Rightarrow P\left(Z > \frac{48-d}{10}\right) = 0.00964$
$\Rightarrow P\left(Z \leq \frac{48-d}{10}\right) = 0.99036$
Using the $\Phi(z)$ table, $\Phi(z) = 0.99036$ for $z = 2.34$.
So, $\frac{48-d}{10} = 2.34 \Rightarrow d = 48 - 2.34 \times 10 = 24.6$

Q11 a) $P(X > w) = 0.91774 \Rightarrow P\left(Z > \frac{w-73}{6}\right) = 0.91774$
$\Rightarrow P\left(Z < \frac{73-w}{6}\right) = 0.91774$
Using the $\Phi(z)$ table, $\Phi(z) = 0.91774$ for $z = 1.39$.
So, $\frac{73-w}{6} = 1.39 \Rightarrow w = 73 - 1.39 \times 6 = 64.66$

b) $P(X > k) = 0.6664 \Rightarrow P\left(Z > \frac{k-73}{6}\right) = 0.6664$
$\Rightarrow P\left(Z < \frac{73-k}{6}\right) = 0.6664$
Using the $\Phi(z)$ table, $\Phi(z) = 0.6664$ for $z = 0.43$.
So, $\frac{73-k}{6} = 0.43 \Rightarrow k = 73 - 0.43 \times 6 = 70.42$

Q12 $P(18 - a < X < 18 + a) = 0.899$
$\Rightarrow P\left(\frac{18-a-18}{0.5} < Z < \frac{18+a-18}{0.5}\right) = 0.899$
$\Rightarrow P\left(\frac{-a}{0.5} < Z < \frac{a}{0.5}\right) = 0.899$
The remaining area = 1 – 0.899 = 0.101.
So, $P\left(Z \geq \frac{a}{0.5}\right) = 0.101 \div 2 = 0.0505$.
$\Rightarrow P\left(Z < \frac{a}{0.5}\right) = 0.9495$
Using the $\Phi(z)$ table, $\Phi(z) = 0.9495$ for $z = 1.64$.
So, $\frac{a}{0.5} = 1.64 \Rightarrow a = 1.64 \times 0.5 = 0.82$

Q13 $P(170 < X < t) = 0.37698$
$\Rightarrow P\left(\frac{170-170}{40} < Z < \frac{t-170}{40}\right) = 0.37698$
$\Rightarrow P\left(0 < Z < \frac{t-170}{40}\right) = 0.37698$
$\Rightarrow P\left(Z < \frac{t-170}{40}\right) - P(Z \leq 0) = 0.37698$
$\Rightarrow P\left(Z < \frac{t-170}{40}\right) = 0.37698 + 0.5 = 0.87698$
Using the $\Phi(z)$ table, $\Phi(z) = 0.87698$ for $z = 1.16$.
So, $\frac{t-170}{40} = 1.16 \Rightarrow t = 1.16 \times 40 + 170 = 216.4$

Q14 $P(107.6 < X < v) = 0.16767$
$\Rightarrow P\left(\frac{107.6-98}{15} < Z < \frac{v-98}{15}\right) = 0.16767$
$\Rightarrow P\left(0.64 < Z < \frac{v-98}{15}\right) = 0.16767$
$\Rightarrow P\left(Z < \frac{v-98}{15}\right) - P(Z \leq 0.64) = 0.16767$
$\Rightarrow P\left(Z < \frac{v-98}{15}\right) = 0.16767 + 0.73891 = 0.90658$
Using the $\Phi(z)$ table, $\Phi(z) = 0.90658$ for $z = 1.32$.
So, $\frac{v-98}{15} = 1.32 \Rightarrow v = 1.32 \times 15 + 98 = 117.8$

Exercise 3.2 — The normal distribution in real-life situations

Q1 a) Let $L \sim N(8.4, 3.1^2)$ represent the length of a worm in cm.
$P(L < 9.5) = P\left(Z < \frac{9.5-8.4}{3.1}\right)$
$= P(Z < 0.35) = 0.63683$

b) $P(L > 10) = P\left(Z > \frac{10-8.4}{3.1}\right) = P(Z > 0.52)$
$= 1 - P(Z \leq 0.52) = 1 - 0.69847 = 0.30153$

c) $P(5 < L < 11) = P\left(\frac{5-8.4}{3.1} < Z < \frac{11-8.4}{3.1}\right)$
$= P(-1.10 < Z < 0.84)$
$= P(Z < 0.84) - P(Z \leq -1.10)$
$= P(Z < 0.84) - P(Z \geq 1.10)$
$= P(Z < 0.84) - [1 - P(Z < 1.10)]$
$= 0.79955 - (1 - 0.86433) = 0.66388$

Q2 a) Let $T \sim N(36, 6^2)$ represent the length of time taken to replace red blood cells, in days.
$P(T < 28) = P\left(Z < \frac{28-36}{6}\right)$
$= P(Z < -1.33) = P(Z > 1.33) = 1 - P(Z \leq 1.33)$
$= 1 - 0.90824 = 0.09176$

b) Let b = the number of days taken by Bella. Then, $P(T > b) = 0.063$.
$\Rightarrow P\left(Z > \frac{b-36}{6}\right) = 0.063$
$\Rightarrow P\left(Z \leq \frac{b-36}{6}\right) = 0.9370$
Using the $\Phi(z)$ table, $\Phi(z) = 0.9370$ (approximately) for $z = 1.53$.
So, $\frac{b-36}{6} = 1.53$
$\Rightarrow b = 1.53 \times 6 + 36 = 45.18$ days (approximately)
Don't forget to say 'days' in your answer — you need to answer the question in the context it was asked.

Q3 a) Let $T \sim N(51, 2.1^2)$ represent the 'personal best' time taken to run 400 m in seconds.

$P(T > 49.3) = P\left(Z > \frac{49.3 - 51}{2.1}\right)$

$= P(Z > -0.81) = P(Z < 0.81) = 0.79103$

So, 79.1% (3 s.f.) are slower than Gary.

b) Let a = the time to beat.

Then, $P(T < a) = 0.2$.

$\Rightarrow P\left(Z < \frac{a - 51}{2.1}\right) = 0.2$

$\Rightarrow P\left(Z > \frac{51 - a}{2.1}\right) = 0.2$

$\Rightarrow P\left(Z \leq \frac{51 - a}{2.1}\right) = 0.8$

Using the percentage-points table,

$p = 0.8$ for $z = 0.8416$

So, $\frac{51 - a}{2.1} = 0.8416$

$\Rightarrow a = 51 - 2.1 \times 0.8416 = 49.2$ s (to 3 s.f.)

Q4 a) Let $L \sim N(300, 50^2)$ represent the lifetime of a battery in hours.

$P(L < 200) = P\left(Z < \frac{200 - 300}{50}\right)$

$= P(Z < -2) = P(Z > 2) = 1 - P(Z \leq 2)$

$= 1 - 0.97725 = 0.02275$

b) $P(L > 380) = P\left(Z > \frac{380 - 300}{50}\right)$

$= P(Z > 1.6) = 1 - P(Z \leq 1.6)$

$= 1 - 0.9452 = 0.0548$

c) Assuming that the lifetimes of the batteries are independent, the probability that both last at least 380 hours = $0.0548 \times 0.0548 = 0.0030$ (to 2 s.f.).

If two things are independent, it means you can multiply their probabilities together.

d) $P(160 < L < h) = 0.97469$

$\Rightarrow P\left(\frac{160 - 300}{50} < Z < \frac{h - 300}{50}\right) = 0.97469$

$\Rightarrow P\left(-2.8 < Z < \frac{h - 300}{50}\right) = 0.97469$

$\Rightarrow P\left(Z < \frac{h - 300}{50}\right) - P(Z \leq -2.8) = 0.97469$

$\Rightarrow P\left(Z < \frac{h - 300}{50}\right) - P(Z \geq 2.8) = 0.97469$

$\Rightarrow P\left(Z < \frac{h - 300}{50}\right) - [1 - P(Z < 2.8)] = 0.97469$

$\Rightarrow P\left(Z < \frac{h - 300}{50}\right) = 0.97469 + (1 - 0.99744)$

$\Rightarrow P\left(Z < \frac{h - 300}{50}\right) = 0.97725$

Using the $\Phi(z)$ table, $\Phi(z) = 0.97725$ for $z = 2.0$.

So, $\frac{h - 300}{50} = 2 \Rightarrow h = 2 \times 50 + 300 = 400$

Q5 a) Let $M \sim N(60, 3^2)$ represent the mass of an egg in grams.

$P(M > 60 - m) = 0.95254$

$\Rightarrow P\left(Z > \frac{60 - m - 60}{3}\right) = 0.95254$

$\Rightarrow P\left(Z > \frac{-m}{3}\right) = 0.95254$

$\Rightarrow P\left(Z < \frac{m}{3}\right) = 0.95254$

Using the $\Phi(z)$ table, $\Phi(z) = 0.95254$ for $z = 1.67$.

So, $\frac{m}{3} = 1.67 \Rightarrow m = 1.67 \times 3 = 5.01$

= 5 grams to the nearest gram.

b) Let c = the maximum mass of an egg in one of farmer Elizabeth's sponge cakes.

Then, $P(M \leq c) = 0.1$.

So, $P\left(Z \leq \frac{c - 60}{3}\right) = 0.1$

$\Rightarrow P\left(Z \geq \frac{60 - c}{3}\right) = 0.1$

$\Rightarrow P\left(Z < \frac{60 - c}{3}\right) = 0.9$

Using the percentage-points table, $p = 0.9$ for $z = 1.2816$

$\Rightarrow \frac{60 - c}{3} = 1.2816 \Rightarrow c = 60 - 3 \times 1.2816$

$= 56.1552 = 56.2$, to 3 s.f.

So, the maximum mass is 56.2 grams.

Exercise 3.3 — Finding the mean and standard deviation of a normal distribution

Q1 a) $P(X < 23) = 0.93319 \Rightarrow P\left(Z < \frac{23 - \mu}{6}\right) = 0.93319$

Using the $\Phi(z)$ table, $\Phi(z) = 0.93319$ for $z = 1.50$.

$\Rightarrow \frac{23 - \mu}{6} = 1.5 \Rightarrow \mu = 23 - 1.5 \times 6 = 14$

b) $P(X < 57) = 0.99702 \Rightarrow P\left(Z < \frac{57 - \mu}{8}\right) = 0.99702$

Using the $\Phi(z)$ table, $\Phi(z) = 0.99702$ for $z = 2.75$.

$\Rightarrow \frac{57 - \mu}{8} = 2.75 \Rightarrow \mu = 57 - 2.75 \times 8 = 35$

c) $P(X > 528) = 0.12924$

$\Rightarrow P\left(Z > \frac{528 - \mu}{100}\right) = 0.12924$

$\Rightarrow P\left(Z \leq \frac{528 - \mu}{100}\right) = 0.87076$

Using the $\Phi(z)$ table, $\Phi(z) = 0.87076$ for $z = 1.13$.

$\Rightarrow \frac{528 - \mu}{100} = 1.13$

$\Rightarrow \mu = 528 - 1.13 \times 100 = 415$

d) $P(X < 11.06) = 0.03216$

$\Rightarrow P\left(Z < \frac{11.06 - \mu}{0.4}\right) = 0.03216$

$\Rightarrow P\left(Z > \frac{\mu - 11.06}{0.4}\right) = 0.03216$

$\Rightarrow P\left(Z \leq \frac{\mu - 11.06}{0.4}\right) = 0.96784$

Using the $\Phi(z)$ table, $\Phi(z) = 0.96784$ for $z = 1.85$.

$\Rightarrow \frac{\mu - 11.06}{0.4} = 1.85$

$\Rightarrow \mu = 1.85 \times 0.4 + 11.06 = 11.8$

e) $P(X > 1.52) = 0.99379$

$\Rightarrow P\left(Z > \frac{1.52 - \mu}{0.02}\right) = 0.99379$

$\Rightarrow P\left(Z < \frac{\mu - 1.52}{0.02}\right) = 0.99379$

Using the $\Phi(z)$ table, $\Phi(z) = 0.99379$ for $z = 2.50$.

$\Rightarrow \frac{\mu - 1.52}{0.02} = 2.5$

$\Rightarrow \mu = 2.5 \times 0.02 + 1.52 = 1.57$

Q2 Start with a sketch showing what you know about X.

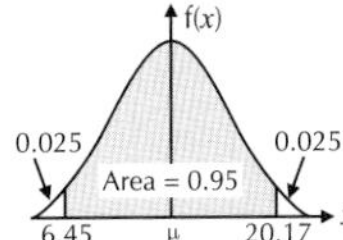

So, $P(X < 20.17) = 0.95 + 0.025 = 0.975$

$\Rightarrow P\left(Z < \frac{20.17 - \mu}{3.5}\right) = 0.975$

Using the percentage-points table, $P(Z \leq z) = 0.975$ for $z = 1.96 \Rightarrow \frac{20.17 - \mu}{3.5} = 1.96$

$\Rightarrow \mu = 20.17 - 1.96 \times 3.5 = 13.31$

There are different ways you could go about this question. For example, you can use the symmetry of the graph. You know that μ is exactly in the middle of 6.45 and 20.17, so you can simply find the average of these 2 values.

Q3 a) $P(X < 53) = 0.89435$

$\Rightarrow P\left(Z < \frac{53 - 48}{\sigma}\right) = P\left(Z < \frac{5}{\sigma}\right) = 0.89435$

Using the $\Phi(z)$ table, $\Phi(z) = 0.89435$ for $z = 1.25$.

$\Rightarrow \frac{5}{\sigma} = 1.25 \Rightarrow \sigma = 5 \div 1.25 = 4$

b) $P(X < 528) = 0.77337$

$\Rightarrow P\left(Z < \frac{528 - 510}{\sigma}\right) = P\left(Z < \frac{18}{\sigma}\right) = 0.77337$

Using the $\Phi(z)$ table, $\Phi(z) = 0.77337$ for $z = 0.75$.

$\Rightarrow \frac{18}{\sigma} = 0.75 \Rightarrow \sigma = 18 \div 0.75 = 24$

c) $P(X > 24) = 0.03673$

$\Rightarrow P\left(Z > \frac{24 - 17}{\sigma}\right) = P\left(Z > \frac{7}{\sigma}\right) = 0.03673$

$\Rightarrow P\left(Z \leq \frac{7}{\sigma}\right) = 0.96327$

Using the $\Phi(z)$ table, $\Phi(z) = 0.96327$ for $z = 1.79$.

$\Rightarrow \frac{7}{\sigma} = 1.79 \Rightarrow \sigma = 7 \div 1.79 = 3.91$ (to 3 s.f.)

d) $P(X < 0.95) = 0.30854$

$\Rightarrow P\left(Z < \frac{0.95 - 0.98}{\sigma}\right) = P\left(Z < -\frac{0.03}{\sigma}\right)$

$= 0.30854$

$\Rightarrow P\left(Z > \frac{0.03}{\sigma}\right) = 0.30854$

$\Rightarrow P\left(Z \leq \frac{0.03}{\sigma}\right) = 0.69146$

Using the $\Phi(z)$ table, $\Phi(z) = 0.69146$ for $z = 0.5$.

$\Rightarrow \frac{0.03}{\sigma} = 0.5 \Rightarrow \sigma = 0.03 \div 0.5 = 0.06$

e) $P(X > 4.85) = 0.83646$

$\Rightarrow P\left(Z > \frac{4.85 - 5.6}{\sigma}\right) = P\left(Z > -\frac{0.75}{\sigma}\right)$

$= 0.83646$

$\Rightarrow P\left(Z < \frac{0.75}{\sigma}\right) = 0.83646$

Using the $\Phi(z)$ table, $\Phi(z) = 0.83646$ for $z = 0.98$.

$\Rightarrow \frac{0.75}{\sigma} = 0.98 \Rightarrow \sigma = 0.75 \div 0.98$

$= 0.765$ (to 3 s.f.)

Q4 Start with a sketch showing what you know about X.

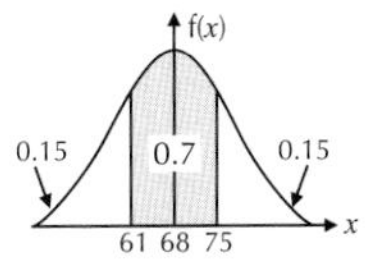

So, $P(X > 75) = 0.15$

$\Rightarrow P\left(Z > \frac{75 - 68}{\sigma}\right) = P\left(Z > \frac{7}{\sigma}\right) = 0.15$

$\Rightarrow P\left(Z \leq \frac{7}{\sigma}\right) = 0.85$

Using the percentage-points table, $p = 0.85$ for $z = 1.0364$.

$\Rightarrow \frac{7}{\sigma} = 1.0364 \Rightarrow \sigma = 7 \div 1.0364 = 6.75$ (to 3 s.f.)

Q5 a) $P(X < 30) = 0.91924 \Rightarrow P\left(Z < \frac{30 - \mu}{\sigma}\right) = 0.91924$

$\Phi(z) = 0.91924$ for $z = 1.40$

$\Rightarrow \frac{30 - \mu}{\sigma} = 1.4 \Rightarrow 30 - \mu = 1.4\sigma$ *(equation 1)*

$P(X < 36) = 0.99534 \Rightarrow P\left(Z < \frac{36 - \mu}{\sigma}\right) = 0.99534$

$\Phi(z) = 0.99534$ for $z = 2.60$

$\Rightarrow \frac{36 - \mu}{\sigma} = 2.6 \Rightarrow 36 - \mu = 2.6\sigma$ *(equation 2)*

Subtracting equation 1 from equation 2 gives:

$36 - 30 - \mu - (-\mu) = 2.6\sigma - 1.4\sigma$

$\Rightarrow 6 = 1.2\sigma \Rightarrow \sigma = 5$

Putting $\sigma = 5$ into equation 1 gives:

$\mu = 30 - 1.4 \times 5 = 23$

So $\mu = 23$ and $\sigma = 5$

b) $P(X < 4) = 0.93319 \Rightarrow P\left(Z < \frac{4-\mu}{\sigma}\right) = 0.93319$
$\Phi(z) = 0.93319$ for $z = 1.50$
$\Rightarrow \frac{4-\mu}{\sigma} = 1.5 \Rightarrow 4 - \mu = 1.5\sigma$ *(equation 1)*
$P(X < 4.3) = 0.99865$
$\Rightarrow P\left(Z < \frac{4.3-\mu}{\sigma}\right) = 0.99865$
$\Phi(z) = 0.99865$ for $z = 3.00$
$\Rightarrow \frac{4.3-\mu}{\sigma} = 3 \Rightarrow 4.3 - \mu = 3\sigma$ *(equation 2)*
Subtracting equation 1 from equation 2 gives:
$4.3 - 4 - \mu - (-\mu) = 3\sigma - 1.5\sigma$
$\Rightarrow 0.3 = 1.5\sigma \Rightarrow \sigma = 0.2$
Putting $\sigma = 0.2$ into equation 1 gives:
$\mu = 4 - 1.5 \times 0.2 = 3.7$
So $\mu = 3.7$ and $\sigma = 0.2$

c) $P(X < 20) = 0.78814$
$\Rightarrow P\left(Z < \frac{20-\mu}{\sigma}\right) = 0.78814$
$\Phi(z) = 0.78814$ for $z = 0.80$
$\Rightarrow \frac{20-\mu}{\sigma} = 0.8 \Rightarrow 20 - \mu = 0.8\sigma$ *(equation 1)*
$P(X < 14) = 0.0548 \Rightarrow P\left(Z < \frac{14-\mu}{\sigma}\right) = 0.0548$
$\Rightarrow P\left(Z > \frac{\mu-14}{\sigma}\right) = 0.0548$
$\Rightarrow P\left(Z \le \frac{\mu-14}{\sigma}\right) = 0.9452$
$\Phi(z) = 0.9452$ for $z = 1.60$
$\Rightarrow \frac{\mu-14}{\sigma} = 1.6 \Rightarrow \mu - 14 = 1.6\sigma$ *(equation 2)*
Adding equations 1 and 2 gives:
$20 - 14 - \mu + \mu = 0.8\sigma + 1.6\sigma$
$\Rightarrow 6 = 2.4\sigma \Rightarrow \sigma = 2.5$
Putting $\sigma = 2.5$ into equation 2 gives:
$\mu = 1.6 \times 2.5 + 14 = 18$
So $\mu = 18$ and $\sigma = 2.5$

d) $P(X < 696) = 0.97128$
$\Rightarrow P\left(Z < \frac{696-\mu}{\sigma}\right) = 0.97128$
$\Phi(z) = 0.97128$ for $z = 1.90$
$\Rightarrow \frac{696-\mu}{\sigma} = 1.9 \Rightarrow 696 - \mu = 1.9\sigma$ *(equation 1)*
$P(X < 592) = 0.24196$
$\Rightarrow P\left(Z < \frac{592-\mu}{\sigma}\right) = 0.24196$
$\Rightarrow P\left(Z > \frac{\mu-592}{\sigma}\right) = 0.24196$
$\Rightarrow P\left(Z \le \frac{\mu-592}{\sigma}\right) = 0.75804$
$\Phi(z) = 0.75804$ for $z = 0.70$
$\Rightarrow \frac{\mu-592}{\sigma} = 0.7 \Rightarrow \mu - 592 = 0.7\sigma$ *(equation 2)*
Adding equations 1 and 2 gives:
$696 - 592 - \mu + \mu = 1.9\sigma + 0.7\sigma$
$\Rightarrow 104 = 2.6\sigma \Rightarrow \sigma = 40$
Putting $\sigma = 40$ into equation 2 gives:
$\mu = 0.7 \times 40 + 592 = 620$
So $\mu = 620$ and $\sigma = 40$

e) $P(X > 33) = 0.10565$
$\Rightarrow P\left(Z > \frac{33-\mu}{\sigma}\right) = 0.10565$
$\Rightarrow P\left(Z \le \frac{33-\mu}{\sigma}\right) = 0.89435$
$\Phi(z) = 0.89435$ for $z = 1.25$
$\Rightarrow \frac{33-\mu}{\sigma} = 1.25 \Rightarrow 33 - \mu = 1.25\sigma$ *(equation 1)*
$P(X > 21) = 0.95994$
$\Rightarrow P\left(Z > \frac{21-\mu}{\sigma}\right) = 0.95994$
$\Rightarrow P\left(Z < \frac{\mu-21}{\sigma}\right) = 0.95994$
$\Phi(z) = 0.95994$ for $z = 1.75$
$\Rightarrow \frac{\mu-21}{\sigma} = 1.75 \Rightarrow \mu - 21 = 1.75\sigma$ *(equation 2)*
Adding equations 1 and 2 gives:
$33 - 21 - \mu + \mu = 1.25\sigma + 1.75\sigma$
$\Rightarrow 12 = 3\sigma \Rightarrow \sigma = 4$
Putting $\sigma = 4$ into equation 2 gives:
$\mu = 1.75 \times 4 + 21 = 28$
So $\mu = 28$ and $\sigma = 4$

f) $P(X > 66) = 0.36317$
$\Rightarrow P\left(Z > \frac{66-\mu}{\sigma}\right) = 0.36317$
$\Rightarrow P\left(Z \le \frac{66-\mu}{\sigma}\right) = 0.63683$
$\Phi(z) = 0.63683$ for $z = 0.35$
$\Rightarrow \frac{66-\mu}{\sigma} = 0.35 \Rightarrow 66 - \mu = 0.35\sigma$ *(equation 1)*
$P(X < 48) = 0.34458$
$\Rightarrow P\left(Z < \frac{48-\mu}{\sigma}\right) = 0.34458$
$\Rightarrow P\left(Z > \frac{\mu-48}{\sigma}\right) = 0.34458$
$\Rightarrow P\left(Z \le \frac{\mu-48}{\sigma}\right) = 0.65542$
$\Phi(z) = 0.65542$ for $z = 0.40$
$\Rightarrow \frac{\mu-48}{\sigma} = 0.4 \Rightarrow \mu - 48 = 0.4\sigma$ *(equation 2)*
Adding equations 1 and 2 gives:
$66 - 48 - \mu + \mu = 0.35\sigma + 0.4\sigma$
$\Rightarrow 18 = 0.75\sigma \Rightarrow \sigma = 24$
Putting $\sigma = 24$ into equation 2 gives:
$\mu = 0.4 \times 24 + 48 = 57.6$
So $\mu = 57.6$ and $\sigma = 24$

Q6 a) Let V = volume of vinegar in ml.
Then $V \sim N(\mu, 5^2)$.
$P(V < 506) = 0.719 \Rightarrow P\left(Z < \frac{506-\mu}{5}\right) = 0.719$
$\Phi(z) = 0.719$ for $z = 0.58$ (approximately)
$\Rightarrow \frac{506-\mu}{5} = 0.58$
$\Rightarrow \mu = 506 - 0.58 \times 5 = 503.1$ ml

b) $P(V < 500) = P\left(Z < \frac{500-503.1}{5}\right)$
$= P(Z < -0.62) = P(Z > 0.62) = 1 - P(Z \le 0.62)$
$= 1 - 0.73237 = 0.26763$
So, 26.76% of bottles contain less than 500 ml.

Q7 a) Let H = height in cm. Then $H \sim N(175, \sigma^2)$.
$P(H > 170) = 0.8$

$\Rightarrow P\left(Z > \frac{170 - 175}{\sigma}\right) = P\left(Z > -\frac{5}{\sigma}\right) = 0.8$

$\Rightarrow P\left(Z < \frac{5}{\sigma}\right) = 0.8$

$p = 0.8$ for $z = 0.8416 \Rightarrow \frac{5}{\sigma} = 0.8416$

$\Rightarrow \sigma = 5 \div 0.8416 = 5.94$ cm (to 3 s.f.)

b) $P(171 < H < 179)$
$= P\left(\frac{171 - 175}{5.94} < Z < \frac{179 - 175}{5.94}\right)$
$= P(-0.67 < Z < 0.67)$
$= P(Z < 0.67) - P(Z \leq -0.67)$
$= P(Z < 0.67) - [1 - P(Z < 0.67)]$
$= 2 \times 0.74857 - 1$
$= 0.49714$

Q8 Let R = rainfall in cm. Then $R \sim N(\mu, \sigma^2)$.
$P(R < 4) = 0.102 \Rightarrow P\left(Z < \frac{4 - \mu}{\sigma}\right) = 0.102$

$\Rightarrow P\left(Z > \frac{\mu - 4}{\sigma}\right) = 0.102 \Rightarrow P\left(Z \leq \frac{\mu - 4}{\sigma}\right) = 0.898$

$\Phi(z) = 0.898$ for $z = 1.27$ (approximately)

$\Rightarrow \frac{\mu - 4}{\sigma} = 1.27 \Rightarrow \mu - 4 = 1.27\sigma$ *(equation 1)*

$P(R > 7) = 0.648 \Rightarrow P\left(Z > \frac{7 - \mu}{\sigma}\right) = 0.648$

$\Rightarrow P\left(Z < \frac{\mu - 7}{\sigma}\right) = 0.648$

$\Phi(z) = 0.648$ for $z = 0.38$ (approximately)

$\Rightarrow \frac{\mu - 7}{\sigma} = 0.38 \Rightarrow \mu - 7 = 0.38\sigma$ *(equation 2)*

Subtracting equation 2 from equation 1 gives:
$\mu - \mu - 4 - (-7) = 1.27\sigma - 0.38\sigma$
$\Rightarrow 3 = 0.89\sigma \Rightarrow \sigma = 3.37$ (to 3 s.f.)
Putting $\sigma = 3.37$ cm into equation 1 gives:
$\mu = 1.27 \times 3.37 + 4 = 8.28$ cm (to 3 s.f.)
So $\mu = 8.28$ cm and $\sigma = 3.37$ cm (to 3 s.f.)

Review Exercise — Chapter 4

Q1 Using the $\Phi(z)$ table:

a) $P(Z < 0.84) = 0.79955$

b) $P(Z < 2.95) = 0.99841$

c) $P(Z > 0.68) = 1 - P(Z \leq 0.68) = 1 - 0.75175$
$= 0.24825$

d) $P(Z \geq 1.55) = 1 - P(Z < 1.55)$
$= 1 - 0.93943 = 0.06057$

e) $P(Z < -2.10) = P(Z > 2.10) = 1 - P(Z \leq 2.10)$
$= 1 - 0.98214 = 0.01786$

f) $P(Z \leq -0.01) = P(Z \geq 0.01)$
$= 1 - P(Z < 0.01) = 1 - 0.50399 = 0.49601$

g) $P(Z > 0.10) = 1 - P(Z \leq 0.10) = 1 - 0.53983$
$= 0.46017$

h) $P(Z \leq 0.64) = 0.73891$

i) $P(Z > 0.23) = 1 - P(Z \leq 0.23) = 1 - 0.59095$
$= 0.40905$

j) $P(0.10 < Z \leq 0.50) = P(Z \leq 0.50) - P(Z \leq 0.10)$
$= 0.69146 - 0.53983 = 0.15163$

k) $P(-0.62 \leq Z < 1.10) = P(Z < 1.10) - P(Z < -0.62)$
$= P(Z < 1.10) - P(Z > 0.62)$
$= P(Z < 1.10) - (1 - P(Z \leq 0.62))$
$= 0.86433 - (1 - 0.73237) = 0.5967$

l) $P(-0.99 < Z \leq -0.74) = P(0.74 \leq Z < 0.99)$
$= P(Z < 0.99) - P(Z < 0.74)$
$= 0.83891 - 0.77035 = 0.06856$

Q2 a) If $P(Z < z) = 0.91309$, then from the $\Phi(z)$ table, $z = 1.36$.

b) If $P(Z < z) = 0.58706$, then from the $\Phi(z)$ table, $z = 0.22$.

c) If $P(Z > z) = 0.03593$, then $P(Z \leq z) = 0.96407$.
From the $\Phi(z)$ table, $z = 1.80$.

d) If $P(Z > z) = 0.01 \Rightarrow P(Z \leq z) = 0.99$, then from the percentage-points table, $z = 2.3263$.

e) If $P(Z \leq z) = 0.40129$, then z must be negative (and so won't be in the $\Phi(z)$ table).
But this means $P(Z \geq -z) = 0.40129$, and so
$P(Z < -z) = 1 - 0.40129 = 0.59871$.
Using the $\Phi(z)$ table, $-z = 0.25$, so $z = -0.25$.
If you need to draw a graph here to make it a bit clearer what's going on, then draw one.

f) If $P(Z \geq z) = 0.995$, then $P(Z \leq -z) = 0.995$
From the percentage-points table, $-z = 2.5758$.
So $z = -2.5758$.
When you've answered a question like this, always ask yourself whether your answer looks 'about right'. Here, you need a number that Z is very very likely to be greater than... so your answer is going to be negative, and it's going to be pretty big. So z = −2.5758 looks about right.

g) If $P(-z < Z < z) = 0.5035$, then the remaining area $= 1 - 0.5035 = 0.4965$,
and $0.4965 \div 2 = 0.24825$.
So, $P(Z < z) = 0.5035 + 0.24825 = 0.75175$.
This is the area between −z and z + the area to the left of −z.

Using the $\Phi(z)$ table, $z = 0.68$.
Or you could divide 0.5035 by 2 to get P(0 < Z < z) = 0.25175. Then add 0.5 to get P(Z < z) = 0.75175.

h) If $P(0.25 < Z < z) = 0.39165$,
$P(Z < z) - P(Z \leq 0.25) = 0.39165$
$\Rightarrow P(Z < z) = 0.39165 + P(Z \leq 0.25)$
$\Rightarrow P(Z < z) = 0.39165 + 0.59871 = 0.99036$

Using the $\Phi(z)$ table, $z = 2.34$.

Q3 **a)** $P(X < 55) = P\left(Z < \frac{55 - 50}{4}\right)$
$= P(Z < 1.25) = 0.89435$

b) $P(X < 42) = P\left(Z < \frac{42 - 50}{4}\right)$
$= P(Z < -2) = P(Z > 2) = 1 - P(Z \leq 2)$
$= 1 - 0.97725 = 0.02275$

c) $P(X > 56) = P\left(Z > \frac{56 - 50}{4}\right)$
$= P(Z > 1.5) = 1 - P(Z \leq 1.5)$
$= 1 - 0.93319 = 0.06681$

d) $P(47 < X < 57) = P\left(\frac{47 - 50}{4} < Z < \frac{57 - 50}{4}\right)$
$= P(-0.75 < Z < 1.75)$
$= P(Z < 1.75) - P(Z \leq -0.75)$
$= P(Z < 1.75) - P(Z \geq 0.75)$
$= P(Z < 1.75) - [1 - P(Z < 0.75)]$
$= 0.95994 - (1 - 0.77337) = 0.73331$

Q4 **a)** $P(X < 0) = P\left(Z < \frac{0 - 5}{7}\right)$
$= P(Z < -0.71) = P(Z > 0.71)$
$= 1 - P(Z \leq 0.71) = 1 - 0.76115 = 0.23885$

b) $P(X < 1) = P\left(Z < \frac{1 - 5}{7}\right)$
$= P(Z < -0.57) = P(Z > 0.57)$
$= 1 - P(Z \leq 0.57) = 1 - 0.71566 = 0.28434$

c) $P(X > 7) = P\left(Z > \frac{7 - 5}{7}\right) = P(Z > 0.29)$
$= 1 - P(Z \leq 0.29) = 1 - 0.61409 = 0.38591$

d) $P(2 < X < 4) = P\left(\frac{2 - 5}{7} < Z < \frac{4 - 5}{7}\right)$
$= P(-0.43 < Z < -0.14)$
$= P(0.14 < Z < 0.43)$
$= P(Z < 0.43) - P(Z \leq 0.14)$
$= 0.66640 - 0.55567$
$= 0.11073$

Q5 **a)** Here $X \sim N(80, 15)$.

If $P(X < a) = 0.99$, then $P\left(Z < \frac{a - 80}{\sqrt{15}}\right) = 0.99$

So $\frac{a - 80}{\sqrt{15}} = 2.3263$ (using percentage points).

Rearrange this to get $a = 80 + 2.3263 \times \sqrt{15}$
$= 89.01$ (to 4 s.f.)

b) $|X - 80| < b$ means that X is 'within b' of 80, i.e. $80 - b < X < 80 + b$.
Since 80 is the mean of X, and since a normal distribution is symmetrical,
$P(80 - b < X < 80 + b) = 0.8$ means that
$P(X \geq 80 + b) = 0.1$

$\Rightarrow P\left(Z \geq \frac{80 + b - 80}{\sqrt{15}}\right) = P\left(Z \geq \frac{b}{\sqrt{15}}\right) = 0.1$

$\Rightarrow P\left(Z < \frac{b}{\sqrt{15}}\right) = 0.9$

So $\frac{b}{\sqrt{15}} = 1.2816$ (using percentage points).

And so $b = 4.964$ (to 4 s.f.)

It's really important you remember that a normal distribution is symmetrical. You often need to use symmetry to work out these sorts of questions.

Q6 If X represents the mass of an item in grams, then $X \sim N(55, 4.4^2)$.

a) $P(X < 55) = P\left(Z < \frac{55 - 55}{4.4}\right) = P(Z < 0) = 0.5$

b) $P(X < 50) = P\left(Z < \frac{50 - 55}{4.4}\right) = P(Z < -1.14)$
$= P(Z > 1.14) = 1 - P(Z \leq 1.14)$
$= 1 - 0.87286 = 0.12714$

c) $P(X > 60) = P\left(Z > \frac{60 - 55}{4.4}\right) = P(Z > 1.14)$
$= 1 - P(Z \leq 1.14) = 1 - 0.87286 = 0.12714$

Q7 If X represents the mass of an egg in kilograms, then $X \sim N(1.4, 0.3^2)$.
Watch out for the units here — you need to make them the same for both the mean and the variance.

$P(X < a) = 0.8830 \Rightarrow P\left(Z < \frac{a - 1.4}{0.3}\right) = 0.8830$

$\Phi(z) = 0.8830$ for $z = 1.19$ (approximately)

$\Rightarrow \frac{a - 1.4}{0.3} = 1.19 \Rightarrow a = 1.19 \times 0.3 + 1.4 = 1.757$

Q8 $P(X < 8) = 0.89251 \Rightarrow P\left(Z < \frac{8 - \mu}{\sqrt{10}}\right) = 0.89251$

$\Phi(z) = 0.89251$ for $z = 1.24$

$\Rightarrow \frac{8 - \mu}{\sqrt{10}} = 1.24 \Rightarrow \mu = 8 - 1.24 \times \sqrt{10}$
$= 4.08$ (to 3 s.f.)

Q9 $P(X > 221) = 0.30854 \Rightarrow P\left(Z > \frac{221 - \mu}{8}\right) = 0.30854$

$\Rightarrow P\left(Z \leq \frac{221 - \mu}{8}\right) = 1 - 0.30854 = 0.69146$

$\Phi(z) = 0.69146$ for $z = 0.5$

$\Rightarrow \frac{221 - \mu}{8} = 0.5 \Rightarrow \mu = 221 - 0.5 \times 8 = 217$

Q10 $P(X < 13) = 0.6$

$\Rightarrow P\left(Z < \frac{13 - 11}{\sigma}\right) = P\left(Z < \frac{2}{\sigma}\right) = 0.6$

$p = 0.6$ for $z = 0.2533$

$\Rightarrow \frac{2}{\sigma} = 0.2533 \Rightarrow \sigma = 2 \div 0.2533 = 7.90$ (to 3 s.f.)

Q11 $P(X \leq 110) = 0.96784$

$\Rightarrow P\left(Z \leq \frac{110 - 108}{\sigma}\right) = P\left(Z \leq \frac{2}{\sigma}\right) = 0.96784$

$\Phi(z) = 0.96784$ for $z = 1.85$

$\Rightarrow \frac{2}{\sigma} = 1.85 \Rightarrow \sigma = 2 \div 1.85 = 1.08$ (to 3 s.f.)

Q12 $P(X < 15.2) = 0.97831 \Rightarrow P\left(Z < \frac{15.2 - \mu}{\sigma}\right) = 0.97831$

$\Phi(z) = 0.97831$ for $z = 2.02$

$\Rightarrow \frac{15.2 - \mu}{\sigma} = 2.02 \Rightarrow 15.2 - \mu = 2.02\sigma$ *(equation 1)*

$P(X > 14.8) = 0.10565 \Rightarrow P\left(Z > \frac{14.8 - \mu}{\sigma}\right) = 0.10565$

$\Rightarrow P\left(Z \le \frac{14.8 - \mu}{\sigma}\right) = 1 - 0.10565 = 0.89435$

$\Phi(z) = 0.89435$ for $z = 1.25$

$\Rightarrow \frac{14.8 - \mu}{\sigma} = 1.25 \Rightarrow 14.8 - \mu = 1.25\sigma$ *(equation 2)*

Subtracting equation 2 from equation 1 gives:

$15.2 - 14.8 - \mu - (-\mu) = 2.02\sigma - 1.25\sigma$
$\Rightarrow 0.4 = 0.77\sigma \Rightarrow \sigma = 0.51948... = 0.519$ (to 3 s.f.)
Putting $\sigma = 0.519...$ into equation 1 gives:
$\mu = 15.2 - 2.02 \times 0.519... = 14.2$ (to 3 s.f.)
So $\mu = 14.2$ and $\sigma = 0.519$ (to 3 s.f.)

Exam-Style Questions — Chapter 4

1 Let X represent the exam marks. Then $X \sim N(50, 15^2)$.

a) $P(X < 30) = P\left(Z < \frac{30 - 50}{15}\right) = P(Z < -1.33)$ ***[1 mark]***
$= P(Z > 1.33) = 1 - P(Z \le 1.33)$ ***[1 mark]***
$= 1 - 0.90824 = 0.09176$ ***[1 mark]***

b) $P(X \ge 41) = P\left(Z \ge \frac{41 - 50}{15}\right) = P(Z \ge -0.6)$ ***[1 mark]***
$= P(Z \le 0.6) = 0.72575$ ***[1 mark]***
So $0.72575 \times 1000 = 726$ is the expected number who passed the exam ***[1 mark]***.

c) If a is the mark needed for a distinction, then:
$P(X \ge a) = 0.1 \Rightarrow P\left(Z \ge \frac{a - 50}{15}\right) = 0.1$ ***[1 mark]***
$\Rightarrow P\left(Z < \frac{a - 50}{15}\right) = 0.9$
$p = 0.9$ for $z = 1.2816$
$\Rightarrow \frac{a - 50}{15} = 1.2816$ ***[1 mark]***
$\Rightarrow a = 69$ (to the nearest whole mark) ***[1 mark]***

2 **a)** $P(X < 50) = 0.12302$
$\Rightarrow P\left(Z < \frac{50 - \mu}{6}\right) = 0.12302$ ***[1 mark]***
$\Rightarrow P\left(Z > \frac{\mu - 50}{6}\right) = 0.12302$
$\Rightarrow P\left(Z \le \frac{\mu - 50}{6}\right) = 1 - 0.12302 = 0.87698$ ***[1 mark]***

$\Phi(z) = 0.87698$ for $z = 1.16$
$\Rightarrow \frac{\mu - 50}{6} = 1.16$ ***[1 mark]***
$\Rightarrow \mu = 1.16 \times 6 + 50 = 56.96$ ***[1 mark]***

b) $P(X > 71) = P\left(Z > \frac{71 - 56.96}{6}\right)$
$= P(Z > 2.34)$ ***[1 mark]***
$= 1 - P(Z \le 2.34)$ ***[1 mark]***
$= 1 - 0.99036 = 0.00964$ ***[1 mark]***

c) Since the distribution is symmetrical about μ,
$P(X < \mu + a) = 0.9$ ***[1 mark]***
$\Rightarrow P\left(Z < \frac{\mu + a - \mu}{6}\right) = P\left(Z < \frac{a}{6}\right) = 0.9$ ***[1 mark]***
$p = 0.9$ for $z = 1.2816$
$\Rightarrow \frac{a}{6} = 1.2816$ ***[1 mark]***
$\Rightarrow a = 7.69$ (to 3 s.f.) ***[1 mark]***

3 **a)** Let X represent the lifetime of a battery in hours. Then $X \sim N(\mu, \sigma^2)$.
$P(X < 20) = 0.4 \Rightarrow P\left(Z < \frac{20 - \mu}{\sigma}\right) = 0.4$ ***[1 mark]***
$\Rightarrow P\left(Z > \frac{\mu - 20}{\sigma}\right) = 0.4$
$\Rightarrow P\left(Z \le \frac{\mu - 20}{\sigma}\right) = 0.6$
Using the percentage-points table,
$p = 0.6$ for $z = 0.2533$
$\Rightarrow \frac{\mu - 20}{\sigma} = 0.2533$ ***[1 mark]***
$\Rightarrow \mu - 20 = 0.2533\sigma$ *(equation 1)*
$P(X < 26) = 0.8 \Rightarrow P\left(Z < \frac{26 - \mu}{\sigma}\right) = 0.8$ ***[1 mark]***
Using the percentage-points table,
$p = 0.8$ for $z = 0.8416$
$\Rightarrow \frac{26 - \mu}{\sigma} = 0.8416$ ***[1 mark]***
$\Rightarrow 26 - \mu = 0.8416\sigma$ *(equation 2)*
Adding equations 1 and 2 gives:
$\mu - \mu - 20 + 26 = 0.2533\sigma + 0.8416\sigma$ ***[1 mark]***
$\Rightarrow 6 = 1.0949\sigma \Rightarrow \sigma = 5.47995... = 5.48$ (to 3 s.f.)
Putting $\sigma = 5.47...$ into equation 1 gives:
$\mu = 0.2533 \times 5.47... + 20 = 21.4$ (to 3 s.f.)
So $\mu = 21.4$ hours ***[1 mark]***
and $\sigma = 5.48$ hours ***[1 mark]*** (to 3 s.f.)

b) From part a), $X \sim N(21.4, 5.48^2)$
So $P(X \ge 15) = P\left(Z \ge \frac{15 - 21.4}{5.48}\right)$ ***[1 mark]***
$= P(Z \ge -1.17) = P(Z \le 1.17)$ ***[1 mark]***
$= 0.8790$ ***[1 mark]***

4 **a)** $P(X > 145) = P\left(Z > \frac{145 - 120}{25}\right)$
$= P(Z > 1)$ ***[1 mark]***
$= 1 - P(Z \leq 1)$ ***[1 mark]***
$= 1 - 0.84134 = 0.15866$ ***[1 mark]***

b) $P(120 < X < j) = 0.46407$
$\Rightarrow P\left(\frac{120 - 120}{25} < Z < \frac{j - 120}{25}\right) = 0.46407$
$\Rightarrow P\left(0 < Z < \frac{j - 120}{25}\right) = 0.46407$ ***[1 mark]***
$\Rightarrow P\left(Z < \frac{j - 120}{25}\right) - P(Z \leq 0) = 0.46407$
$\Rightarrow P\left(Z < \frac{j - 120}{25}\right) = 0.46407 + 0.5$
$\Rightarrow P\left(Z < \frac{j - 120}{25}\right) = 0.96407$ ***[1 mark]***
$\Phi(z) = 0.96407$ for $z = 1.80$
$\Rightarrow \frac{j - 120}{25} = 1.8$ ***[1 mark]***
$\Rightarrow j = 1.8 \times 25 + 120 = 165$ ***[1 mark]***

5 **a)** For a normal distribution, mean = median, so median = 12 inches ***[1 mark]***.

b) Let X represent the base diameters.
Then $X \sim N(12, \sigma^2)$. $P(X > 13) = 0.05$ ***[1 mark]***,
so $P\left(Z > \frac{13 - 12}{\sigma}\right) = P\left(Z > \frac{1}{\sigma}\right) = 0.05$ ***[1 mark]***
and $P\left(Z \leq \frac{1}{\sigma}\right) = 0.95$
Using the percentage-points table,
$p = 0.95$ for $z = 1.6449$
$\Rightarrow \frac{1}{\sigma} = 1.6449$ ***[1 mark]***
$\Rightarrow \sigma = 1 \div 1.6449 = 0.608$ (to 3 s.f.) ***[1 mark]***

c) $P(X < 10.8) = P\left(Z < \frac{10.8 - 12}{0.608}\right)$
$= P(Z < -1.97)$ ***[1 mark]***
$= P(Z > 1.97) = 1 - (Z \leq 1.97)$
$= 1 - 0.97558 = 0.02442$ ***[1 mark]***
So you would expect $0.02442 \times 100 \approx 2$ pizza bases to be discarded ***[1 mark]***.

d) P(at least 1 base too small)
= 1 – P(no bases too small).
P(base not too small) = 1 – 0.02442 = 0.97558.
P(no bases too small) = $0.97558^3 = 0.9285$
[1 mark]
P(at least 1 base too small) = 1 – 0.9285 ***[1 mark]***
= 0.0715 ***[1 mark]***.

6 **a)** Let X represent the volume of compost in a bag.
Then $X \sim N(50, 0.4^2)$.
$P(X < 49) = P\left(Z < \frac{49 - 50}{0.4}\right)$
$= P(Z < -2.5)$ ***[1 mark]***
$= P(Z > 2.5) = 1 - P(Z \leq 2.5)$ ***[1 mark]***
$= 1 - 0.99379 = 0.00621$ ***[1 mark]***

b) $P(X > 50.5) = P\left(Z > \frac{50.5 - 50}{0.4}\right)$
$= P(Z > 1.25)$ ***[1 mark]***
$= 1 - P(Z \leq 1.25)$ ***[1 mark]***
$= 1 - 0.89435 = 0.10565$ ***[1 mark]***
So in 1000 bags, 0.10565×1000 ***[1 mark]***
≈ 106 bags ***[1 mark]*** (approximately) would be expected to contain more than 50.5 litres of compost.

c) $P(Y < 74) = 0.1$
$\Rightarrow P\left(Z < \frac{74 - 75}{\sigma}\right) = P\left(Z < -\frac{1}{\sigma}\right) = 0.1$
$\Rightarrow P\left(Z > \frac{1}{\sigma}\right) = 0.1 \Rightarrow P\left(Z \leq \frac{1}{\sigma}\right) = 0.9$ ***[1 mark]***
Using the percentage-points table,
$p = 0.9$ for $z = 1.2816$
$\Rightarrow \frac{1}{\sigma} = 1.2816$ ***[1 mark]***
$\Rightarrow \sigma = 1 \div 1.2816$
$= 0.780$ litres (to 3 s.f.) ***[1 mark]***

Chapter 5: Estimation

2. Statistics

Exercise 2.1 — Estimating a population mean (μ) and population variance (σ^2)

Q1 **a)** Yes.
b) No — the mean is unknown.
c) Yes.
d) No — the standard deviation is unknown.

Q2 First find the sample mean $\bar{x}$ (which will be your unbiased estimate of the population mean).

$$\bar{x} = \frac{\sum x}{n} = \frac{240}{10} = 24$$

Now you can find the sample variance s^2 (which will be your unbiased estimate of the population variance).

$$s^2 = \frac{n}{n-1}\left[\frac{\sum x^2}{n} - \left(\frac{\sum x}{n}\right)^2\right]$$
$$= \frac{10}{9}\left[\frac{5790}{10} - \left(\frac{240}{10}\right)^2\right]$$
$$= 3.3333... = 3.33 \text{ (to 3 sig. fig.)}.$$

Q3 **a)** You'll need to add some rows to your table:

Marks	31-40	41-50	51-60	61-70	71-80	81-90
Frequency (f)	2	4	5	8	6	5
Class mid-point (x)	35.5	45.5	55.5	65.5	75.5	85.5
fx	71	182	277.5	524	453	427.5
x^2	1260.25	2070.25	3080.25	4290.25	5700.25	7310.25
fx^2	2520.5	8281	15401.25	34322	34201.5	36551.25

Then you can work out that:
$n = \sum f = 30,\ \sum fx = 1935,\ \sum fx^2 = 131277.5$
So the sample mean $\bar{x}$ (which will be your unbiased estimate of the population mean) is:
$$\bar{x} = \frac{\sum fx}{\sum f} = \frac{1935}{30} = 64.5 \text{ marks}$$

b) Now find the sample variance s^2 (which will be your unbiased estimate of the population variance).
$$s^2 = \frac{n}{n-1}\left[\frac{\sum fx^2}{n} - \left(\frac{\sum fx}{n}\right)^2\right]$$
$$= \frac{30}{29}\left[\frac{131277.5}{30} - \left(\frac{1935}{30}\right)^2\right]$$
$$= 223.1034... = 223 \text{ (to 3 sig. fig.)}.$$

3. Confidence Intervals

Exercise 3.1 — Standard error and the sampling distribution of $\bar{X}$ if $X \sim N(\mu, \sigma^2)$

Q1 The population variance (σ^2) is 32.5, and the sample size (n) is 20. So the standard error of the sample mean is
$$\frac{\sigma}{\sqrt{n}} = \frac{\sqrt{32.5}}{\sqrt{20}} = 1.27 \text{ (to 3 sig. fig.)}$$

Q2 The population standard deviation (σ) is 2 cm, and the sample size (n) is 60. So the standard error of the sample mean is
$$\frac{\sigma}{\sqrt{n}} = \frac{2}{\sqrt{60}} = 0.258 \text{ cm (to 3 sig. fig.)}$$

Q3 a) The population of heights is a normally distributed population following $N(\mu, \sigma^2) = N(164, 57)$.
So if the sample size is $n = 30$, the sample mean ($\bar{X}$) must follow $N(\mu, \frac{\sigma^2}{n}) = N(164, \frac{57}{30})$.

b) First find the probability of a random sample having a mean of less than 162 cm.
$$P(\bar{X} < 162) = P\left(Z < \frac{162 - 164}{\sqrt{57/30}}\right) = P(Z < -1.45)$$
This equals $P(Z > 1.45) = 1 - P(Z \le 1.45)$
$= 1 - 0.92647 = 0.07353$
So out of 100 samples, you would expect $100 \times 0.07353 = 7.4$ (to 1 d.p.) (i.e. approximately 7) to have a mean of less than 162 cm.

Q4 a) The population of volumes is normally distributed, so the sampling distribution of the mean will be:
$$\bar{X} \sim N\left(500, \frac{2.63^2}{10}\right)$$
i.e. $\bar{X} \sim N(500, 0.692)$ (to 3 sig. fig.)

b) $P(\bar{X} > 501) = P\left(Z > \frac{501 - 500}{\sqrt{0.692}}\right)$
$= P(Z > 1.20) = 1 - P(Z \le 1.20)$
$= 1 - 0.88493 = 0.11507$

Exercise 3.2 — Confidence intervals for μ if $X \sim N(\mu, \sigma^2)$

Q1 a) The formula for a confidence interval is:
$$\left(\bar{X} - z\frac{\sigma}{\sqrt{n}}, \bar{X} + z\frac{\sigma}{\sqrt{n}}\right)$$
Here, since you need a 95% confidence interval, you need to find z with $P(-z < Z < z) = 0.95$, so use your tables to look up the value of z with $P(Z < z) = 0.975$ — this gives $z = 1.9600$.

You also know that $\sigma = 20$, $n = 30$ and $\bar{x} = 510$.

So the confidence interval you need is:
$$\left(510 - 1.9600 \times \frac{20}{\sqrt{30}}, 510 + 1.9600 \times \frac{20}{\sqrt{30}}\right)$$
$= (503 \text{ kg}, 517 \text{ kg})$ (to 3 sig. fig.)

b) The whole confidence interval is greater than 500, so this claim seems valid, based on this evidence.

Q2 a) Here, since you need a 98% confidence interval, you need to find z with $P(-z < Z < z) = 0.98$, so use your tables to look up the value of z with $P(Z < z) = 0.99$ — this gives $z = 2.3263$.

You also know that $\sigma^2 = 3600$ (and so $\sigma = 60$), $n = 50$ and $\bar{x} = 1600$.

So the confidence interval you need is:
$$\left(1600 - 2.3263 \times \frac{60}{\sqrt{50}}, 1600 + 2.3263 \times \frac{60}{\sqrt{50}}\right)$$
$= (1580 \text{ N}, 1620 \text{ N})$ (to 3 sig. fig.)

b) If $\bar{x} - z\frac{\sigma}{\sqrt{n}} = 1585$, then $1600 - z\frac{60}{\sqrt{50}} = 1585$
This means that $z = 1.77$ (to 2 d.p.).
(You get the same value for z if you solve $\bar{x} + z\frac{\sigma}{\sqrt{n}} = 1615$.)

So you need to find $P(-1.77 < Z < 1.77)$.
$P(-1.77 < Z < 1.77) = P(Z < 1.77) - P(Z \le -1.77)$
$= P(Z < 1.77) - P(Z \ge 1.77)$
$= P(Z < 1.77) - (1 - P(Z < 1.77))$
$= 2 \times P(Z < 1.77) - 1$
From your tables, you know that $P(Z < 1.77) = 0.96164$.
So $P(-1.77 < Z < 1.77) = 2 \times 0.96164 - 1$
$= 0.92328$

So the probability that this interval contains the true mean breaking strength of the cable is 92.3% (to 3 sig. fig.) (i.e. it is a 92.3% confidence interval).

Q3 a) Since the confidence interval is symmetrical about the sample mean, the sample mean is $(1023.3 + 1101.7) \div 2 = 1062.5$ hours

b) The confidence interval extends a distance of '$z \times$ standard error' from the sample mean in both directions. This distance is $1062.5 - 1023.3 = 1101.7 - 1062.5 = 39.2$
Since this is a 95% confidence interval, you know that $z = 1.9600$ (since $P(-1.9600 < Z < 1.9600) = 0.95$).

So $1.96 \times$ standard error $= 39.2$, which means the standard error of the sample mean ($= \frac{\sigma}{\sqrt{n}}$) must be $39.2 \div 1.96 = 20$ hours.

c) Since $\frac{\sigma}{\sqrt{n}} = 20$ and $n = 36$, the population standard deviation must be given by $\sigma = 20 \times \sqrt{n} = 20 \times 6 = 120$ hours.

d) For a 99% confidence interval, you need to find z with $P(-z < Z < z) = 0.99$. This means $z = 2.5758$. So the 99% confidence interval is:
$(1062.5 - 2.5758 \times 20, 1062.5 + 2.5758 \times 20)$
$= (1011 \text{ h}, 1114 \text{ h})$ (to 4 sig. fig.)

e) 1020 hours is contained within the 99% confidence interval. This means that the manufacturer cannot be 99% certain that the average life is more than 1020 hours based on this sample.

4. Large Samples and the Central Limit Theorem

Exercise 4.1 — The Central Limit Theorem

Q1 a) The sample size is large, so the Central Limit Theorem tells you that the sampling distribution of the mean is approximately
$N(55, \frac{12}{80}) = N(55, 0.15)$.

You need to use the Central Limit Theorem here because you are not told that the population follows a normal distribution.

b) $P(\overline{X} > 54) = P\left(Z > \frac{54 - 55}{\sqrt{0.15}}\right)$
$= P(Z > -2.58)$
$= P(Z < 2.58) = 0.99506$

Q2 Since the population follows a normal distribution $N(55, 12)$, the sampling distribution of the sample mean where the sample size is 80 must be
$N(55, \frac{12}{80}) = N(55, 0.15)$.
You do **not** need to use the Central Limit Theorem here because the population is itself normally distributed.

Exercise 4.2 — Confidence intervals for μ — with a large sample and known variance

Q1 The Central Limit Theorem tells you that the sampling distribution of the sample mean will follow
$N(\mu, \frac{4.1^2}{80})$.
For a 99% confidence interval, you need to find z such that $P(-z < Z < z) = 0.99$, which means using your tables to look up $P(Z < z) = 0.995$.
This gives $z = 2.5758$.
So your confidence interval is:

$$\left(\overline{x} - z\frac{\sigma}{\sqrt{n}}, \overline{x} + z\frac{\sigma}{\sqrt{n}}\right)$$
$$= \left(513 - 2.5758 \times \frac{4.1}{\sqrt{80}}, 513 + 2.5758 \times \frac{4.1}{\sqrt{80}}\right)$$
$$= (511.8\text{ g}, 514.2\text{ g}) \text{ (to 1 d.p.)}$$

Q2 The population has mean 30 and variance 10. Since the question does not tell you that the population follows a normal distribution, you can use the Central Limit Theorem and the large sample size to say that the sampling distribution of the sample mean is approximately $N(30, \frac{10}{n})$.
$P(\overline{X} > 30.5) = 0.02$ means $P(\overline{X} \le 30.5) = 0.98$.

$$P(\overline{X} \le 30.5) = P\left(Z \le \frac{30.5 - 30}{\sqrt{10/n}}\right) = 0.98$$

Looking up 0.98 in the normal percentage-points table tells you that
$\frac{30.5 - 30}{\sqrt{10/n}} = 2.0537$

Solving for n gives:
$\frac{10}{n} = \left[\frac{(30.5 - 30)}{2.0537}\right]^2 = 0.05927...$
i.e. $n = 168.707...$
So $n = 169$ (approximately).

Q3 a) To estimate the sample mean, start by adding some rows to the table showing the class mid-points (x) and fx:

Age (years)	15-19	20-24	25-29	30-39	40-49	50-69
Frequency, f	12	17	17	10	14	10
x	17	22	27	34.5	44.5	59.5
fx	204	374	459	345	623	595

This means $n = \sum f = 80$ and $\sum fx = 2600$, and so:
$$\overline{x} = \frac{\sum fx}{\sum f} = \frac{2600}{80} = 32.5 \text{ years}$$

b) For a 95% confidence interval, you need to find z such that $P(-z < Z < z) = 0.95$, which means $z = 1.9600$. So your confidence interval is:

$$\left(\bar{x} - z\frac{\sigma}{\sqrt{n}}, \bar{x} + z\frac{\sigma}{\sqrt{n}}\right)$$

$$= \left(32.5 - 1.9600 \times \frac{\sqrt{184}}{\sqrt{80}}, 32.5 + 1.9600 \times \frac{\sqrt{184}}{\sqrt{80}}\right)$$

$$= (29.5, 35.5) \text{ (to 1 d.p.)}$$

5. Large Samples and Estimating the Standard Error

Exercise 5.1 — Estimating the standard error

Q1 The sample variance is given by:

$$s^2 = \frac{n}{n-1}\left[\frac{\sum x^2}{n} - \left(\frac{\sum x}{n}\right)^2\right]$$

$$= \frac{50}{49}\left[\frac{5460}{50} - \left(\frac{506}{50}\right)^2\right]$$

$$= 6.924...$$

So an estimate of the standard error of the sample mean is given by:

$$\frac{s}{\sqrt{n}} = \frac{\sqrt{6.924...}}{\sqrt{50}} = 0.372 \text{ cm (to 3 sig. fig.)}$$

Q2 Add some extra rows to the table for the class mid-points (x), fx, x^2 and fx^2.

Length in cm	5-6	7-8	9-10	11-12	13-14
Frequency (f)	6	9	14	10	7
x	5.5	7.5	9.5	11.5	13.5
fx	33	67.5	133	115	94.5
x^2	30.25	56.25	90.25	132.25	182.25
fx^2	181.5	506.25	1263.5	1322.5	1275.75

Then $\sum f = 46$, $\sum fx = 443$, $\sum fx^2 = 4549.5$.

This means the sample variance (s^2) is given by:

$$s^2 = \frac{n}{n-1}\left[\frac{\sum fx^2}{\sum f} - \left(\frac{\sum fx}{\sum f}\right)^2\right]$$

$$= \frac{46}{45}\left[\frac{4549.5}{46} - \left(\frac{443}{46}\right)^2\right]$$

$$= 6.29371...$$

So an estimate of the standard error of the sample mean is:

$$\frac{s}{\sqrt{n}} = \frac{\sqrt{6.29371...}}{\sqrt{46}} = 0.370 \text{ cm (to 3 sig. fig.)}$$

Exercise 5.2 — Confidence intervals for μ — with large n but unknown σ^2

Q1 a) You are not told the population standard deviation, so you are going to have to estimate it using the sample standard deviation s.
The formula for a confidence interval is:

$$\left(\bar{x} - z\frac{s}{\sqrt{n}}, \bar{x} + z\frac{s}{\sqrt{n}}\right)$$

Here, since you need a 95% confidence interval, you need to find z with $P(-z < Z < z) = 0.95$, so use your tables to look up the value of z with $P(Z < z) = 0.975$ — this gives $z = 1.9600$.

So the confidence interval you need is:

$$\left(63 - 1.9600 \times \frac{5}{\sqrt{70}}, 63 + 1.9600 \times \frac{5}{\sqrt{70}}\right)$$

$$= (61.8 \text{ beats}, 64.2 \text{ beats}) \text{ (to 3 sig. fig.)}$$

It is not stated that the population has a normal distribution, so you do need to use the Central Limit Theorem here.

b) You can use the same formula for the confidence interval here, but you need a different value of z. You need a 99% confidence interval, so find z with $P(-z < Z < z) = 0.99$ — use your tables to look up the value of z with $P(Z < z) = 0.995$ — this gives $z = 2.5758$.

So the confidence interval you need is:

$$\left(63 - 2.5758 \times \frac{5}{\sqrt{70}}, 63 + 2.5758 \times \frac{5}{\sqrt{70}}\right)$$

$$= (61.5 \text{ beats}, 64.5 \text{ beats}) \text{ (to 3 sig. fig.)}$$

Q2 a) Add some extra rows to the table for fx, x^2 and fx^2.

x	82	83	84	85	86	87
f	6	9	19	27	22	17
fx	492	747	1596	2295	1892	1479
x^2	6724	6889	7056	7225	7396	7569
fx^2	40344	62001	134064	195075	162712	128673

Then $\sum f = 100$, $\sum fx = 8501$, and $\sum fx^2 = 722869$.

The sample mean provides an unbiased estimate of the population mean.

$$\bar{x} = \frac{\sum fx}{\sum f} = \frac{8501}{100} = 85.01$$

b) An unbiased estimate of the population variance is given by the sample variance (s^2):

$$s^2 = \frac{n}{n-1}\left[\frac{\sum fx^2}{\sum f} - \bar{x}^2\right]$$

$$= \frac{100}{99}\left[\frac{722869}{100} - 85.01^2\right]$$

$$= 2.01$$

c) You need a 98% confidence interval, so find z with $P(-z < Z < z) = 0.98$ — use your tables to look up the value of z with $P(Z < z) = 0.99$ — this gives $z = 2.3263$.
Since the sample size is large, the Central Limit Theorem tells you the mean follows an approximately normal distribution, and you can safely use $\frac{s}{\sqrt{n}}$ to estimate the standard error of the mean. The confidence interval you need is given by:

$$\left(\overline{x} - z\frac{s}{\sqrt{n}}, \overline{x} + z\frac{s}{\sqrt{n}}\right)$$

This means your confidence interval is:

$$\left(85.01 - 2.3263 \times \frac{\sqrt{2.01}}{\sqrt{100}}, 85.01 + 2.3263 \times \frac{\sqrt{2.01}}{\sqrt{100}}\right)$$

$= (84.7, 85.3)$ (to 3 sig. fig.)

Q3 a) The sample mean provides an unbiased estimate of the population mean.

So $\overline{x} = \frac{\sum x}{n} = \frac{634}{50} = 12.68$ cm

An unbiased estimate of the population variance is given by the sample variance (s^2):

$$s^2 = \frac{n}{n-1}\left[\frac{\sum x^2}{n} - \left(\frac{\sum x}{n}\right)^2\right]$$
$$= \frac{50}{49}\left[\frac{8356}{50} - \left(\frac{634}{50}\right)^2\right]$$
$$= 6.4669... = 6.47 \text{ (to 3 sig. fig.)}$$

b) You need a 99% confidence interval, so find z with $P(-z < Z < z) = 0.99$ — this gives $z = 2.5758$.
Using $\frac{s}{\sqrt{n}}$ to estimate the standard error of the mean, the confidence interval you need is given by:

$$\left(\overline{x} - z\frac{s}{\sqrt{n}}, \overline{x} + z\frac{s}{\sqrt{n}}\right)$$

This means your confidence interval is:

$$\left(12.68 - 2.5758 \times \frac{\sqrt{6.4669...}}{\sqrt{50}}, 12.68 + 2.5758 \times \frac{\sqrt{6.4669...}}{\sqrt{50}}\right)$$

$= (11.8 \text{ cm}, 13.6 \text{ cm})$ (to 3 sig. fig.)

c) Since all of the confidence interval is above 11.5 cm the claim is justified, based on this evidence.

Q4 a) The sample mean ($\overline{x}$) is given by:

$$\overline{x} = \frac{\sum x}{n} = \frac{1884}{60} = 31.4 \text{ minutes}$$

The sample variance (s^2) is given by:

$$s^2 = \frac{\sum(x - \overline{x})^2}{n-1} = \frac{57200}{59}$$
$$= 969.49... = 969.5 \text{ (to 4 sig. fig.)}$$

b) You need a 95% confidence interval, so use $z = 1.96$. Then the confidence interval you need is given by:

$$\left(\overline{x} - z\frac{s}{\sqrt{n}}, \overline{x} + z\frac{s}{\sqrt{n}}\right)$$

This means your confidence interval is:

$$\left(31.4 - 1.96 \times \frac{\sqrt{969.49...}}{\sqrt{60}}, 31.4 + 1.96 \times \frac{\sqrt{969.49...}}{\sqrt{60}}\right)$$

$= (23.5 \text{ minutes}, 39.3 \text{ minutes})$ (to 3 sig. fig.)

c) Since 30 lies within the confidence interval, the company have no reason to be dissatisfied with the time taken by this painter.

d) It is not stated that the times are normally distributed. So the Central Limit Theorem is needed to ensure that the sampling distribution of the sample mean is approximately normal (and the Central Limit Theorem can be used here due to the large sample size).

Review Exercise — Chapter 5

Q1 a) All the members of the tennis club.

b) By using a random sample.

Q2 A simple random sample is one where every member of the population has an equal chance of being in the sample and each selection is independent.

Q3 a) Yes

b) No — it contains the unknown parameter σ.

c) No — it contains the unknown parameter μ.

d) Yes

You've just got to look for any unknown parameters — if you find one, it's not a statistic.

Q4 The sample mean is an unbiased estimate of the population mean — this is: $\frac{\sum x}{n} = \frac{80.5}{10} = 8.05$

An unbiased estimate of the population variance is:

$$\frac{n}{n-1}\left[\frac{\sum x^2}{n} - \left(\frac{\sum x}{n}\right)^2\right] = \frac{10}{9}\left[\frac{653.13}{10} - \left(\frac{80.5}{10}\right)^2\right]$$
$= 0.567$ (to 3 d.p.).

Q5 a) Standard error of sample mean $= \frac{\sigma}{\sqrt{n}}$

$$= \frac{5}{\sqrt{15}} = 1.29 \text{ (to 3 sig. fig.)}$$

b) Because the population follows a normal distribution, the sampling distribution of the sample mean is also normal.

$$\overline{X} \sim N\left(7.2, \frac{25}{15}\right) = N\left(7.2, \frac{5}{3}\right)$$

c) $P(\overline{X} < 7.5) = P\left(Z < \frac{7.5 - 7.2}{\sqrt{5/3}}\right)$
$= P(Z < 0.23) = 0.59095$

Q6 a) Because the sample size is large, the Central Limit Theorem tells you that the sampling distribution of the sample mean will be approximately normal.

$\overline{X} \sim N\left(18, \frac{4^2}{80}\right) = N(18, 0.2)$ (approximately)

b) $P(\overline{X} > 19) = P\left(Z > \frac{19 - 18}{\sqrt{0.2}}\right) = P(Z > 2.24)$

$= 1 - P(Z \leq 2.24)$

$= 1 - 0.98745$

$= 0.01255$

Q7 This is a normal distribution with a known standard deviation, so a 99% confidence interval is given by:

$\left(\overline{x} - z\frac{\sigma}{\sqrt{n}}, \overline{x} + z\frac{\sigma}{\sqrt{n}}\right)$, where $z = 2.5758$.

Since the sample mean is 18.2, the confidence interval is:

$\left(18.2 - 2.5758 \times \frac{0.4}{\sqrt{25}}, 18.2 + 2.5758 \times \frac{0.4}{\sqrt{25}}\right)$

$= (17.99, 18.41)$ (to 2 d.p.).

Q8 Here, the population itself may not be normally distributed, but the Central Limit Theorem tells you that the sampling distribution of the sample mean will still be approximately normal — meaning a 95% confidence interval is given by:

$\left(\overline{x} - z\frac{\sigma}{\sqrt{n}}, \overline{x} + z\frac{\sigma}{\sqrt{n}}\right)$, where $z = 1.96$.

Since the sample mean is 33.8, the confidence interval is:

$\left(33.8 - 1.96 \times \frac{3}{\sqrt{120}}, 33.8 + 1.96 \times \frac{3}{\sqrt{120}}\right)$

$= (33.26, 34.34)$ (to 2 d.p.).

Q9 First work out an unbiased estimate of the population variance.

$$s^2 = \frac{n}{n-1}\left[\frac{\sum x^2}{n} - \left(\frac{\sum x}{n}\right)^2\right]$$

$$= \frac{100}{99}\left[\frac{122.1}{100} - \left(\frac{104}{100}\right)^2\right]$$

$$= 0.140808...$$

So an estimate of the population standard deviation is $s = \sqrt{0.140808...}$.

Now you can estimate the sample mean's standard error — this is:

$$\frac{s}{\sqrt{n}} = \frac{\sqrt{0.140808...}}{\sqrt{100}} = 0.0375 \text{ (to 3 sig. fig.)}.$$

Q10 Sample mean $= \frac{\sum x}{n} = \frac{24.2}{80} = 0.3025$

And the sample variance is:

$$s^2 = \frac{n}{n-1}\left[\frac{\sum x^2}{n} - \left(\frac{\sum x}{n}\right)^2\right]$$

$$= \frac{80}{79}\left[\frac{41.3}{80} - \left(\frac{24.2}{80}\right)^2\right] = 0.43012...$$

This means the sample standard deviation is: $s = 0.655...$

Because the sample size is large, you can assume that the sampling distribution of $\overline{X}$ is approximately normal and your estimate of the population standard deviation is reasonably good, which means that a 95% confidence interval for the population mean is given by:

$\left(\overline{x} - z\frac{s}{\sqrt{n}}, \overline{x} + z\frac{s}{\sqrt{n}}\right)$, where $z = 1.96$

$$= \left(0.3025 - 1.96 \times \frac{0.655...}{\sqrt{80}}, 0.3025 + 1.96 \times \frac{0.655...}{\sqrt{80}}\right)$$

$= (0.16, 0.45)$ (to 2 d.p.).

Exam-Style Questions — Chapter 5

1 a) You need to use mid-interval values. So add some extra rows to your table.

Height, h (cm)	0-40	40-80	80-100	100-140	140-160
Frequency, f	5	8	11	19	7
Mid-interval value, x	20	60	90	120	150
fx	100	480	990	2280	1050
x^2	400	3600	8100	14400	22500
fx^2	2000	28 800	89 100	273 600	157 500

$\sum f = 50, \sum fx = 4900, \sum fx^2 = 551000$.

This gives an (unbiased) estimate of the mean of:

$\frac{\sum fx}{\sum f} = \frac{4900}{50} = 98$ cm ***[1 mark]***

b) An unbiased estimate of the population variance is given by the sample variance. This is:

$$\frac{n}{n-1}\left[\frac{\sum fx^2}{\sum f} - \left(\frac{\sum fx}{\sum f}\right)^2\right]$$

$= \frac{50}{49}\left[\frac{551000}{50} - \left(\frac{4900}{50}\right)^2\right]$ ***[1 mark]***

$= 1445$ (to 4 sig. fig.) ***[1 mark]***

2 a) The mean weight of the frogs in the sample is:

$\frac{3840}{30} = 128$ g ***[1 mark]***

b) The standard error of the sample mean weight is:

$\frac{\sigma}{\sqrt{n}} = \frac{8.5}{\sqrt{30}}$ ***[1 mark]*** $= 1.55$ g (to 2 d.p.) ***[1 mark]***

c) A 95% confidence interval is given by:

$\left(\bar{x} - z\frac{\sigma}{\sqrt{n}}, \bar{x} + z\frac{\sigma}{\sqrt{n}}\right)$ ***[1 mark]***

$= \left(128 - 1.96 \times \frac{8.5}{\sqrt{30}}, 128 + 1.96 \times \frac{8.5}{\sqrt{30}}\right)$ ***[1 mark]***

$= (125.0\,\text{g}, 131.0\,\text{g})$ (to 1d.p.) ***[1 mark]***.

d) The weights of the frogs are normally distributed, so if the random variable Y represents the weights of the individual frogs, then $Y \sim N(128, 8.5^2)$ (using the estimated mean) ***[1 mark]***. If you transform this to the standard normal distribution (by subtracting the mean and dividing by the standard deviation), then you need to find z with:

$P\left(-z \leq \frac{Y - 128}{8.5} \leq z\right) = 0.99$,

i.e. $P(-z \leq Z \leq z) = 0.99$, or $P(Z \leq z) = 0.995$

Using the normal percentage-points table, this gives

$z = 2.5758$ ***[1 mark]***.

Since $-2.5758 \leq \frac{Y - 128}{8.5} \leq 2.5758$,

the range for Y you need is:

$(128 - 2.5758 \times 8.5, 128 + 2.5758 \times 8.5)$

$= (106.1\text{ g}, 149.9\text{ g})$ (to 1 d.p.) ***[1 mark]***

3 a) $s^2 = \frac{n}{n-1}\left[\frac{\sum x^2}{n} - \left(\frac{\sum x}{n}\right)^2\right]$

$= \frac{60}{59}\left[\frac{620}{60} - \left(\frac{184}{60}\right)^2\right]$ ***[1 mark]***

$= 0.94463...$ ***[1 mark]***

So an estimate of the sample mean's standard error is:

$\frac{s}{\sqrt{n}} = \frac{\sqrt{0.94463...}}{\sqrt{60}}$ ***[1 mark]***

$= 0.125\,\text{m}$ (to 3 sig. fig.) ***[1 mark]***

b) Since the sample size is large, the estimate of the standard error should be reasonably good ***[1 mark]***, and the sampling distribution of the sample mean should be approximately normal ***[1 mark]***. This means that a 98% confidence interval for the population mean is given by:

$\left(\bar{x} - z\frac{s}{\sqrt{n}}, \bar{x} + z\frac{s}{\sqrt{n}}\right)$, where $z = 2.3263$ ***[1 mark]***

$= \left(\frac{184}{60} - 2.3263 \times 0.125, \frac{184}{60} + 2.3263 \times 0.125\right)$ ***[1 mark]***

$= (2.78\,\text{m}, 3.36\,\text{m})$ (to 2 d.p.). ***[1 mark]***

c) Because part of this confidence interval is below 3 metres ***[1 mark]***, these results do not provide evidence that the average distance covered in 10 minutes is above 3 metres ***[1 mark]*** (although they do not provide evidence that the manager is wrong either).

4 a) $s^2 = \frac{\sum(x - \bar{x})^2}{n - 1} = \frac{1382}{39}$

$= 35.4$ (to 3 sig. fig.) ***[1 mark]***

b) The population is modelled by a normal distribution and so the sampling distribution of the sample mean will also be normal ***[1 mark]***, so a 99% confidence interval for the mean is given by:

$\left(\bar{x} - z\frac{s}{\sqrt{n}}, \bar{x} + z\frac{s}{\sqrt{n}}\right)$, where $z = 2.5758$ ***[1 mark]***

$= \left(\frac{1676}{40} - 2.5758 \times \frac{\sqrt{1382/39}}{\sqrt{40}}, \frac{1676}{40} + 2.5758 \times \frac{\sqrt{1382/39}}{\sqrt{40}}\right)$ ***[1 mark]***

$= (39.5\,\text{mins}, 44.3\,\text{mins})$ (to 3 sig. fig.) ***[1 mark]***

c) Since this confidence interval does not include 46 minutes, these results do not support the claim of Ravi's manager ***[1 mark]***. Since 42 minutes is within the confidence interval, these results provide no reason to doubt Ravi's claim ***[1 mark]***.

5 a) To estimate the mean and standard deviation, start by adding some extra columns showing the class mid-points (x), as well as fx, x^2 and fx^2. (Here, the number of customers is the frequency, f.)

Time (seconds)	Number of customers, f	Class mid-point (x)	fx	x^2	fx^2
$0 \leq t \leq 30$	33	15	495	225	7425
$30 < t \leq 60$	17	45	765	2025	34425
$60 < t \leq 90$	20	75	1500	5625	112500
$90 < t \leq 120$	7	105	735	11025	77175
$120 < t \leq 150$	2	135	270	18225	36450
$150 < t \leq 180$	1	165	165	27225	27225

$n = \sum f = 80$, $\sum fx = 3930$, $\sum fx^2 = 295200$

[1 mark for $\sum fx$ and $\sum fx^2$ correct]

So an estimate of the sample mean is given by:

$\bar{x} = \frac{\sum fx}{\sum f} = \frac{3930}{80} = 49.125$ seconds ***[1 mark]***

And an estimate of the sample variance (s^2) is:

$s^2 = \frac{n}{n-1}\left[\frac{\sum fx^2}{n} - \left(\frac{\sum fx}{n}\right)^2\right]$

$= \frac{80}{79}\left[\frac{295200}{80} - \left(\frac{3930}{80}\right)^2\right] = 1292.89...$

[1 mark]

So an estimate of the sample standard deviation (s) is:

$\sqrt{1292.89...} = 35.95...$

$= 36.0$ seconds (to 3 sig. fig.)

[1 mark]

b) The table shows that the waiting times do not seem to be normally distributed because the distribution seems very asymmetrical ***[1 mark]***.

c) The sample size is large, so by the Central Limit Theorem the distribution of the sample mean will follow a normal distribution (approximately) ***[1 mark]***.

d) (i) Use the sample mean as an estimate of the population mean. So your estimate will be 49.125 seconds ***[1 mark]***

(ii) Use the estimator $\frac{S}{\sqrt{n}}$.

So your estimate of the standard error of the mean will be:

$\frac{35.95...}{\sqrt{80}}$ ***[1 mark]***

$= 4.020... = 4.02$ s (to 3 sig. fig.) ***[1 mark]***

e) A 95% confidence interval for the population mean is given by:

$\left(\overline{x} - z\frac{s}{\sqrt{n}}, \overline{x} + z\frac{s}{\sqrt{n}}\right)$, where $z = 1.96$ ***[1 mark]***

$= \begin{pmatrix} 49.125 - 1.96 \times 4.020..., \\ 49.125 + 1.96 \times 4.020... \end{pmatrix}$ ***[1 mark]***

$= (41.2\text{ s}, 57.0\text{ s})$ (to 1d.p.). ***[1 mark]***

Chapter 6: Correlation and Regression

1. Correlation

Exercise 1.1 — Scatter diagrams and correlation

Q1 a)

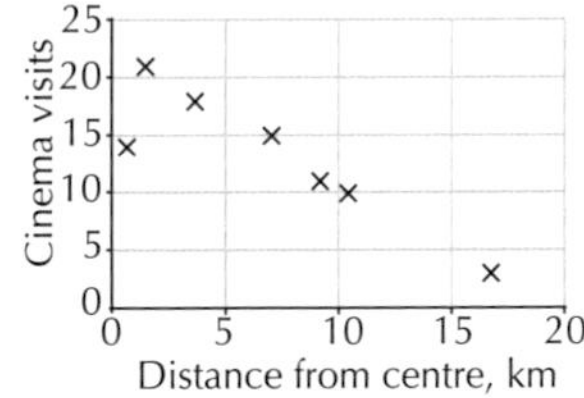

b) Negative correlation

Q2 a)

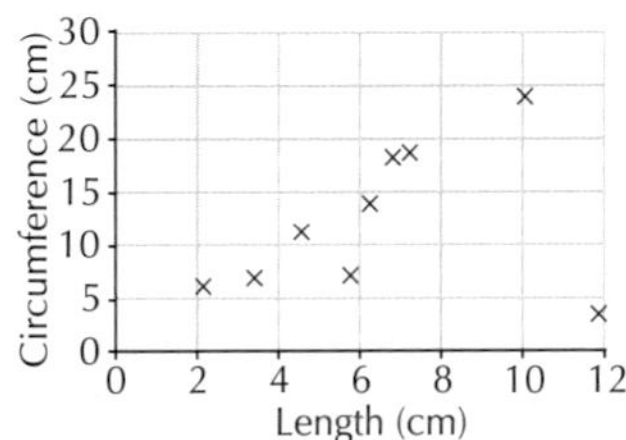

b) Positive correlation

c) The circumference of 3.5 cm <u>or</u> the length of 11.9 cm.

Exercise 1.2 — S_{xx}, S_{yy} and S_{xy}

Q1 a) Add rows to the table for x^2, y^2 and xy. And include a column showing the total of each row.

x	11	6	9	4	8	2	5	45
y	24	13	18	5	19	1	12	92
x^2	121	36	81	16	64	4	25	347
y^2	576	169	324	25	361	1	144	1600
xy	264	78	162	20	152	2	60	738

So $\sum x = 45$, $\sum y = 92$, $\sum x^2 = 347$, $\sum y^2 = 1600$ and $\sum xy = 738$.

b) $S_{xy} = \sum xy - \frac{\sum x \sum y}{n} = 738 - \frac{45 \times 92}{7}$

$= 146.57$ (to 2 d.p.)

$S_{xx} = \sum x^2 - \frac{(\sum x)^2}{n} = 347 - \frac{45^2}{7}$

$= 57.71$ (to 2 d.p.)

$S_{yy} = \sum y^2 - \frac{(\sum y)^2}{n} = 1600 - \frac{92^2}{7}$

$= 390.86$ (to 2 d.p.)

Q2 a) $S_{xy} = \sum xy - \frac{\sum x \sum y}{n} = 589 - \frac{29 \times 109}{5}$

$= -43.2$

$S_{xx} = \sum x^2 - \frac{(\sum x)^2}{n} = 167 - \frac{29^2}{5} = -1.2$

$S_{yy} = \sum y^2 - \frac{(\sum y)^2}{n} = 2031 - \frac{109^2}{5} = -345.2$

b) $S_{xy} = \sum xy - \frac{\sum x \sum y}{n} = 1013 - \frac{206 \times 50}{10} = -17$

$S_{xx} = \sum x^2 - \frac{(\sum x)^2}{n} = 4504 - \frac{206^2}{10} = 260.4$

$S_{yy} = \sum y^2 - \frac{(\sum y)^2}{n} = 326 - \frac{50^2}{10} = 76$

c) $S_{xy} = \sum xy - \frac{\sum x \sum y}{n}$

$= 1880 - \frac{115 \times 114}{6} = -305$

$S_{xx} = \sum x^2 - \frac{(\sum x)^2}{n} = 2383 - \frac{115^2}{6}$

$= 178.83$ (to 2 d.p.)

$S_{yy} = \sum y^2 - \frac{(\sum y)^2}{n} = 2762 - \frac{114^2}{6} = 596$

Exercise 1.3 — Product moment correlation coefficient

Q1 $S_{xy} = \sum xy - \frac{\sum x \sum y}{n} = 1515 - \frac{313 \times 75}{15} = -50$

$S_{xx} = \sum x^2 - \frac{(\sum x)^2}{n} = 6875 - \frac{313^2}{15}$

$= 343.7333...$

$S_{yy} = \sum y^2 - \frac{(\sum y)^2}{n} = 473 - \frac{75^2}{15} = 98$

This means:

$r = \frac{S_{xy}}{\sqrt{S_{xx}S_{yy}}}$

$= \frac{-50}{\sqrt{343.7333... \times 98}} = -0.272$ (to 3 sig.fig.)

Q2 a)

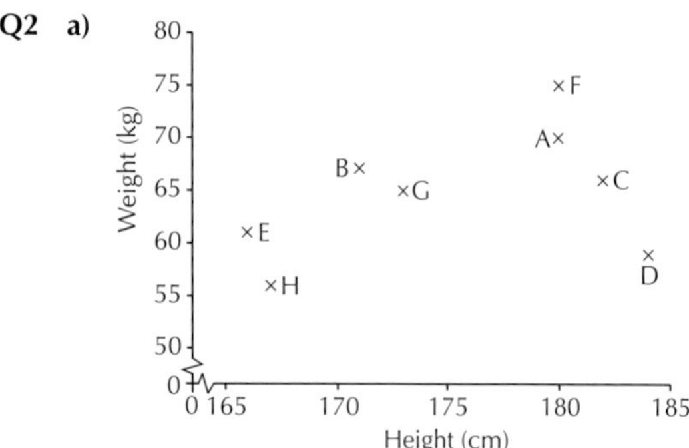

b) Make a table including x^2, y^2 and xy. Include a final column showing the total of each row.

x	180	171	182	184	166	180	173	167	1403
y	70	67	66	59	61	75	65	56	519
x^2	32400	29241	33124	33856	27556	32400	29929	27889	246395
y^2	4900	4489	4356	3481	3721	5625	4225	3136	33933
xy	12600	11457	12012	10856	10126	13500	11245	9352	91148

$$S_{xy} = \sum xy - \frac{\sum x \sum y}{n} = 91148 - \frac{1403 \times 519}{8}$$
$$= 128.375$$
$$S_{xx} = \sum x^2 - \frac{(\sum x)^2}{n} = 246\,395 - \frac{1403^2}{8}$$
$$= 343.875$$
$$S_{yy} = \sum y^2 - \frac{(\sum y)^2}{n} = 33\,933 - \frac{519^2}{8} = 262.875$$

c) This means:

$$r = \frac{S_{xy}}{\sqrt{S_{xx}S_{yy}}}$$
$$= \frac{128.375}{\sqrt{343.875 \times 262.875}} = 0.427 \text{ (to 3 sig.fig.)}$$

Q3 a) Make a table including x^2, y^2 and xy. Include a final column showing the total of each row.

x	13	9	15	10	8	11	12	14	92
y	5	7	2	4	3	8	1	2	32
x^2	169	81	225	100	64	121	144	196	1100
y^2	25	49	4	16	9	64	1	4	172
xy	65	63	30	40	24	88	12	28	350

So $\sum x = 92$, $\sum y = 32$, $\sum x^2 = 1100$, $\sum y^2 = 172$, $\sum xy = 350$

b) $$S_{xy} = \sum xy - \frac{\sum x \sum y}{n} = 350 - \frac{92 \times 32}{8} = -18$$
$$S_{xx} = \sum x^2 - \frac{(\sum x)^2}{n} = 1100 - \frac{92^2}{8} = 42$$
$$S_{yy} = \sum y^2 - \frac{(\sum y)^2}{n} = 172 - \frac{32^2}{8} = 44$$

c) This means:

$$r = \frac{S_{xy}}{\sqrt{S_{xx}S_{yy}}}$$
$$= \frac{-18}{\sqrt{42 \times 44}} = -0.419 \text{ (to 3 sig.fig.)}$$

Q4 a) First find $\sum x = 43$ and $\sum y = 30.4$.

Then:

$$S_{xy} = \sum xy - \frac{\sum x \sum y}{n} = 181.75 - \frac{43 \times 30.4}{8}$$
$$= 18.35$$
$$S_{xx} = \sum x^2 - \frac{(\sum x)^2}{n} = 258 - \frac{43^2}{8} = 26.875$$
$$S_{yy} = \sum y^2 - \frac{(\sum y)^2}{n} = 128.2 - \frac{30.4^2}{8} = 12.68$$

b) This means:

$$r = \frac{S_{xy}}{\sqrt{S_{xx}S_{yy}}}$$
$$= \frac{18.35}{\sqrt{26.875 \times 12.68}} = 0.994 \text{ (to 3 sig.fig.)}$$

c) This value for r is very close to 1, which shows that there is a very strong positive correlation between the length of a leaf (x) and its width (y). The longer a leaf is (i.e. the higher the value of x), the wider it tends to be (i.e. the higher the value of y).

Q5 a) This looks like a fairly random scattering of points, so the correlation coefficient will be close to zero — accept any answer between –0.3 and 0.3 (the actual answer is $r = 0.048$).

b) This looks like a fairly strong negative correlation, so the correlation coefficient will be close to –1 — accept any answer between –0.5 and –0.95 (the actual answer is –0.892).

c) If you draw lines showing (roughly) $x = \bar{x}$ and $y = \bar{y}$, then you can see that most of the points lie in the top-right and bottom-left quadrants — this means the correlation coefficient will be positive.

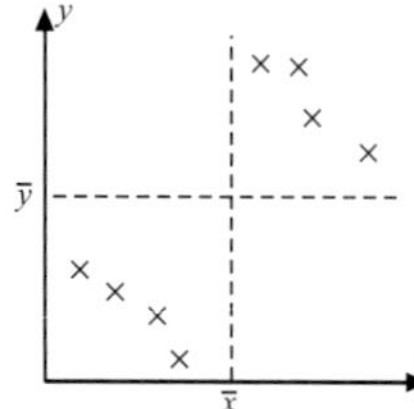

But the points don't really lie close to a straight line, so the answer won't be too close to 1 — accept any answer between 0.3 and 0.7 (the actual answer is 0.589).

Exercise 1.4 — Linear scaling

Q1 Create a new table showing the scaled data values x and y. Include extra rows for x^2, y^2 and xy.

x	3	7	2	9	1	5	27
y	4	1	8	7	3	6	29
x^2	9	49	4	81	1	25	169
y^2	16	1	64	49	9	36	175
xy	12	7	16	63	3	30	131

So $\sum x = 27$, $\sum y = 29$, $\sum x^2 = 169$,
$\sum y^2 = 175$, $\sum xy = 131$

Then:

$$S_{xy} = \sum xy - \frac{\sum x \sum y}{n} = 131 - \frac{27 \times 29}{6} = 0.5$$

$$S_{xx} = \sum x^2 - \frac{(\sum x)^2}{n} = 169 - \frac{27^2}{6} = 47.5$$

$$S_{yy} = \sum y^2 - \frac{(\sum y)^2}{n} = 175 - \frac{29^2}{6}$$

$$= 34.8333...$$

This means:

$$r = \frac{S_{xy}}{\sqrt{S_{xx}S_{yy}}}$$

$$= \frac{0.5}{\sqrt{47.5 \times 34.8333...}} = 0.012 \text{ (to 3 d.p.)}$$

Because u and v are related by linear transformations to x and y (where the value of b is positive for both transformations), this means that the PMCC between u and v must also be 0.012 (to 3 d.p.).

Q2 Create a new table showing the scaled data values x and y. Include extra rows for x^2, y^2 and xy.

x	4	6	5	3	2	9	11	8	48
y	7	21	9	13	19	15	20	16	120
x^2	16	36	25	9	4	81	121	64	356
y^2	49	441	81	169	361	225	400	256	1982
xy	28	126	45	39	38	135	220	128	759

So $\sum x = 48$, $\sum y = 120$, $\sum x^2 = 356$,
$\sum y^2 = 1982$, $\sum xy = 759$

Then:

$$S_{xy} = \sum xy - \frac{\sum x \sum y}{n} = 759 - \frac{48 \times 120}{8} = 39$$

$$S_{xx} = \sum x^2 - \frac{(\sum x)^2}{n} = 356 - \frac{48^2}{8} = 68$$

$$S_{yy} = \sum y^2 - \frac{(\sum y)^2}{n} = 1982 - \frac{120^2}{8} = 182$$

This means:

$$r = \frac{S_{xy}}{\sqrt{S_{xx}S_{yy}}}$$

$$= \frac{39}{\sqrt{68 \times 182}} = 0.351 \text{ (to 3 sig.fig.)}$$

Because u and v are related by linear transformations to x and y (where the value of b is positive for both transformations), this means that the PMCC between u and v must also be 0.351 (to 3 sig.fig.).

Q3 Create a new table showing the scaled data values x and y. Include extra rows for x^2, y^2 and xy.

x	0	1	2	3	4	5	6	7	8	36
y	32	25	21	17	7	12	8	4	2	128
x^2	0	1	4	9	16	25	36	49	64	204
y^2	1024	625	441	289	49	144	64	16	4	2656
xy	0	25	42	51	28	60	48	28	16	298

So $\sum x = 36$, $\sum y = 128$, $\sum x^2 = 204$,
$\sum y^2 = 2656$, $\sum xy = 298$

Then:

$$S_{xy} = \sum xy - \frac{\sum x \sum y}{n} = 298 - \frac{36 \times 128}{9} = -214$$

$$S_{xx} = \sum x^2 - \frac{(\sum x)^2}{n} = 204 - \frac{36^2}{9} = 60$$

$$S_{yy} = \sum y^2 - \frac{(\sum y)^2}{n} = 2656 - \frac{128^2}{9}$$

$$= 835.5555...$$

This means:

$$r = \frac{S_{xy}}{\sqrt{S_{xx}S_{yy}}}$$

$$= \frac{-214}{\sqrt{60 \times 835.5555...}} = -0.956 \text{ (to 3 sig.fig.)}$$

Because s and t are related by linear transformations to x and y (where the value of b is positive for both transformations), this means that the PMCC between s and t must also be –0.956 (to 3 sig.fig.).

Q4 Create a new table showing the scaled data values x and y. Include extra rows for x^2, y^2 and xy.

x	16	4	20	19	7	12	9	14	101
y	4	13	22	8	17	5	28	23	120
x^2	256	16	400	361	49	144	81	196	1503
y^2	16	169	484	64	289	25	784	529	2360
xy	64	52	440	152	119	60	252	322	1461

So $\sum x = 101$, $\sum y = 120$, $\sum x^2 = 1503$,
$\sum y^2 = 2360$, $\sum xy = 1461$

Then:

$$S_{xy} = \sum xy - \frac{\sum x \sum y}{n} = 1461 - \frac{101 \times 120}{8} = -54$$

$$S_{xx} = \sum x^2 - \frac{(\sum x)^2}{n} = 1503 - \frac{101^2}{8} = 227.875$$

$$S_{yy} = \sum y^2 - \frac{(\sum y)^2}{n} = 2360 - \frac{120^2}{8} = 560$$

This means:

$$r = \frac{S_{xy}}{\sqrt{S_{xx}S_{yy}}}$$

$$= \frac{-54}{\sqrt{227.875 \times 560}} = -0.151 \text{ (to 3 sig.fig.)}$$

Because w and s are related by linear transformations to x and y (where the value of b is positive for both transformations), this means that the PMCC between w and s must also be –0.151 (to 3 sig.fig.).

Q5 Your scaling needs to make the numbers easier to use. So use the scaling: $x = u - 4000$, and $y = \frac{v}{100}$
Then create a new table showing the scaled data values x and y. Include extra rows for x^2, y^2 and xy.

x	8	10	11	15	18	21	83
y	1	4	8	3	7	2	25
x^2	64	100	121	225	324	441	1275
y^2	1	16	64	9	49	4	143
xy	8	40	88	45	126	42	349

So $\sum x = 83$, $\sum y = 25$, $\sum x^2 = 1275$, $\sum y^2 = 143$, $\sum xy = 349$
Then:

$$S_{xy} = \sum xy - \frac{\sum x \sum y}{n} = 349 - \frac{83 \times 25}{6}$$
$$= 3.1666...$$

$$S_{xx} = \sum x^2 - \frac{(\sum x)^2}{n} = 1275 - \frac{83^2}{6}$$
$$= 126.8333...$$

$$S_{yy} = \sum y^2 - \frac{(\sum y)^2}{n} = 143 - \frac{25^2}{6} = 38.8333...$$

This means:

$$r = \frac{S_{xy}}{\sqrt{S_{xx}S_{yy}}}$$
$$= \frac{3.1666...}{\sqrt{126.8333... \times 38.8333...}} = 0.0451 \text{(to 3 sig.fig.)}$$

Because u and v are related by linear transformations to x and y (where the value of b is positive for both transformations), the correlation coefficient for u and v is 0.0451 (to 3 sig. fig.).

2. Linear Regression

Exercise 2.1 — Explanatory and response variables

Q1 **Explanatory variable**: the time spent practising the piano each week
Response variable: the number of mistakes made in a test at the end of the week

It is the amount of practice that would determine the performance in the test, not the other way around.

Q2 **Explanatory variable**: the age of a second-hand car
Response variable: the value of a second-hand car

It is the age of the car that would affect its value, not the other way around.

Q3 **Explanatory variable**: the population of a town
Response variable: the number of phone calls made in a town in a week

It is the population that would affect the number of calls, not the other way around.

Q4 **Explanatory variable**: the amount of sunlight falling on a plant in an experiment
Response variable: the growth rate of a plant in an experiment

It is the amount of sunlight that would affect the growth rate, not the other way around.
(Or you could say that the amount of sunlight can be directly controlled, as this is an experiment.)

Exercise 2.2 — Regression lines

Q1 Call the equation of the regression line $y = a + bx$.
Then the gradient of the regression line is b, where:

$$b = \frac{S_{xy}}{S_{xx}} = \frac{254.9}{139.4} = 1.82855... = 1.83 \text{ (to 3 sig. fig.)}$$

And the intercept of the regression line is a, where:

$$a = \bar{y} - b\bar{x} = \frac{\sum y}{n} - b\frac{\sum x}{n}$$
$$= \frac{115}{7} - (1.82855...) \times \frac{54}{7}$$
$$= 2.32 \text{ (to 3 sig. fig.)}.$$

So the equation of the regression line of y on x is: $y = 2.32 + 1.83x$

Q2 a)

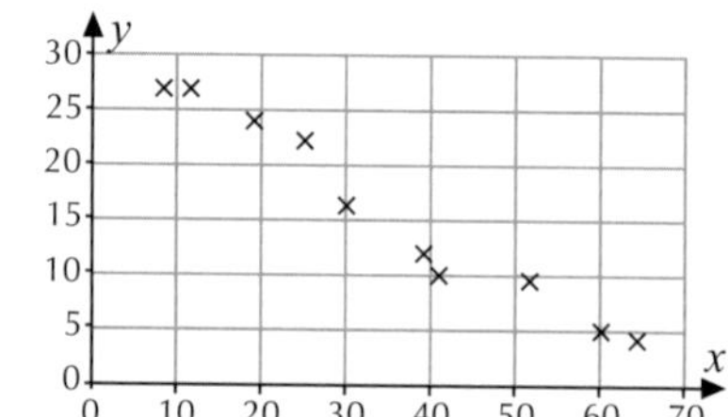

b) Start by working out the four summations $\sum x$, $\sum y$, $\sum x^2$, and $\sum xy$.
It's best to draw a table.

x	8	30	19	41	64	12	60	25	52	39	350
y	27	16	24	10	4	27	5	22	9	12	156
x^2	64	900	361	1681	4096	144	3600	625	2704	1521	15696
xy	216	480	456	410	256	324	300	550	468	468	3928

So $\sum x = 350$, $\sum y = 156$, $\sum x^2 = 15\,696$, $\sum xy = 3928$
Then:

$$S_{xy} = \sum xy - \frac{\sum x \sum y}{n} = 3928 - \frac{350 \times 156}{10}$$
$$= -1532$$

$$S_{xx} = \sum x^2 - \frac{(\sum x)^2}{n} = 15696 - \frac{350^2}{10} = 3446$$

Call the equation of the regression line $y = a + bx$.
Then the gradient of the regression line is b, where:

$$b = \frac{S_{xy}}{S_{xx}} = \frac{-1532}{3446} = -0.44457...$$
$= -0.445$ (to 3 sig. fig.)

And the intercept of the regression line is a, where:

$$a = \bar{y} - b\bar{x} = \frac{\sum y}{n} - b\frac{\sum x}{n}$$
$$= \frac{156}{10} - (-0.44457...) \times \frac{350}{10}$$
$$= 31.16006... = 31.2 \text{ (to 3 sig. fig.)}.$$

So the equation of the regression line of y on x is: $y = 31.2 - 0.445x$

c) The value of b tells you that the temperature decreases by approximately 0.445 °C for every extra degree of latitude (since when x increases by 1, y decreases by 0.445).

The value of a suggests that on the equator (when $x = 0$) the mean annual temperature is about 31.2 °C.

d) (i) When $x = 19$, the residual is:
$e = 24 - (31.16006... - 0.44457... \times 19)$
$= 1.29$ (to 3 sig. fig.)

(ii) When $x = 41$, the residual is:
$e = 10 - (31.16006... - 0.44457... \times 41)$
$= -2.93$ (to 3 sig. fig.)

Q3 a) You first need to find S_{xy} and S_{xx}.

$$S_{xy} = \sum xy - \frac{\sum x \sum y}{n} = 2596 - \frac{92 \times 264}{10}$$
$$= 167.2$$

$$S_{xx} = \sum x^2 - \frac{(\sum x)^2}{n} = 1072 - \frac{92^2}{10} = 225.6$$

If the equation of the regression line is $y = a + bx$, then the gradient of the regression line is b, where:

$$b = \frac{S_{xy}}{S_{xx}} = \frac{167.2}{225.6} = 0.741134...$$
$$= 0.741 \text{ (to 3 sig. fig.)}$$

And the intercept of the regression line is a, where:

$$a = \bar{y} - b\bar{x} = \frac{\sum y}{n} - b\frac{\sum x}{n}$$
$$= \frac{264}{10} - (0.741134...) \times \frac{92}{10}$$
$$= 19.6 \text{ (to 3 sig. fig.)}.$$

So the equation of the regression line of y on x is: $y = 19.6 + 0.741x$

b) The value of b tells you that a graduate employee's salary will generally increase by £741 per year (since when x increases by 1, y increases by 0.741, which is equivalent to £741, as the salaries are given in thousands of pounds).

The value of a tells you that a newly employed graduate (when $x = 0$) typically earns a salary of £19 600.

Exercise 2.3 — Interpolation and extrapolation

Q1 a) y is the response variable (since this is the regression line of y on x).

b) (i) $1.67 + 0.107 \times 5 = 2.205$

(ii) $1.67 + 0.107 \times 20 = 3.81$

Q2 a) $103 - 4.57 \times 4 = 84.72$
This is interpolation (since 4 is between 2 and 15), and the percentage residuals are very small. This estimate should be reliable.

b) $103 - 4.57 \times 20 = 11.6$
This is extrapolation (since 20 is greater than the largest observed value of x, which was 15). This estimate may not be reliable.

c) $103 - 4.57 \times 7 = 71.01$
This is interpolation (since 7 is between 2 and 15), and the percentage residuals are very small. This estimate should be reliable.

Q3 a) $1.4 \times 20 + 7 = 35$
This is interpolation (since 20 is between 17 and 35, which are the values of x between which data was collected). Although this estimate may be reliable, there are some large residuals and this means that you need to be careful (for example, if the error in the above value of 35 were as large as 14, this would be 40% of the response variable's value).

b) $1.4 \times 50 + 7 = 77$
This is extrapolation (since 50 is greater than the largest value of x for which data was collected). This estimate may not be reliable.

Q4 a) $58.8 - 2.47 \times 7 = 41.51$ — so the volunteer would be predicted to have approximately 42 spots. This is interpolation (since 7 is between 2 and 22, which are the values of x between which data was collected), and the size of the residuals is small. This estimate should be reliable.

b) $58.8 - 2.47 \times 0 = 58.8$ — so the volunteer would be predicted to have approximately 59 spots. This is extrapolation (since 0 is less than 2, which was the smallest value of x for which data was collected). This estimate may not be reliable.

c) Using the formula for $x = 30$ is extrapolation, since 30 is greater than 22, the largest value of x for which data was collected. The model isn't valid for $x = 30$, since you can't have a negative number of spots. But this doesn't mean that the regression equation is wrong.

Exercise 2.4 — Regression and linear scaling

Q1 Substitute the expressions defining p and q into the equation of the regression line for q on p. This gives you an equation involving just x and y.
$q = 40 + 2p$, so $y - 50 = 40 + 2(x - 7)$

Now rearrange this so it is in the form $y = a + bx$, where a and b are constants.
$y = 40 + 2x - 14 + 50 = 76 + 2x$
So the equation of the regression line of y on x is $y = 76 + 2x$.

Q2 $q = -0.9 + 0.1p$,
and so $10y - 3 = -0.9 + 0.1 \times \frac{x - 20}{2}$
Now rearrange this into the form $y = a + bx$.
So $10y = -0.9 + 0.05x - (0.05 \times 20) + 3$
i.e. $10y = 0.05x + 1.1$
Or $y = 0.005x + 0.11$

Q3 $y = 17.4 - 0.78x$, so $t - 45 = 17.4 - 0.78(w - 60)$
Rearrange this to give:
$t = 17.4 - 0.78w + (0.78 \times 60) + 45$,
or $t = -0.78w + 109.2$

Q4 a) $S_{xy} = \sum xy - \frac{\sum x \sum y}{n} = 618 - \frac{28 \times 124}{10}$
$= 270.8$

$S_{xx} = \sum x^2 - \frac{(\sum x)^2}{n} = 140 - \frac{28^2}{10} = 61.6$

Call the equation of the regression line $y = a + bx$. Then the gradient of the regression line is b, where:

$b = \frac{S_{xy}}{S_{xx}} = \frac{270.8}{61.6} = 4.396103...$
$= 4.396$ (to 4 sig. fig.)

And the intercept of the regression line is a, where:

$a = \bar{y} - b\bar{x} = \frac{\sum y}{n} - b\frac{\sum x}{n}$
$= \frac{124}{10} - (4.396103...) \times \frac{28}{10}$
$= 0.090909... = 0.09091$ (to 4 sig. fig.).

So the equation of the regression line of y on x is: $y = 0.09091 + 4.396x$

b) $v - 7 = 0.09091 + 4.396 \times (\frac{s}{100} - 2)$
So $v = -1.70 + 0.0440s$

Q5 a) Start by working out the four summations $\sum x$, $\sum y$, $\sum x^2$, and $\sum xy$.
It's best to draw a table.

x	1	2	3	5	7	10	28
y	19	11	9	–1	–14	–24	0
x^2	1	4	9	25	49	100	188
xy	19	22	27	–5	–98	–240	–275

So $\sum x = 28$, $\sum y = 0$, $\sum x^2 = 188$, $\sum xy = -275$
Then:

$S_{xy} = \sum xy - \frac{\sum x \sum y}{n} = -275 - \frac{28 \times 0}{6}$
$= -275$

$S_{xx} = \sum x^2 - \frac{(\sum x)^2}{n} = 188 - \frac{28^2}{6} = 57.333...$

Call the equation of the regression line $y = a + bx$. Then the gradient of the regression line is b, where:

$b = \frac{S_{xy}}{S_{xx}} = \frac{-275}{57.333...} = -4.796511...$
$= -4.80$ (to 3 sig. fig.)
And the intercept of the regression line is a, where:
$a = \bar{y} - b\bar{x} = \frac{\sum y}{n} - b\frac{\sum x}{n}$
$= \frac{0}{6} - (-4.796511...) \times \frac{28}{6}$
$= 22.4$ (to 3 sig. fig.).

So the equation of the regression line of y on x is: $y = 22.4 - 4.80x$

b) Substitute expressions for x and y into your regression equation: $t - 29 = 22.4 - 4.80\frac{s}{10}$
This means that: $t = 51.4 - 0.480s$

Review Exercise — Chapter 6

Q1 **a)**

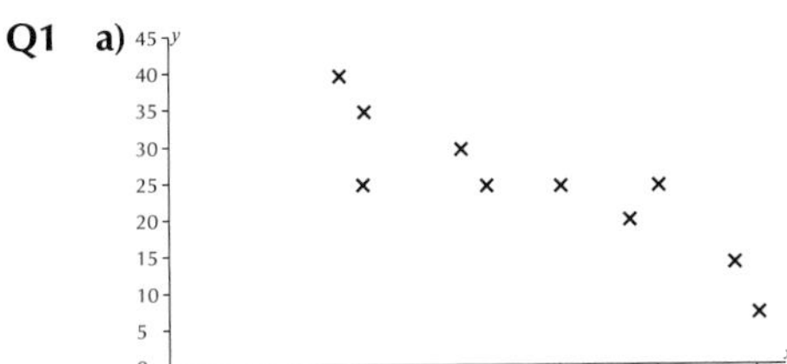

b) First you need to find these values:

$\sum x = 1880$, $\sum y = 247$, $\sum x^2 = 410\,400$,

$\sum y^2 = 6899$ and $\sum xy = 40\,600$.

Then

$$S_{xy} = \sum xy - \frac{\sum x \sum y}{n} = 40\,600 - \frac{1880 \times 247}{10}$$
$$= -5836$$

$$S_{xx} = \sum x^2 - \frac{(\sum x)^2}{n} = 410\,400 - \frac{1880^2}{10}$$
$$= 56\,960$$

$$S_{yy} = \sum y^2 - \frac{(\sum y)^2}{n} = 6899 - \frac{247^2}{10} = 798.1$$

This means:

$$r = \frac{S_{xy}}{\sqrt{S_{xx}S_{yy}}}$$
$$= \frac{-5836}{\sqrt{56\,960 \times 798.1}} = -0.866 \text{ (to 3 sig.fig.)}$$

c) The PMCC tells you that there is a strong negative correlation between drink volume and alcohol concentration — cocktails with smaller volumes tend to have higher concentrations of alcohol.
Don't panic about that PMCC formula — you need to know how to USE it, but they give you the formula in the exam, so you don't need to REMEMBER it.

Q2 **a)** **Explanatory**: the annual number of sunny days
Response: the annual number of volleyball-related injuries

b) **Explanatory**: the annual number of rainy days
Response: the annual number of Monopoly-related injuries

c) **Explanatory**: a person's disposable income
Response: a person's spending on luxuries

d) **Explanatory**: the number of cups of tea drunk per day
Response: the number of trips to the loo per day

e) **Explanatory**: the number of festival tickets sold
Response: the number of pairs of Wellington boots bought

Q3 **a)** **(i)** $S_{xx} = 26816.78 - \frac{517.4^2}{10} = 46.504$

(ii) $S_{xy} = 57045.5 - \frac{517.4 \times 1099}{10} = 183.24$

b) $\text{b} = \frac{S_{xy}}{S_{xx}} = \frac{183.24}{46.504} = 3.9403...$
$= 3.94$ (to 3 sig. fig.).

c) $\text{a} = \bar{y} - \text{b}\bar{x}$, where $\bar{y} = \frac{\sum y}{10} = 109.9$

and $\bar{x} = \frac{\sum x}{10} = 51.74$

So $\text{a} = 109.9 - 3.9403... \times 51.74$
$= -93.9711... = -94.0$ (to 3 sig. fig.).

d) The equation of the regression line is:
$y = 3.94x - 94.0$

e) When $x = 60$, the regression line gives an estimate for y of:
$y = 3.94 \times 60 - 94.0 = 142.4$ g

f) This estimate might not be very reliable because it uses an x-value from outside the range of the original data. It is extrapolation.
You'll be given the equations for finding a regression line — but you still need to know how to use them, otherwise the formula booklet will just be a blur. And you need to practise USING them of course...

Q4 Rearrange the expressions $P = x - 5$ and $Q = \frac{y}{8}$ to get formulas for x and y. These are $x = P + 5$ and $y = 8Q$.

Substitute these expressions for x and y into the regression line's equation from Question 3.
$y = 3.9403... \times x - 93.9711...$,
and so $8Q = 3.9403... \times (P + 5) - 93.9711...$

Now rearrange to get an equation of the form $Q = \text{a} + \text{b}P$:
$8Q = 3.9403... \times P + (3.9403... \times 5 - 93.9711...)$
i.e. $Q = 0.493P - 9.28$.

Exam-Style Questions — Chapter 6

1 **a)**

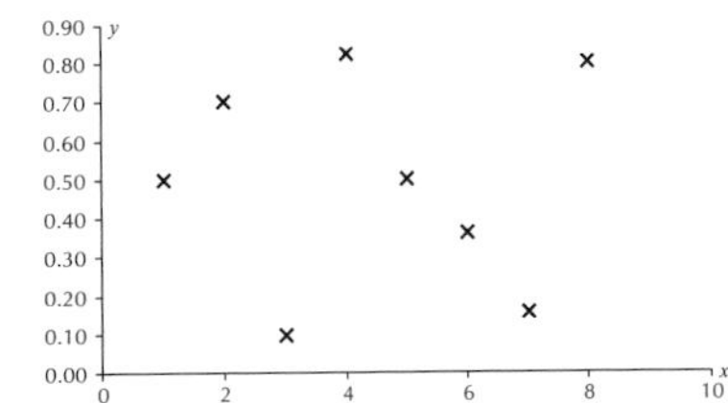

[2 marks for all points plotted correctly, or 1 mark if at least 3 points are plotted correctly.]

b) You need to work out these sums:

$\sum x = 36, \sum y = 3.94,$
$\sum x^2 = 204, \sum y^2 = 2.4676, \sum xy = 17.66$

Then:

$$S_{xy} = \sum xy - \frac{\sum x \sum y}{n} = 17.66 - \frac{36 \times 3.94}{8}$$
$$= -0.07$$

$$S_{xx} = \sum x^2 - \frac{(\sum x)^2}{n} = 204 - \frac{36^2}{8} = 42$$

$$S_{yy} = \sum y^2 - \frac{(\sum y)^2}{n} = 2.4676 - \frac{3.94^2}{8} = 0.52715$$

[3 marks available — 1 for each correct term]

This means:

$$r = \frac{S_{xy}}{\sqrt{S_{xx}S_{yy}}} = \frac{-0.07}{\sqrt{42 \times 0.52715}}$$
$$= -0.015 \text{ (to 3 d.p.)}.$$ ***[1 mark]***

c) This very small value for the correlation coefficient tells you that there appears to be only a very weak linear relationship between the two variables (or perhaps no linear relationship at all) ***[1 mark]***.

2 a)

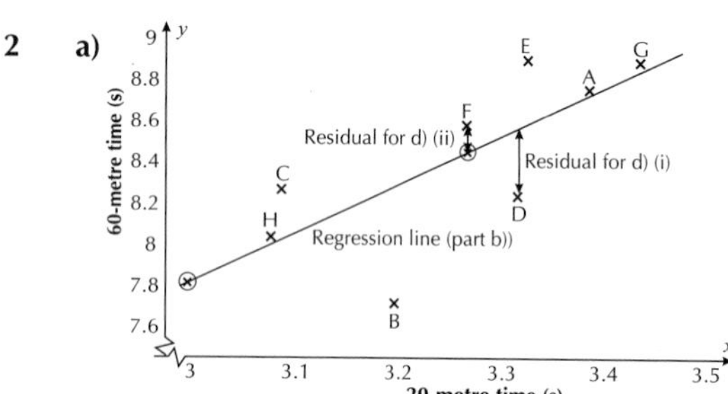

[2 marks for all points plotted correctly, or 1 mark if at least 3 points are plotted correctly.]

b) It's best to make a table like this one first:

	A	B	C	D	E	F	G	H
x	3.39	3.20	3.09	3.32	3.33	3.27	3.44	3.08
y	8.78	7.73	8.28	8.25	8.91	8.59	8.90	8.05
x^2	11.4921	10.24	9.5481	11.0224	11.0889	10.6929	11.8336	9.4864
xy	29.7642	24.736	25.5852	27.39	29.6703	28.0893	30.616	24.794

So $\sum x = 26.12$, $\sum y = 67.49$,
$\sum x^2 = 85.4044$, and $\sum xy = 220.645$.

[2 marks for at least three correct totals, or 1 mark if one total found correctly.]

Then:

$$S_{xy} = 220.645 - \frac{26.12 \times 67.49}{8} = 0.29015$$

[1 mark]

$$S_{xx} = 85.4044 - \frac{26.12^2}{8} = 0.1226$$

[1 mark]

Then the gradient b is given by:

$$b = \frac{S_{xy}}{S_{xx}} = \frac{0.29015}{0.1226} = 2.36663...$$
$$= 2.367 \text{ (to 3 d.p.)}.$$

[1 mark]

And the intercept a is given by:

$$a = \bar{y} - b\bar{x} = \frac{\sum y}{n} - b\frac{\sum x}{n}$$
$$= \frac{67.49}{8} - 2.36663... \times \frac{26.12}{8}$$
$$= 0.709 \text{ (to 3 d.p.)}.$$

[1 mark]

So the regression line has equation:
$y = 2.367x + 0.709$
[1 mark]

To plot the line, find two points that the line passes through. A regression line always passes through $(\bar{x}, \bar{y})$, which here is (3.27, 8.44). Then put $x = 3$ (say) to find that the line also passes through (3, 7.81).
Now plot these points (in circles) on your scatter diagram, and draw the regression line through them ***[1 mark for plotting the line correctly]***.

Remember, you get marks for method as well as correct answers, so take it step by step and show all your workings.

c) (i) $y = 2.367 \times 3.15 + 0.709$
$= 8.17$ (to 3 sig. fig.),
(or 8.16 if $b = 2.36663...$ used) ***[1 mark]***

This should be reliable, since we are using interpolation within the range of x for which we have data and the residuals are fairly small ***[1 mark]***.

(ii) $y = 2.367 \times 3.88 + 0.709 = 9.89$ (to 3 sig. fig.)
[1 mark]

This could be unreliable, since we are extrapolating beyond the range of the data ***[1 mark]***.

d) (i) residual = 8.25 – (2.367 × 3.32 + 0.709)
= –0.317 (3 sig. fig.),
(or –0.316 if $b = 2.36663...$ used)
[1 mark for calculation, 1 mark for plotting residual correctly]

(ii) residual = 8.59 – (2.367 × 3.27 + 0.709)
= 0.141 (3 sig. fig.),
(or 0.142 if $b = 2.36663...$ used)
[1 mark for calculation, 1 mark for plotting residual correctly]

3 a) Put the values into the PMCC formula:

$$r = \frac{S_{xy}}{\sqrt{S_{xx}S_{yy}}} = \frac{12666}{\sqrt{310880 \times 788.95}}$$
$$= 0.809 \text{ (to 3 sig. fig.)}.$$

[1 mark for correctly substituting the values into the PMCC formula, and 1 mark for the correct final answer.]

b) There is a strong positive correlation between the miles cycled in the morning and calories consumed for lunch. Generally, the further they cycled, the more they ate ***[1 mark]***.

c) 0.809 (to 3 sig. fig.) ***[1 mark]***
Remember — the PMCC won't be affected if you multiply a set of data values by the same positive number, so changing the data from miles to km doesn't change it.

4 a) At $x = 12.5$,
$y = 211.599 + (9.602 \times 12.5) = 331.624$
At $x = 14.7$,
$y = 211.599 + (9.602 \times 14.7) = 352.7484$
[1 mark for each value of y correctly calculated]

b) Using the equation:
'Residual = Observed y – Estimated y':
At $x = 12.5$:
Residual = 332.5 – 331.624 = 0.876 ***[1 mark]***
At $x = 14.7$: Residual = 352.1 – 352.7484
= –0.6484 ***[1 mark]***

5 a) Find the summations $\sum x = 65$ ***[1 mark]*** and $\sum y = 0$ ***[1 mark]***.
Then:

$$S_{xy} = \sum xy - \frac{\sum x \sum y}{n} = 843 - \frac{65 \times 0}{10}$$

[1 mark]

= 843 ***[1 mark]***

$$S_{xx} = \sum x^2 - \frac{(\sum x)^2}{n} = 571 - \frac{65^2}{10}$$

= 148.5 ***[1 mark]***

$$S_{yy} = \sum y^2 - \frac{(\sum y)^2}{n} = 548\,586 - \frac{0^2}{10}$$

= 548 586 ***[1 mark]***

b) $r = \frac{S_{xy}}{\sqrt{S_{xx}S_{yy}}}$
$= \frac{843}{\sqrt{148.5 \times 548\,586}}$ ***[1 mark]***
$= 0.0934$ (to 3 sig.fig.) ***[1 mark]***

c) 0.0934 (to 3 sig. fig.) ***[1 mark]***
Because x and y are related by linear transformations to d and t (where the value of b is positive for both transformations), this means that the PMCC between d and t must be the same as that between x and y ***[1 mark]***.

d) The PMCC between d and t is very low ***[1 mark]***, which suggests that the length of a run the day before a race has little impact upon the performance of these athletes ***[1 mark]***.

6 a)

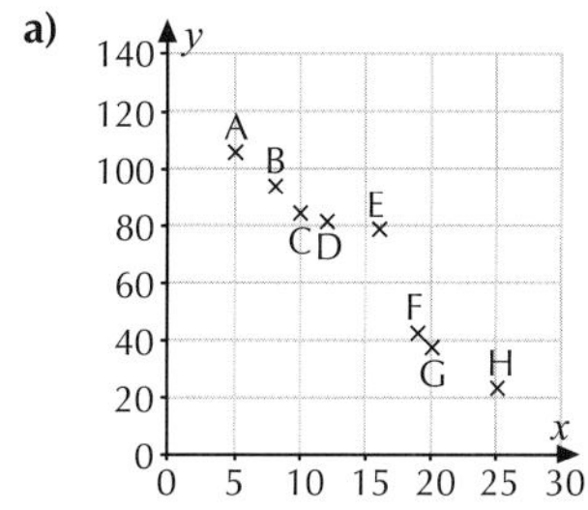

[1 mark for at least 4 points plotted correctly, or 2 marks if all points plotted correctly.]

b) Start by working out the summations $\sum x = 115$ ***[1 mark]*** and $\sum y = 544$ ***[1 mark]***.
Then:

$$S_{xy} = \sum xy - \frac{\sum x \sum y}{n}$$
$$= 6446 - \frac{115 \times 544}{8} \textbf{ [1 mark]}$$
$$= -1374 \textbf{ [1 mark]}$$

$$S_{xx} = \sum x^2 - \frac{(\sum x)^2}{n}$$
$$= 1975 - \frac{115^2}{8} = 321.875 \textbf{ [1 mark]}$$

c) The gradient of the regression line is b, where:
$b = \frac{S_{xy}}{S_{xx}} = \frac{-1374}{321.875}$ ***[1 mark]*** = –4.26873...
= –4.27 (to 3 sig. fig.) ***[1 mark]***
And the intercept of the regression line is a, where:
$a = \bar{y} - b\bar{x} = \frac{\sum y}{n} - b\frac{\sum x}{n}$
$= \frac{544}{8} - (-4.26873...) \times \frac{115}{8}$ ***[1 mark]***
$= 129$ (to 3 sig. fig.) ***[1 mark]***.

d) The regression line must pass through the point $(\bar{x}, \bar{y}) = (14.375, 68)$. It must also pass through the point (0, 129).

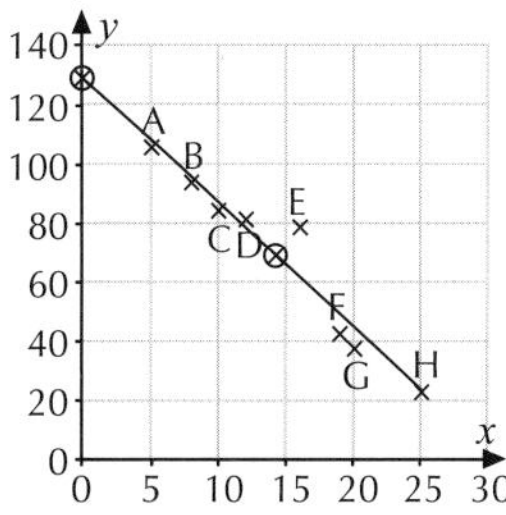

[1 mark if the line passes through one correct point, or 2 marks if line is drawn correctly.]

e) Brand E appears to be overpriced ***[1 mark]*** — it is much higher than the line, whereas the other points lie very close to it ***[1 mark]***.

Glossary

Addition law
A formula linking the probability of the **union** and the probability of the **intersection** of events A and B:
$P(A \cup B) = P(A) + P(B) - P(A \cap B)$

Binomial coefficient
The number of orders in which x objects of one type and $(n - x)$ objects of a different type can be arranged.
Equal to $\binom{n}{x} = \frac{n!}{x!(n-x)!}$

Binomial distribution B(n, p)
A discrete **probability distribution** which models the number of successes x in n independent trials when the probability of success in each trial is p.

Bivariate data
Data that comes as an ordered pair of **variables** (x, y).

Complement (of an event A)
The group of all **outcomes** corresponding to event A not happening.

Conditional probability
A probability is conditional if it depends on whether or not another **event** happens.

Confidence interval
A range of values, calculated from **sample** data, with a specified probability of containing a population **parameter**.

Continuous random variable
A **random variable** which is measured on a continuous scale. It may take any value in a given range (i.e. with no 'gaps' between possible values).

Correlation
A linear relationship between two **variables** showing that they change together to some extent.
(A correlation does not necessarily mean a causal relationship.)

Cumulative distribution function
A function, F(x), which gives the probability that a **random variable**, X, will be less than or equal to a particular value, x.

Dependent variable
Another name for the **response variable**.

Discrete random variable
A **random variable** with 'gaps' between its possible values.

Dispersion
Measures of dispersion describe how spread out data values are.

Estimator
A **statistic** that's used to estimate the value of a **parameter**.

Event
An event is a 'group' of one or more possible **outcomes**.

Expected value
The expected value of a **random variable** is the 'expected' mean of a large number of readings.

Explanatory variable
In an experiment, the **variable** you can control, or the one that you think is affecting the other.

Extrapolation
Predicting a value of y corresponding to a value of x outside the range for which you have data.

Independent events
If the probability of an **event** B happening doesn't depend on whether or not an **event** A happens, **events** A and B are independent.

Independent variable
Another name for the **explanatory variable**.

Interpolation
Predicting a value of y corresponding to a value of x within the range for which you have data.

Interquartile range
A measure of **dispersion**. It's the difference between the **upper quartile** and the **lower quartile**.

Intersection (of events A and B)
The set of **outcomes** corresponding to both **event** A and **event** B happening.

Linear regression
A method for finding the equation of a line of best fit on a **scatter diagram**.

Linear scaling
Linear scaling means transforming all the readings in a data set (x) using a linear transformation $y = \frac{x - a}{b}$.

Location
Measures of location show where the 'centre' of the data lies.

Lower quartile
The value that 25% of data values in a data set are less than or equal to.

Mean
A measure of **location** — it's the sum of a set of data values, divided by the number of data values.

Mean of a random variable
The 'expected' **mean** of a large number of readings.
Also known as the **expected value**.

Median
A measure of **location** — it's the value in the middle of the data set when all the data values are in order of size.

Mode
A measure of **location** — it's the most frequently occurring data value.

Multiplication law
A formula used to work out the probability of two **events** both happening: $P(A \cap B) = P(A) \times P(B|A)$

Mutually exclusive
Events are mutually exclusive (or just 'exclusive') if they have no **outcomes** in common, and so can't happen at the same time.

Normal distribution
A continuous 'bell-shaped' **probability distribution** where the further from the **mean** a value is, the less likely it is to occur.

Outcome
One of the possible results of a **trial** or experiment.

Outlier
A freak piece of data lying a long way from the majority of the values in a data set.

Parameter
A quantity that describes a characteristic of a **population**.

Population
The whole group that you want to investigate, consisting of every single person/item/animal.

Probability distribution
A description of the possible values a random variable can take, along with a means to find the probability of those values (e.g. a **probability function**).

Probability function
A function that generates the probabilities of a **discrete random variable** taking each of its possible values.

Product moment correlation coefficient
A measure of the strength of the **correlation** between two **variables**.

Qualitative variable
A **variable** that takes non-numerical values.

Quantitative variable
A **variable** that takes numerical values.

Random variable
A **variable** taking different values with different probabilities.

Range
A measure of **dispersion**. It's the difference between the highest value and the lowest value.

Regression line
A line of best fit found using **linear regression**.

Relative frequency
Can be used to estimate the probability of an **event** happening. Calculated by dividing the number of **trials** in which the event happened by the total number of trials carried out.

Representative
A **sample** is representative of a **population** if it resembles it in the ways that matter for the study.

Residual
The difference between a real-life observation and what a **regression line** predicts.

Response variable
In an experiment, the **variable** you think is being affected.

Sample
A selection of the people or items in a **population**.

Sample space
The set of all possible **outcomes** of a **trial**.

Sampling distribution
The **probability distribution** of a **statistic**.

Scatter diagram
Graph showing the two **variables** in a **bivariate** data set plotted against each other.

Simple random sample
A **sample** where members are chosen at random from a full list of the **population**.

Standard deviation
A measure of **dispersion** calculated by taking the square root of the **variance.**

Standard error
The **standard deviation** of the **sampling distribution** of a **statistic**.

Standard normal variable, *Z*
A **random variable** that follows a **normal distribution** with **mean** 0 and **variance** 1.

Statistic
A quantity that is calculated using only observations from a **sample**.

Trial
A process (e.g. an experiment) with different possible **outcomes**.

Unbiased
An **estimator** is unbiased if its **expected value** equals the **parameter** it is trying to estimate.

Union (of events A and B)
The set of **outcomes** corresponding to either **event** A or **event** B (or both) happening.

Upper quartile
The value that 75% of data values in a data set are less than or equal to.

Variable
A quantity that can take a variety of values — its value is not fixed.

Variance
A measure of **dispersion** from the **mean**.

Variance of a random variable
The 'expected' **variance** of a large number of readings.

Venn diagram
A Venn diagram shows how a collection of objects is split up into different groups, where everything in a group has something in common. In probability, the objects are **outcomes**, and the groups are **events**.

***Z*-tables**
Tables relating to the **standard normal variable** (Z) — such as the **cumulative distribution function** $\Phi(z)$, and the percentage-points table.

Index

S1 Formula Sheet

The formulas below will be included in the formula book for your exams — make sure you know exactly **when you need them** and **how to use them**.

Probability $P(A \cup B) = P(A) + P(B) - P(A \cap B)$ $P(A \cap B) = P(A) \times P(B \mid A)$

Sampling Distributions For a random sample $X_1, X_2, ..., X_n$ of n independent observations from a distribution with mean μ and variance σ^2:

$\overline{X}$ is an unbiased estimator of μ, with $\mathrm{Var}(\overline{X}) = \frac{\sigma^2}{n}$

S^2 is an unbiased estimator of σ^2, where $S^2 = \dfrac{\Sigma(X_i - \overline{X})^2}{n-1}$

Discrete Distributions

Standard discrete distribution:

Distribution of X	$P(X = x)$	Mean	Variance
Binomial $B(n, p)$	$\binom{n}{x} p^x (1-p)^{n-x}$	np	$np(1-p)$

Continuous Distributions

Standard continuous distribution:

Distribution of X	P.D.F.	Mean	Variance
Normal $N(\mu, \sigma^2)$	$\frac{1}{\sigma\sqrt{2\pi}} e^{-\frac{1}{2}\left(\frac{x-\mu}{\sigma}\right)^2}$	μ	σ^2

Correlation and Regression

For a set of n pairs of values (x_i, y_i):

$$S_{xx} = \Sigma(x_i - \bar{x})^2 = \Sigma x_i^2 - \frac{(\Sigma x_i)^2}{n} \qquad S_{yy} = \Sigma(y_i - \bar{y})^2 = \Sigma y_i^2 - \frac{(\Sigma y_i)^2}{n}$$

$$S_{xy} = \Sigma(x_i - \bar{x})(y_i - \bar{y}) = \Sigma x_i y_i - \frac{(\Sigma x_i)(\Sigma y_i)}{n}$$

The **product moment correlation coefficient** is:

$$r = \frac{S_{xy}}{\sqrt{S_{xx}S_{yy}}} = \frac{\Sigma(x_i - \bar{x})(y_i - \bar{y})}{\sqrt{\{\Sigma(x_i - \bar{x})^2\}\{\Sigma(y_i - \bar{y})^2\}}} = \frac{\Sigma x_i y_i - \frac{(\Sigma x_i)(\Sigma y_i)}{n}}{\sqrt{\left(\Sigma x_i^2 - \frac{(\Sigma x_i)^2}{n}\right)\left(\Sigma y_i^2 - \frac{(\Sigma y_i)^2}{n}\right)}}$$

The **regression coefficient** of y on x is $b = \dfrac{S_{xy}}{S_{xx}} = \dfrac{\Sigma(x_i - \bar{x})(y_i - \bar{y})}{\Sigma(x_i - \bar{x})^2}$

Least squares regression line of y on x is $y = a + bx$ where $a = \bar{y} - b\bar{x}$

MAS1T51